ADVANCES IN LIPID RESEARCH

Volume 11

Advances in Lipid Research

Volume 11

Edited by

Rodolfo Paoletti

Institute of Pharmacology
Milan, Italy

David Kritchevsky

The Wistar Institute
Philadelphia, Pennsylvania

 1973

ACADEMIC PRESS • New York and London
A Subsidiary of Harcourt Brace Jovanovich, Publishers

ACADEMIC PRESS, INC.
111 Fifth Avenue, New York, New York 10003

United Kingdom Edition published by
ACADEMIC PRESS, INC. (LONDON) LTD.
24/28 Oval Road, London NW1

LIBRARY OF CONGRESS CATALOG CARD NUMBER: 63-22330

PRINTED IN THE UNITED STATES OF AMERICA

CONTENTS

The Metabolic Role of Lecithin : Cholesterol Acyltransferase: Perspectives from Pathology

John A. Glomset and Kaare R. Norum

Lipoprotein-Polyanion-Metal Interactions

M. Burstein and H. R. Scholnick

Uptake and Transport of Fatty Acids into the Brain and the Role of the Blood—Brain Barrier System

Govind A. Dhopeshwarkar and James F. Mead

Microbiological Transformation of Bile Acids

Shohei Hayakawa

Phytosterols

George A. Bean

Metabolism of Steroids in Insects

M. J. Thompson, J. N. Kaplanis, W. E. Robbins, and
J. A. Svoboda

Lipids in Viruses

Herbert A. Blough and John M. Tiffany

LIST OF CONTRIBUTORS

Numbers in parentheses indicate the pages on which the authors' contributions begin.

GEORGE A. BEAN, *Department of Botany, University of Maryland, College Park, Maryland* (193)

HERBERT A. BLOUGH, *Division of Biochemical Virology and Membrane Research, Scheie Eye Institute of the Presbyterian–University of Pennsylvania Medical Center, Philadelphia, Pennsylvania* (267)

M. BURSTEIN, *Centre National de Transfusion Sanguine, Paris, France* (67)

GOVIND A. DHOPESHWARKAR, *Laboratory of Nuclear Medicine and Radiation Biology, and Department of Nutrition, School of Public Health, University of California at Los Angeles, Los Angeles, California* (109)

JOHN A. GLOMSET, *Department of Medicine and Regional Primate Research Center, University of Washington, Seattle, Washington* (1)

SHOHEI HAYAKAWA, *Shionogi Research Laboratory, Shionogi & Co., Ltd., Fukushima-ku, Osaka, Japan* (143)

J. N. KAPLANIS, *Insect Physiology Laboratory, Plant Protection Institute, ARS, USDA, Agricultural Research Center, Beltsville, Maryland* (219)

JAMES F. MEAD, *Laboratory of Nuclear Medicine and Radiation Biology, and Department of Biological Chemistry, School of Medicine, University of California at Los Angeles, Los Angeles, California* (109)

KAARE R. NORUM, *Institute for Nutrition Research, School of Medicine, University of Oslo, Oslo, Norway* (1)

W. E. ROBBINS, *Insect Physiology Laboratory, Plant Protection Institute, ARS, USDA, Agricultural Research Center, Beltsville, Maryland* (219)

ix

H. R. SCHOLNICK, *Albert Einstein College of Medicine, New York, New York* (67)

J. A. SVOBODA, *Insect Physiology Laboratory, Plant Protection Institute, ARS, USDA, Agricultural Research Center, Beltsville, Maryland* (219)

M. J. THOMPSON, *Insect Physiology Laboratory, Plant Protection Institute, ARS, USDA, Agricultural Research Center, Beltsville, Maryland* (219)

JOHN M. TIFFANY, *Division of Biochemical Virology and Membrane Research, Scheie Eye Institute of the Presbyterian–University of Pennsylvania Medical Center, Philadelphia, Pennsylvania* (267)

PREFACE

This volume of *Advances in Lipid Research* contains discussions of a wide range of topics, all of which are part of the broad lipid field.

The first review concerns itself with a serum enzyme whose action had been described over 35 years ago but whose characterization is more recent. This enzyme is lecithin:cholesterol acyltransferase, or LCAT. The article reviews the metabolic role of this enzyme. The second chapter covers a topic which is becoming increasingly important in metabolic and clinical research, namely, simple means of separation and quantitation of serum lipoproteins. This chapter offers a guide to the many variations of the reaction involving lipoproteins, divalent cations, and polyanionic substances, organic and inorganic. It systematizes the current knowledge. In the third article the metabolism of fatty acids by brain tissue is reviewed. The concept of the blood–brain barrier is discussed critically and its role in fatty acid uptake is assessed. As our knowledge of the metabolic role of bile acids deepens, it becomes increasingly evident that the production or excretion of these steroids may be important in the establishment of cholesteremia, lithogenesis, and possibly cancer. Many of the alterations in bile acid structure are due to their interaction with the intestinal microflora, and this relationship is the basis of the fourth review. The plant sterols may play more than a simple structural role. As research reveals the multiple aspects of plant sterol function it becomes important for us to have a better understanding of their chemistry and metabolism. The fifth chapter provides such a review of the phytosterols. For normal metabolism insects require an exogenous source of sterol, being incapable of sterol synthesis. Insects can utilize and metabolize dietary sterol, and how this is accomplished is reviewed in the sixth chapter. The last chapter covers a field which has intrigued biologists for decades—the lipids of viruses. The elucidation of the role lipids play in viral structure and metabolism has had to wait for the development of sophisticated methodology. Now that we have the analytical tools, this entire area will open up. As this chapter shows, ubiquitous lipid is important even in the smallest of integrated biological units.

RODOLFO PAOLETTI
DAVID KRITCHEVSKY

CONTENTS OF PREVIOUS VOLUMES

The Metabolic Role of Lecithin : Cholesterol Acyltransferase: Perspectives from Pathology

JOHN A. GLOMSET

*Department of Medicine and Regional Primate
Research Center, University of Washington,
Seattle, Washington*

AND

KAARE R. NORUM

*Institute for Nutrition Research,
School of Medicine, University of Oslo,
Oslo, Norway*

I. Introduction

The blood plasma of many species contains an enzyme that can catalyze esterification of lipoprotein cholesterol (Glomset, 1968, 1972). Although the detailed lipid substrate specificity, apoprotein effector requirements, and physical properties of the enzyme are still being investigated (Nichols and Gong, 1971; Raz, 1971; Fielding *et al.*, 1972a,b; Fielding and Fielding, 1971), several facts are reasonably well estab-

1

lished. The enzyme is a lecithin:cholesterol acyltransferase (LCAT)[1] that preferentially utilizes fatty acids from the C-2 position of lecithin. It is mainly extracellular, and is secreted into plasma by the liver (Simon and Boyer, 1971; Osuga and Portman, 1971). It circulates in plasma as a high density lipoprotein (HDL) complex and acts directly on the smaller HDL (Glomset *et al.*, 1966; Fielding and Fielding, 1971). It *indirectly* diminishes the unesterified cholesterol and lecithin of other plasma lipoproteins (Glomset *et al.*, 1970), apparently because these lipids readily equilibrate among lipoproteins (Eder, 1957; Roheim *et al.*, 1963) and transfer nonenzymatically to HDL that have been attacked by LCAT (Fig. 1). It also indirectly promotes nonenzymatic exchange of HDL cholesteryl ester for the triglyceride of other lipoproteins for reasons that are still unclear (Rehnborg and Nichols, 1964; Nichols and Smith, 1965).

Despite the rapidly accumulating evidence concerning the LCAT reac-

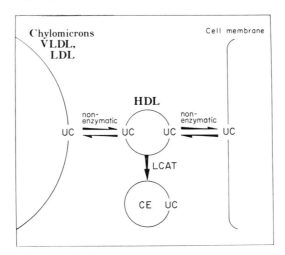

FIG. 1. Schematic illustration showing equilibria between the unesterified cholesterol (UC) of plasma lipoproteins and plasma membranes and the effect of coupling these equilibria to the formation of HDL cholesteryl ester (CE) by the LCAT reaction.

---

[1] The following abbreviations will be used: LCAT = lecithin:cholesterol acyltransferase; LPL = lipoprotein lipase; VLDL = very low density lipoproteins; LDL = low density lipoproteins; HDL = high density lipoproteins; apo-A = apolipoprotein A (terminology of Alaupovic, 1971); apo-B = apolipoprotein B; apo-C = apolipoprotein C; UC = unesterified cholesterol; CE = cholesteryl ester; PC = lecithin (phosphatidylcholine); TG = triglyceride; S = sphingomyelin; PL = phospholipid; FFA = free fatty acids; PCMPS = p-chloromercuriphenylsulfonate; NEM = N-ethylmaleimide; ME = mercaptoethanol.

tion, its physiological role is not yet understood. One problem is that we still know little about the uptake and catabolism of plasma lipoproteins. Thus, LCAT might affect the properties and thereby the subsequent metabolism of circulating lipoproteins by altering their polar and nonpolar lipids. However, the fact that most of the cholesterol of freshly isolated lipoproteins is already esterified has hampered *in vitro* investigation of the effects of the LCAT reaction on the properties of lipoproteins; and even if clear-cut effects could be established, the problem of determining their influence on the subsequent fate of lipoproteins would remain. A second and more fundamental problem is that the physiological significance of plasma cholesterol itself has never been adequately clarified. Thus, LCAT clearly affects the content of unesterified cholesterol in plasma and tissues and the content of cholesteryl ester in plasma, but the effect of the precise regulation of these components is not immediately apparent. Fortunately, the recent discovery of familial LCAT deficiency (Norum and Gjone, 1967a,b; Gjone and Norum, 1968) has provided a unique opportunity to study the metabolic role of the LCAT reaction. The plasma lipoproteins of patients with this disease are highly abnormal, apparently because they have never been altered by the LCAT reaction, and *in vivo* and *in vitro* experiments designed to perturb the lipoproteins have yielded some striking effects. Furthermore, lipoprotein and tissue abnormalities similar to those in familial LCAT deficiency have been found in cholesterol-fed guinea pigs and in patients with cholestasis, and this has provided new insight into the role and significance of the factors that regulate the concentration of plasma unesterified cholesterol. The aim of this review is to summarize the abnormalities found in familial LCAT deficiency, to compare them with those of cholesterol-fed guinea pigs and patients with cholestasis, and then to put the metabolic role of the LCAT reaction into provisional perspective by considering the possible mechanisms and effects of these abnormalities.

II. Familial LCAT Deficiency

Six living patients in three Scandinavian families have familial LCAT deficiency (Norum and Gjone, 1967a,b; Gjone and Norum, 1968; Torsvik *et al.*, 1968; Hamnström *et al.*, 1969; Norum *et al.*, 1970, 1972). All of the patients have abnormal plasma lipids and lipoproteins; all have corneal opacities; all have anemia with a hemolytic component associated with approximately twofold increases in erythrocyte unesterified cholesterol and lecithin and with the presence of lipid vacuoles in the cells of the bone marrow and spleen (Gjone *et al.*, 1968; Jacobson *et al.*, 1972); and all have proteinuria associated with intra- and extracellular lipid in the glomeruli (Norum *et al.*, 1972; Hovig and Gjone, 1972). Moreover, a seventh patient died at 41 years of age in renal failure, and one of the living patients developed renal failure when she was 36 years old and has been treated by dialysis for three years.

Most of the studies summarized below were done on the five Norwegian patients whose plasma contains no LCAT activity. The one Swedish patient, M. L., has been studied less extensively. She may have a different genetic defect since her plasma contains low but detectable amounts of cholesterol esterifying activity and a higher relative amount of cholesteryl ester (about 30% of the plasma cholesterol is esterified as compared to about 10% in the plasma of the Norwegian patients; Hamnström *et al.*, 1969).

A. PLASMA LIPIDS

Almost all of the plasma lipid and lipoprotein abnormalities are consistent with present knowledge concerning the LCAT reaction. Thus, the relative content of unesterified cholesterol in plasma is high and that of cholesteryl ester is extremely low, while the fatty acid composition of the few cholesteryl esters present (Table I) resembles that of human chylomicron cholesteryl esters (formed in the intestinal mucosa) rather than that of HDL or low density lipoprotein (LDL) cholesteryl esters (nor-

Table I

CHOLESTERYL ESTERS OF NORMAL HUMAN PLASMA HDL; THORACIC DUCT LIPOPROTEINS; AND WHOLE PLASMA FROM A PATIENT WITH FAMILIAL LCAT DEFICIENCY

| | Fatty acids (mole %) | | |
	Saturated	Mono-unsaturated	Poly-unsaturated
Normal HDL[a]	12.6	23.6	62.6
Whole thoracic duct lymph[b]	28.7	60.4	10.8
Thoracic duct lipoproteins of d < 1.005 gm/ml[c]	62.0	29.0	7.0
Whole plasma, patient M. R.[d]	35.4	45.5	18.9

[a] Lipoproteins of d < 1.063–1.21 gm/ml from subject E. H. (Goodman and Shiratori, 1964.)

[b] Whole thoracic lymph sampled during active fat absorption—patient A. (Blomstrand and Dahlbäck, 1960.)

[c] Thoracic lymph lipoproteins of d < 1.005 gm/ml from patient B (Kayden *et al.*, 1963) after an overnight fast. The tabulated figures are taken from the authors' Fig. 5.

[d] Plasma from M. R. taken after an overnight fast. The patient was on an ordinary diet.

mally formed by the LCAT reaction). Moreover, the patients' plasma cholesteryl esters are probably formed within mucosal cells since they become labeled following oral administration of radioactive cholesterol, but not following intravenous administration of radioactive mevalonic acid (Norum and Gjone, 1967b) and since, in contrast to normal, they are largely present in lipoproteins of $d < 1.006$ gm/ml (Table II). The composition of the plasma phospholipids also is consistent with the ab-

Table II

MAJOR LIPIDS OF LIPOPROTEINS FROM SIX NORMAL FEMALES AND FIVE PATIENTS WITH FAMILIAL LCAT DEFICIENCY[a]

	UC[b]	CE[b]	PC[b]	TG[b]
	(μmole/ml of plasma)			
d < 1.006 gm/ml				
Normal[c]	0.084 ± 0.074	0.066 ± 0.060	0.077 ± 0.008	0.220 ± 0.223
Patient M. R.	0.233	0.101	0.186	0.331
Patient A. R.	6.390	0.930	3.450	—
Patient I. S.	2.430	0.414	1.710	3.510
Patient A. A.	2.060	0.381	1.210	4.680
Patient L. G.	1.890	0.398	1.280	3.730
d 1.006–1.019				
Normal[c]	0.020 ± 0.008	0.026 ± 0.009	0.010 ± 0.005	0.009 ± 0.003
Patient M. R.	0.113	0.042	0.095	0.099
Patient A. R.	0.711	0.039	0.390	—
Patient I. S.	0.270	0.032	0.205	0.249
Patient A. A.	0.482	0.063	0.231	0.375
Patient L. G.	0.176	0.022	0.144	0.158
d 1.019–1.063				
Normal[c]	0.627 ± 0.134	1.369 ± 0.366	0.336 ± 0.088	0.071 ± 0.012
Patient M. R.	1.730	0.164	1.210	0.261
Patient A. R.	4.500	0.099	2.560	—
Patient I. S.	6.960	0.101	4.530	0.685
Patient A. A.	1.760	0.025	0.910	0.366
Patient L. G.	1.740	0.039	1.150	0.258
d 1.063–1.21				
Normal[c]	0.514 ± 0.085	1.460 ± 0.260	1.07 ± 0.151	0.052 ± 0.009
Patient M. R.	0.748	0.053	0.661	0.078
Patient A. R.	0.337	0.012	0.302	—
Patient I. S.	0.576	0.018	0.529	0.100
Patient A. A.	0.506	0.029	0.397	0.690
Patient L. G.	0.728	0.017	0.636	0.091

[a] Samples taken after an overnight fast; all subjects on ordinary diets.

[b] Abbreviations: UC = unesterified cholesterol; CE = cholesteryl ester; PC = lecithin (phosphatidylcholine); TG = triglyceride.

[c] Mean ± SD from six normal females (Glomset *et al.*, 1970).

sence of LCAT activity: lecithin constitutes more (82–86%) and lyso-
lecithin less (1.3–2.8%) of the total lipid phosphorus than in normal
plasma. However, the plasma triglycerides also are high, particularly in
the five patients who have hyperlipemia and this is not readily explained
by the enzyme lack. Instead, the hyperlipemia seems to be a late, secondary defect, dependent on renal dysfunction. Thus, the youngest patient, M. R., has not yet developed hyperlipemia; and the plasma triglycerides of A. R., her formerly hyperlipemic sister, increased as renal
function deteriorated, then decreased to slightly above normal concentrations when all renal function ceased, and have subsequently remained
low during treatment by dialysis (E. Gjone, unpublished observations).

B. Very Low Density Lipoproteins (VLDL)

Each of the plasma lipoprotein classes separated by preparative ultracentrifugation is abnormal by at least two criteria. The lipoproteins of
$d < 1.006$ gm/ml (VLDL) are abnormal in both lipid composition and
electrophoretic mobility. The lipid abnormalities are best illustrated by
the VLDL of the nonlipemic patient, M. R. (Glomset et al., 1973a).
Upon being filtered through 2% agarose gel, these lipoproteins yield subfractions (Fig. 2, A–C) showing at least three compositional abnormalities. First, the large lipoproteins excluded from the gel contain much
more unesterified cholesterol and lecithin relative to triglyceride and
much more of all lipids measured relative to protein than corresponding
normal lipoproteins. (Fig. 2, D–F). These large lipoproteins appear to
be related to large LDL present in the patients' plasma (see below).
Second, the content of cholesteryl ester relative to triglyceride or unesterified cholesterol does not increase as the VLDL become progressively
smaller. Since circulating VLDL probably diminish progressively in size
as they are successively attacked by lipoprotein lipase (LPL) (Nichols
et al., 1968), and since in vitro experiments (Rehnborg and Nichols,
1964; Nichols and Smith, 1965; Glomset et al., 1970) show that LCAT
can indirectly increase VLDL cholesteryl ester and decrease VLDL triglyceride and unesterified cholesterol, this abnormality probably is directly caused by the LCAT deficiency. A third compositional abnormality,
also probably caused by the LCAT deficiency (see Section II,F), is the
continuous increase in the content of lecithin relative to unesterified
cholesterol as the VLDL decrease in size. The lipoproteins of $d < 1.006$
gm/ml of the hyperlipemic patients show compositional abnormalities
similar to those of the VLDL of M. R., but are comprised of a much
higher proportion of large molecules. Many of the latter are probably
chylomicrons since they diminish in concentration on fat-free diets, which
also decrease the plasma triglycerides (Section II,E).

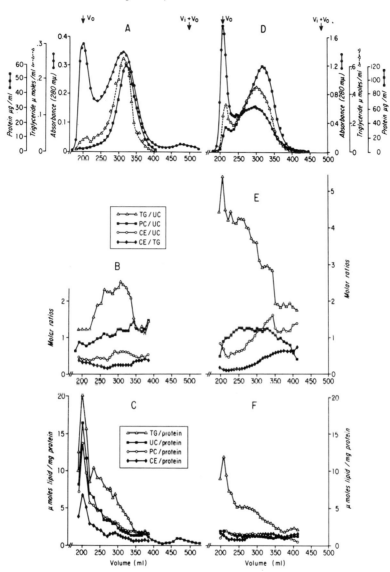

Fig. 2. Compositional abnormalities of VLDL from a patient with familial LCAT deficiency. VLDL from patient M. R., filtered through 2% agarose gel, were analyzed for lipids and protein (parts A–C) and compared with VLDL from a normal female (parts D–F). From Glomset *et al.* (1973a).

The smaller VLDL of both the nonlipemic and hyperlipemic patients migrate as β-lipoproteins on electrophoresis. The cause of this abnormally slow mobility has not been definitely established, but incubation with LCAT in the presence of normal HDL increases the mobility to that of normal pre-β VLDL (Section II,F), and preliminary studies of VLDL apoproteins have thus far disclosed no abnormalities.

C. Low Density Lipoproteins

The patients' LDL of d 1.006–1.019 gm/ml are abnormal in size distribution and in lipid composition. Abnormally large lipoproteins are present (Fig. 3), which contain a significant proportion of the total lipid of this LDL subclass (Table III) and which are particularly rich in unesterified cholesterol and lecithin (Table IV). Normal-sized lipoproteins also are present, but they contain abnormally small amounts of cholesteryl ester and large amounts of triglyceride relative to unesterified cholesterol and lecithin. These abnormalities seem to be analogous to the VLDL abnormalities mentioned above. Their relation to the LCAT deficiency, and the relation of the lipoprotein abnormalities described below, will be discussed in Section II,F.

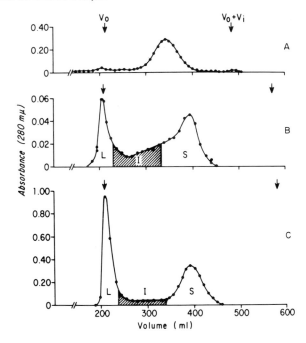

Fig. 3. Gel filtration of LDL of d 1.006–1.019 gm/ml. Part A shows LDL from a normal subject filtered through a column of 2% agarose gel. Parts B and C show similar experiments with the LDL of patients with familial LCAT deficiency (M. R. and L. G. respectively). Large, intermediate, and small molecular weight subfractions indicated by "L," "I," and "S." From Glomset *et al.* (1973a).

Table III

DISTRIBUTION OF TOTAL CHOLESTEROL AMONG LDL SUBFRACTIONS FROM
PATIENTS WITH FAMILIAL LCAT DEFICIENCY[a]

LDL Subclass	Large molecular weight	Intermediate molecular weight	Small molecular weight
	(μmoles total cholesterol/ml plasma)		
Patient M. R.			
d 1.006–1.019 gm/ml	0.008	0.019	0.087
d 1.019–1.063 gm/ml	0.624	0.942	0.268
Patient L. G.			
d 1.006–1.019 gm/ml	0.051	0.023	0.093
d 1.019–1.063 gm/ml	1.252	0.370	0.156

[a] Plasma taken after an overnight fast; patients on no special diet. (See Glomset *et al.*, 1973a.)

[b] Subfractions labeled "L," "I," and "S" in Figs. 3, 4, and 5.

The LDL of d 1.019–1.063 gm/ml are present in much larger concentrations than those of d 1.006–1.019 gm/ml and have been studied more extensively. They resemble the LDL of d 1.006–1.019 gm/ml in that much of the lipid is present in highly abnormal, large particles and that the size distribution of the large particles is related to the presence or absence of hyperlipemia. Thus, most of the LDL of the hyperlipemic patients, e.g., L. G. (Fig. 4A and Table III) or A. A. (Norum *et al.*, 1971a), are so large that they are completely excluded from 2% agarose gel. In contrast, most of the LDL of the nonlipemic patient, M. R. (Fig. 5A, peak "I" and Table III), are of intermediate size and emerge somewhat later. The LDL of d 1.019–1.063 gm/ml also resemble those of d 1.006–1.019 gm/ml in that small lipoproteins similar to normal LDL are present. However, these lipoproteins contain less than 10% of the total LDL cholesterol, and their total concentration in the plasma, expressed in terms of protein (Table V), is much less than that of normal LDL.

As in the case of the VLDL and the LDL of d 1.006–1.019 gm/ml, the lipid compositions of all of the subfractions of d 1.019–1.063 gm/ml are abnormal. The subfractions that emerge with the void volume primarily contain unesterified cholesterol and lecithin, sometimes in extremely large amounts compared to protein (Table IV). The subfractions of intermediate molecular size contain less of these lipids and more protein, but their content still differs distinctly from that of the smaller molecular weight LDL which is more nearly normal despite an abnormally high content of triglyceride and an abnormally low content of cholesteryl ester.

Table IV

RELATIVE COMPOSITION OF LDL SUBFRACTIONS FROM TWO PATIENTS WITH FAMILIAL LCAT DEFICIENCY

	Patient M. R.				Patient L. G.			
	UC/ protein	PC/ protein	CE/ protein	TG/ protein	UC/ protein	PC/ protein	CE/ protein	TG/ protein
	(μmoles/mg)				(μmoles/mg)			
Large molecular weight								
d 1.006–1.019[a]	4.85	2.50	1.08	1.65	15.9	9.15	0.60	5.45
d 1.019–1.063[a]	14.8	8.70	0.61	0.90	54.7	31.0	0.43	2.45
Intermediate molecular weight								
d 1.006–1.019[a]	4.89	3.50	1.32	3.28	5.64	3.41	0.46	3.31
d 1.019–1.063[a]	7.84	4.83	0.48	0.91	5.13	3.34	0.11	0.65
Small molecular weight								
d 1.006–1.019[a]	3.92	3.43	1.72	4.95	2.20	1.89	0.36	3.71
d 1.019–1.063[a]	1.14	1.07	0.61	1.33	0.89	0.85	0.15	1.21
Normal lipoproteins[b]								
d 1.019–1.063	1.44	0.482	1.77	0.114	1.44	0.482	1.77	0.114

[a] Lipoproteins of d 1.006–1.019 gm/ml and 1.019–1.063 gm/ml subfractionated by filtration on 2% agarose gel. (See Glomset et al., 1973a.)

[b] From Norum et al. (1971a). These data are mean values from six normal females.

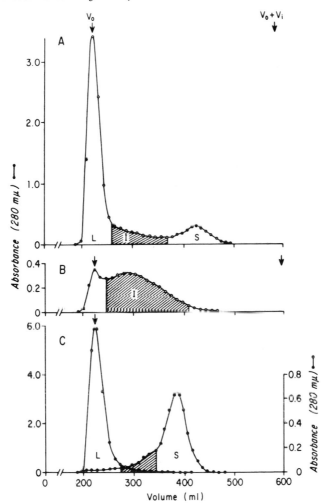

F<small>IG</small>. 4. Gel filtration of LDL of d 1.019–1.063 gm/ml from a lipemic patient with familial LCAT deficiency. Part A shows LDL of patient L. G. filtered through 2% agarose gel. Parts B and C show refiltration experiments with the intermediate ("I"), large ("L"), and small ("S") molecular weight subfractions from the experiment shown in part A. From Glomset *et al.* (1973a).

Electron microscopic studies of the LDL of d 1.019–1.063 gm/ml (Fig. 6) have confirmed the differences in lipoprotein size suggested by the gel filtration experiments. The void volume subfraction contains material that yields flat discs, >1000 Å in diameter, upon being negatively stained with phosphotungstic acid. Occasionally, these discs show lamellar or "myelin-type" structure. The intermediate LDL subfraction largely yields

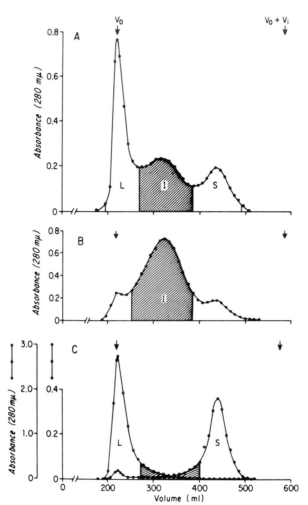

Fig. 5. Gel filtration of LDL of d 1.019–1.063 gm/ml from a nonlipemic patient with familial LCAT deficiency. Part A shows LDL of patient M. R. filtered through 2% agarose gel. Parts B and C show refiltration experiments with the intermediate ("I"), large ("L"), and small ("S") molecular weight subfractions from the experiment shown in part A. From Glomset *et al.* (1973a).

particles 450–600 Å in diameter, although the total range of particle diameters extends from about 340 to 1000 Å. Occasionally the particles form stacks. The smaller molecular weight subfraction contains particles of essentially the same diameter as normal LDL, i.e., mainly 210–250 Å.

The abnormalities in size appear largely to account for the bizarre flotation patterns obtained on analytical ultracentrifugation (Figs. 7, 8). Most of the LDL are of $S_f > 12$ and, particularly in the patients who

Table V

PLASMA CONCENTRATION OF NORMAL LDL AND OF SMALL MOLECULAR WEIGHT
LDL OF d 1.019–1.063 gm/ml FROM THREE PATIENTS WITH
FAMILIAL LCAT DEFICIENCY

Subjects	Total cholesterol (μmoles per ml plasma; ±S.D.)	Protein (mg per ml plasma; ±S.D.)
Normal[a]	3.62 ± 0.82	0.83 ± 0.25
Patient M. R.[b]	0.268	0.15
Patient I. S.[b]	0.350	0.15
Patient L. G.[b]	0.156	0.15

[a] Data from Lees (1970).
[b] Note that the values for cholesterol and protein probably underestimate the true values since they do not take into account small LDL present in the intermediate fraction (see Fig. 5B).

have hyperlipemia (Fig. 7), much is of $S_f > 20$. This is in contrast to normal LDL of d 1.019–1.063 gm/ml which are of S_f 0–12. Figures 7D and 8D indicate that the fast floating material in the patients' unsubfractionated LDL is contributed by the large and intermediate subfractions isolated by gel filtration.

The apoproteins of the three LDL subfractions have not yet been completely characterized, but those of the intermediate subfraction appear to be comprised of about 65% albumin and 35% apo-C and yield a reaction of immunological identity with the abnormal LDL of cholestasis (Torsvik *et al.*, 1972; see Section IV). The composition of the large molecular weight subfraction has not been established, but the small molecular weight subfraction appears to contain only apo-B (J. A. Glomset, unpublished observations).

D. HIGH DENSITY LIPOPROTEINS

The patients' HDL, like their LDL, are abnormal by several criteria. First, the size distribution is abnormal. When the HDL are filtered through Sephadex G 200 (Fig. 9), a large peak emerges either with the void volume or slightly after it, well ahead of the peak typically obtained with normal HDL. A smaller peak emerges considerably later in a position similar to that of the smaller HDL of normal plasma. The patients' large and small molecular weight HDL subfractions are both abnormal in lipid composition (Fig. 9; Table VI). Both mainly contain unesterified cholesterol and lecithin, but the proportion of these lipids relative to protein is much higher in the large molecular weight subfraction than in the small molecular weight subfraction. As a result of the high proportion of unesterified cholesterol in the HDL subfractions, the total concentration

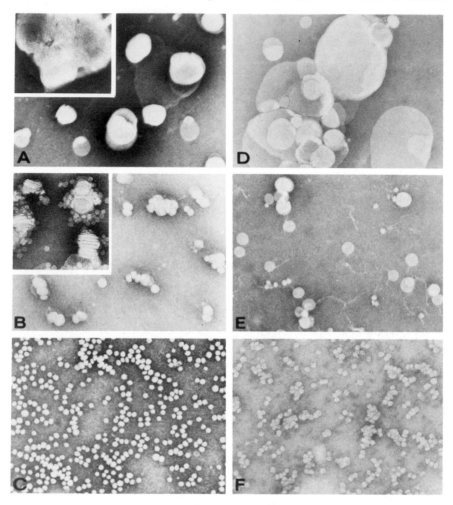

FIG. 6. Electron micrographs of LDL subfractions of two patients with familial
LCAT deficiency. Refiltered large, intermediate, and small molecular weight LDL
of d 1.019–1.063 gm/ml from patients M. R. (parts A–C) and L. G. (Parts D–F)
(see Figs. 4 and 5) negatively stained with phosphotungstic acid. Inset, part A,
shows lamellar structure. Inset, part B, shows stacking phenomena. Magnification
61,500 ×. Insets, 81,500 ×. From Glomset *et al.* (1973a).

of HDL unesterified cholesterol is in the normal range (Table II), even
though the total concentration of HDL protein appears to be only about
one-third of normal (Torsvik, 1969, 1970, 1972).

Upon electron microscopy, the large HDL (Fig. 10A) have the appearance of stacked discs, 150–200 Å in diameter, whereas the small HDL
(Fig. 10B) appear to be round particles, 45–60 Å in diameter, consider-

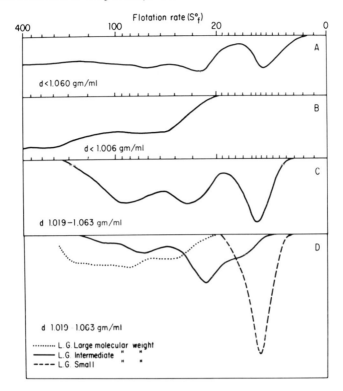

Fig. 7. Analytical ultracentrifugation of VLDL and LDL of patient with familial LCAT deficiency. Lipoproteins of L. C. obtained by preparative ultracentrifugation (parts A–C) and preparative ultracentrifugation and gel filtration (part D, see Fig. 4B and C). From Glomset *et al.* (1973a).

ably smaller than normal HDL (Forte *et al.*, 1971a; Forte and Nichols, 1972). As expected from their abnormal composition and size, the HDL subfractions are abnormal on analytical ultracentrifugation (Fig. 11). The large molecular weight subfraction yields material in the range of $F_{1.20}$ 3–20, whereas the small molecular weight HDL float at $F_{1.20}$ 0–3. Thus, both differ from normal HDL, which float in the range of $F_{1.20}$ 0–9 and yield peaks at $F_{1.20}$ 2(HDL₃) and approximately $F_{1.20}$ 5(HDL₂).

Torsvik (1972) has studied the apoproteins of the two HDL subfractions by immunochemistry, gel filtration, and amino acid analysis. Using specific antisera to the main apoproteins of normal HDL, apo A-I and apo A-II, he observed reactions of immunological identity between the precipitin bands of the large and small molecular weight subfractions and also between these bands and those obtained with purified normal apo A-I and apo A-II. He also filtered delipidized apoproteins of the large

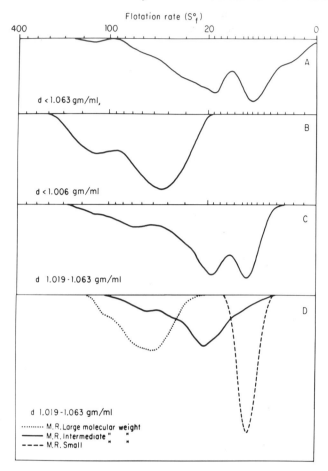

FIG. 8.   Analytical ultracentrifugation of VLDL and LDL of patient with familial LCAT deficiency. Lipoproteins of M. R. obtained by preparative ultracentrifugation (parts A–C) and preparative ultracentrifugation and gel filtration (part D, see Fig. 5B and C). From Glomset *et al.* (1973a).

molecular weight subfraction through Sephadex G 200 in 8 M urea and found a pattern very similar to that obtained with delipidized normal HDL of d 1.063–1.195 gm/ml (Fig. 12). In contrast, the small molecular weight subfraction was mainly comprised of apo A-I, i.e., material corresponding to peak III, Fig. 12A. The amino acid composition of the major peaks isolated by gel filtration of the delipidized apoproteins (Table VII) was generally similar to that obtained in comparable experiments with normal HDL (Torsvik, 1972).

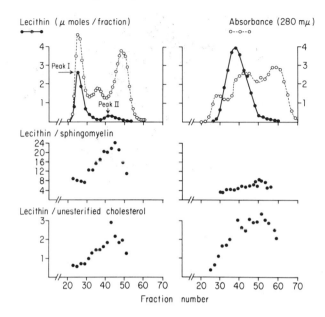

Fɪɢ. 9. Gel filtration of HDL. Left, plasma proteins of d > 1.063 gm/ml of patient with LCAT deficiency (M. R.). Right, corresponding proteins from a normal female. From Glomset *et al.* (1970); see also Torsvik (1969).

E. Dɪᴇᴛᴀʀʏ Exᴘᴇʀɪᴍᴇɴᴛs

Hamnström (1970) studied the effects of different diets on the plasma lipids of the Swedish patient, M. L. The diets were isocaloric in most cases and were characterized as (1) "ordinary hospital food"; (2) "high

Table VI

Lɪᴘɪᴅ:Pʀᴏᴛᴇɪɴ Rᴀᴛɪᴏs ᴏғ Nᴏʀᴍᴀʟ HDL ᴀɴᴅ HDL Sᴜʙғʀᴀᴄᴛɪᴏɴs
ғʀᴏᴍ ᴀ Pᴀᴛɪᴇɴᴛ ᴡɪᴛʜ Fᴀᴍɪʟɪᴀʟ LCAT Dᴇғɪᴄɪᴇɴᴄʏ[a]

	UC	CE	PC	S[b]	TG
	(μmoles lipid/mg protein)				
Normal	0.268	0.703	0.475	0.088	0.025
Patient A. A.					
Large HDL	3.33	—[c]	2.29	0.33	0.076
Small HDL	0.30	—[c]	0.67	0.04	0.089

[a] Data from Norum *et al.* (1971a). Patient had been on a low fat diet for 1 week.
[b] S = sphingomyelin.
[c] Amount present in sample below reliable limit of detection.

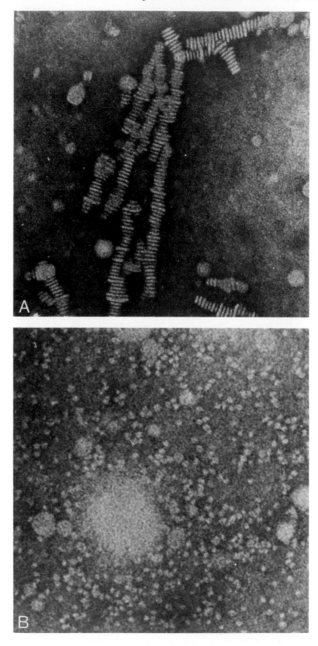

Fig. 10.   Electron micrographs of HDL subfractions from a patient with familial
LCAT deficiency. A, large molecular weight HDL of patient A. A. negatively stained
with phosphotungstic acid; approx. 189,000 ×. B, small molecular weight HDL of
patient A. A.; approx. 231,000 ×. From Forte *et al.* (1971a); see also Torsvik *et al.*
(1970).

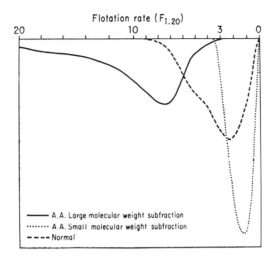

Flotation rate ($F_{1.20}$)

——— A.A. Large molecular weight subfraction
········ A.A. Small molecular weight subfraction
— — — Normal

FIG. 11. Analytical ultracentrifugation of HDL subfractions from a patient with familial LCAT deficiency. Large and small molecular weight subfractions from patient A. A. (see also Fig. 10) compared with normal HDL. From Norum *et al.* (1971a).

fat" (140–155 gm fat/50–60 gm carbohydrate, or 125–145 gm fat/50–60 gm carbohydrate); and (3) "high carbohydrate" (40–50 gm fat/325–350 gm carbohydrate, or 40–55 gm fat/220–300 gm carbohydrate). The high fat diets somewhat decreased the concentrations of plasma triglyceride and cholesterol as well as the relative amount of triglyceride (chylomicron triglyceride ?) in the top portion of a polyvinylpyrrolidone gradient, whereas high carbohydrate diets had the opposite effect. No changes occurred in the concentration of plasma cholesteryl esters, the electrophoretic mobility of the "broad β" lipoprotein band, or the cholesterol concentration of the proteins of d > 1.063 gm/ml. Unfortunately, detailed studies of the lipoproteins of this patient have not yet been carried out, and no more is known concerning the effects of diet. However, several dietary studies (Glomset *et al.*, 1973b) have been performed on four of the Norwegian patients with striking results. In these patients, isocaloric, low fat (approximately 6% of calories from fat) or fat-free (less than 1% of calories from fat) diets *decreased* plasma triglycerides and cholesterol (Table VIII), whereas subsequent hypercaloric, high carbohydrate diets or isocaloric diets in which the fat was provided by medium chain triglyceride increased the concentration of plasma triglyceride toward its starting value without affecting the concentration of cholesterol. However, the diets caused the most marked effects on the LDL and HDL subfractions. Thus, when patient A. A. was successively fed (a) an isocaloric

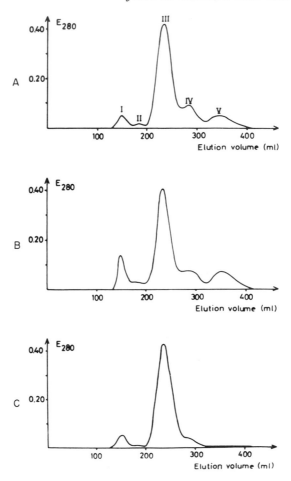

Fig. 12.   HDL apoproteins separated by gel filtration in 8 *M* urea. A, Apoproteins from normal HDL; B, large molecular weight HDL apoproteins from a patient (A. R.) with familial LCAT deficiency; C, small molecular weight HDL apoproteins from patient A. R. From Torsvik (1972).

diet containing 35% of the total calories as fat, (b) an isocaloric, fat-free diet, and (c) a hypercaloric, fat-free diet, the fat-free diets markedly *decreased* the concentration of the large molecular weight LDL, decreased the concentration of the intermediate molecular weight LDL to a lesser extent, and *increased* the small molecular weight LDL (Fig. 13, Table IX). Similarly, an isoelectric, fat-free diet given to patient M. R. caused a parallel reduction in the large molecular weight subfractions of d < 1.006 gm/ml, d 1.006–1.019 gm/ml, and d 1.019–1.063 gm/ml, and a

Table VII

Apoprotein Amino Acid Composition of Normal HDL and HDL Subfractions from a Patient (A. R.) with Familial LCAT Deficiency[a]

	Apo-A I			Apo-A II		
	Normal HDL	Large HDL	Small HDL	Normal HDL	Large HDL	Small HDL
	(moles/1000 moles amino acid)					
Lys	58.7	63.0	57.7	69.4	64.5	73.8
His	22.1	25.7	31.7	7.3	6.7	11.6
Arg	72.3	74.1	80.3	20.1	25.1	46.6
Asp	83.1	89.8	91.5	65.2	61.8	86.3
Thr	45.5	47.3	48.5	69.8	69.0	54.2
Ser	62.1	65.2	66.4	74.9	73.8	66.6
Gln	191.9	178.1	189.8	198.7	190.8	189.4
Pro	44.5	44.5	41.5	58.9	57.6	50.9
Gly	45.6	46.2	45.5	45.7	50.9	53.3
Ala	84.1	84.3	81.7	71.1	68.5	69.5
Val	58.2	61.8	64.0	73.0	81.6	65.7
Met	13.6	13.9	14.5	15.5	16.8	15.5
Ile	1.1	2.6	0.0	12.5	15.5	10.2
Leu	157.8	159.7	172.7	114.3	121.3	128.1
Tyr	30.7	30.6	34.2	46.3	44.5	35.1
Phe	26.6	28.0	29.5	45.3	46.2	35.0
Cys	0.7	2.3	0.5	13.9	14.9	8.1

[a] Data from Torsvik (1972). Normal HDL = lipoproteins of d 1.063–1.195 gm/ml. Large and small molecular weight HDL obtained by gel filtration on Sephadex G 200. Apo-A I and apo-A II obtained by gel filtration of the delipidized HDL by gel filtration on Sephadex G 200 in 8 M urea (see Fig. 12).

diet which contained 35% of the calories as low cholesterol fat caused changes in the opposite direction.

The effects of diet on the HDL of A. A. and M. R. also have been studied. Fat-free diets caused relatively little change in the large molecular weight HDL subfraction, but markedly decreased the concentration of the small molecular weight HDL, as shown by gel filtration (Fig. 14), disc gel electrophoresis (Fig. 15), and analytical ultracentrifugation (Fig. 16). In patient A. A., a diet that provided about 35% of the total calories in the form of medium chain triglyceride had the same general effect.

Several alternate mechanisms might account for the effect of dietary fat on the large molecular weight VLDL and the large and intermediate molecular weight LDL. One possibility is that dietary fat directly stimulates formation and secretion of a family of abnormal lipoproteins by the intestine and/or the liver. Another possibility is that dietary fat af-

Table VIII

EFFECT OF DIET ON LIPOPROTEIN LIPIDS AND PROTEIN OF A PATIENT
(A. A.) WITH FAMILIAL LCAT DEFICIENCY

	UC	PC	CE	TG	Protein
		(μmoles/ml plasma)			(μg/ml plasma)
VLDL					
Isocaloric, 35% fat[a]	2.369	1.436	0.442	7.025	384
Isocaloric, fat-free	1.440	1.251	0.349	3.284	352
Hypercaloric, fat-free	2.178	1.840	0.343	5.275	7.8
LDL (d 1.006–1.019 gm/ml)					
Isocaloric, 35% fat	0.121	0.081	0.008	0.127	50
Isocaloric, fat-free	0.226	0.220	0.035	0.301	169
Hypercaloric, fat-free	0.131	0.119	0.012	0.165	73
LDL (d 1.019–1.063 gm/ml)					
Isocaloric, 35% fat	0.861	0.585	0.009	0.191	172
Isocaloric, fat-free	0.463	0.386	0.034	0.269	336
Hypercaloric, fat-free	0.343	0.335	0.019	0.267	271
HDL					
Isocaloric, 35% fat	0.757	0.698	0.006	0.067	—
Isocaloric, fat-free	0.578	0.506	0.009	0.052	—
Hypercaloric, fat-free	0.409	0.465	0.004	0.052	—

[a] 35% of calories provided by fat (see Glomset et al., 1973b).

fects the rate of removal of the abnormal lipoproteins from the circulation. However, the most attractive possibility at the moment is that the abnormal lipoproteins are directly or indirectly derived from the surfaces of chylomicrons. This possibility is supported by the fact that the large and intermediate lipoproteins, like chylomicron surfaces (Zilversmit, 1965), contain large amounts of unesterified cholesterol and lecithin, and is in line with the concept of Schumaker and Adams (1970) that a relative excess of unesterified cholesterol and lecithin develops as the triglycerides of chylomicrons or VLDL are progressively hydrolyzed by LPL. Thus, in the absence of LCAT, the agent presumed to dispose of this excess lipid, unesterified cholesterol, phospholipid, and apo C might "bud off" chylomicrons or VLDL and ultimately form abnormal, intermediate and large molecular weight aggregates (Fig. 17).

A further extension of this concept, also shown in Fig. 17, is that small molecular weight HDL also may be derived from chylomicrons.[2] The

[2] The alternate mechanisms proposed to account for the changes in abnormal VLDL and LDL also must be considered, and especially the possibility that the small HDL may be secreted by the liver in response to chylomicrons.

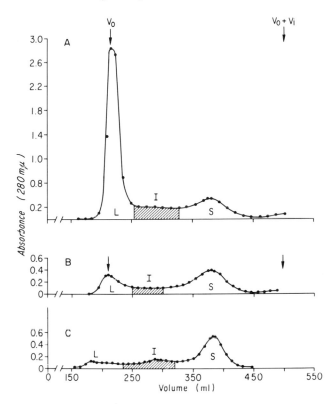

Fɪɢ. 13. Effect of fat-free diets on the LDL of a patient with familial LCAT deficiency. Patient A. A. was successively fed a diet containing (A) 35% of the total calories as fat, (B) an isocaloric, fat-free diet, and (C) a hypercaloric, fat-free diet for periods of approximately 1 week each. At the end of each dietary period the LDL of d 1.019–1.063 gm/ml were prepared by ultracentrifugation and subfractionated by gel filtration on 2% agarose gel. From Glomset *et al.* (1973b).

observation (Kostner and Holasec, 1972) that human chylomicrons contain isoleucine-free apo A-I is compatible with this possibility since the small molecular weight HDL, but apparently not the large molecular weight HDL, also appear to contain isoleucine-free apo A-I (Table VIII). Thus, the small molecular weight HDL, the best substrates of LCAT (Glomset *et al.*, 1966, 1970), also might be released during the intravascular catabolism of chylomicrons and, by being acted upon by LCAT, contribute to the disposal of "excess" unesterified cholesterol and lecithin. This possibility is supported by the *in vitro* incubation studies described below.

Table IX

CONCENTRATION OF LIPIDS AND PROTEIN OF LDL SUBFRACTIONS OF A PATIENT
(A. A.) WITH FAMILIAL LCAT DEFICIENCY AS AFFECTED BY THREE
DIFFERENT DIETS[a]

	UC	PC	CE	TG	Protein
					(µg/ml
		(µmoles/ml plasma)			plasma)
Large LDL					
Isocaloric, 35% fat	0.4777	0.2027	0.0016	0.0201	14.27
Isocaloric, fat-free	0.0999	0.0436	0.0004	0.0044	5.31
Hypercaloric, fat-free	0.0288	0.0136	0.0002	0.0017	3.24
Intermediate LDL					
Isocaloric, 35% fat	0.1681	0.0912	0.0010	0.0156	14.49
Isocaloric, fat-free	0.0977	0.0529	0.0013	0.0114	12.50
Hypercaloric, fat-free	0.1199	0.0711	0.0010	0.0142	10.61
Small LDL					
Isocaloric, 35% fat	0.1407	0.1143	0.0088	0.1287	91.28
Isocaloric, fat-free	0.1892	0.1590	0.0278	0.1765	147.25
Hypercaloric, fat-free	0.1557	0.1632	0.0193	0.1951	144.28

[a] Patient A. A. was successively given the diets indicated for periods of 7, 7, and 5 days, respectively, and the LDL subfractions of d 1.019–1.063 gm/ml were subsequently isolated by preparative ultracentrifugation and filtration through 2% agarose gel (see Glomset *et al.*, 1973b).

F. INCUBATION EXPERIMENTS

Early *in vitro* experiments (Norum and Gjone, 1967b) indicated that the abnormal cholesterol and phospholipid composition of the patients' lipoproteins is not caused by inability to react directly with normal LCAT; and subsequent experiments (Glomset *et al.*, 1970) showed that the LCAT reaction indirectly promotes nonenzymatic transfer of unesterified cholesterol, lecithin, cholesteryl ester, and triglyceride among the patient's lipoproteins in the same way as it does among normal plasma lipoproteins. However, recent studies have gone considerably further (Norum *et al.*, 1971b, 1973). Incubation of the patients' isolated VLDL with normal plasma proteins of d > 1.063 gm/ml has been found to increase the electrophoretic mobility of the VLDL to that of pre-β-lipoproteins (Fig. 18), and this increase is markedly enhanced by the presence of active LCAT. The increase is not affected by washing of the reisolated VLDL in the presence of fatty acid-poor albumin, and appears to be associated with very little change in flotation rate. However, lipid transfers occur and lipoproteins of d 1.006–1.063 gm/ml are formed (Table X).

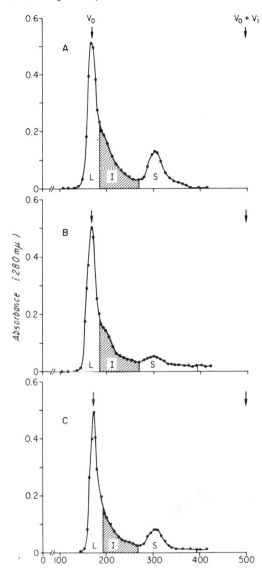

FIG. 14. Effect of diet on the HDL of a patient with familial LCAT deficiency. Patient M. R. was successively fed a diet containing (A) 35% of the total calories as fat, (B) an isocaloric, fat-free diet, and (C) a diet containing 35% of the total calories as low cholesterol fat. At the end of each dietary period (2, 5, and 4 days respectively) the HDL were prepared by ultracentrifugation and subfractionated by gel filtration on Sephadex G 200. From Glomset *et al.* (1973b).

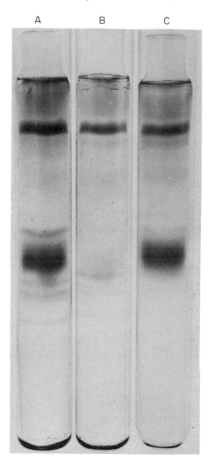

Fig. 15. Effect of diet on the HDL of a patient with familial LCAT deficiency, same dietary experiment as shown in Fig. 14. HDL of patient M. R. were analyzed by disc gel electrophoresis. Separating gel = 10% polyacrylamide. Protein applied to gels: 148, 128, and 148 μg respectively. Note that the fast moving component is comparable to the small molecular weight HDL isolated by gel filtration. From Glomset *et al.* (1973b).

Changes in lipid composition (Table XI) also occur when the patients' LDL subfractions are incubated with normal plasma proteins of d > 1.063 gm/ml. In the case of the large and intermediate LDL, changes in unesterified cholesterol occur in the absence of equimolar changes in cholesteryl ester or triglyceride. In the case of the small LDL, major changes in unesterified cholesterol and lecithin occur and a large proportion of the triglyceride is replaced by cholesteryl ester. These changes are accompanied by only slight changes in flotation rate and no changes in electrophoretic mobility.

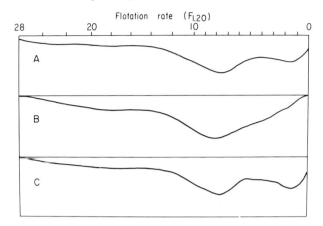

Fɪɢ. 16. Effect of diet on the HDL of a patient with familial LCAT deficiency. Same dietary experiment as shown in Figs. 14 and 15. HDL analyzed by analytical ultracentrifugation. Note that the slow moving component of $F_{1.20}$ 1–2 is comparable to the small molecular weight HDL isolated by gel filtration. From Glomset *et al.* (1973b).

The above changes in isolated VLDL and LDL, taken in conjunction with similar changes in the composition of the large molecular weight HDL demonstrated earlier (Glomset *et al.*, 1970), provide a basis for understanding the effects of incubating the patients' unfractionated plasma in the presence of normal proteins of d > 1.063 gm/ml or d > 1.25 gm/ml. Thus, incubation with plasma proteins of d > 1.063 gm/ml

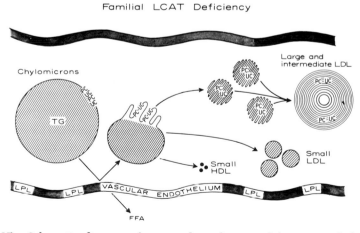

Fɪɢ. 17. Schematic diagram of proposed mechanism of formation of abnormal LDL and HDL in familial LCAT deficiency. TG = triglyceride, PC = lecithin, UC = unesterified cholesterol, LPL = lipoprotein lipase. From Glomset *et al.* (1973b).

Normal   A. A.   A. A. VLDL incubated with
⊢VLDL⊣⊢VLDL ⊢————————normal d >1.063 proteins ————⊣

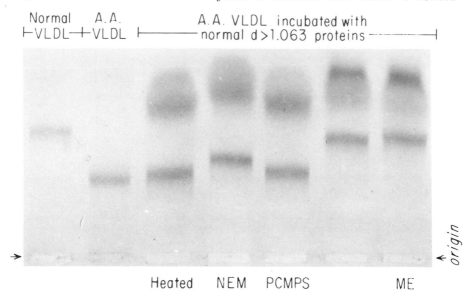

Heated   NEM   PCMPS   ME

Fig. 18. Effect of incubation on VLDL of a patient with familial LCAT deficiency. VLDL of patient A. A. incubated for 24 hours at 37°C with normal plasma proteins of d > 1.063 gm/ml. The LCAT activity present in the normal plasma proteins was inactivated by heating at 56°C, or by adding 0.1 M N-ethylmaleimide (NEM) or 2 mM p-chloromercuriphenylsulfonate (PCMPS) or its activity was maintained by adding 0.01 M mercaptoethanol (ME). After the incubation the VLDL were reisolated by ultracentrifugation and analyzed by electrophoresis on agarose gel. From Norum et al. (1973).

in the presence of LCAT decreases the LDL of $S_f > 12$ and increases the LDL of S_f 0–12 (Fig. 19); these changes are accompanied by major decrements in the unesterified cholesterol and lecithin of the large and intermediate LDL obtained by gel filtration (Fig. 20, Table XII), and by two- to threefold increments in the lecithin, cholesteryl ester, triglyceride, and *protein* of the small LDL.

Similar though less extensive effects are obtained when the patients' plasma is incubated with normal plasma proteins of d > 1.25 gm/ml in the presence of LCAT; and these experiments permit analysis of the effects of incubation on the patients' HDL. The most striking change observed is the disappearance of the stacked discs of large molecular weight HDL and the appearance of particles that resemble normal HDL on electron microscopy (Fig. 21). In addition, one experiment in which the pattern of HDL obtained on gel filtration was analyzed (Fig. 22) was of particular interest in that it showed a decrement in the large molecular weight subfraction and a *disproportionate* increment in the protein of HDL of intermediate size (Table XIII). Although the total

Table X

EFFECT OF INCUBATION WITH NORMAL PLASMA PROTEINS OF d > 1.063 gm/ml
OR d > 1.25 gm/ml ON THE VLDL OF A PATIENT WITH FAMILIAL
LCAT DEFICIENCY[a]

	UC	PC	S	CE	TG	Protein (µg/ml incubation medium)
	(mµmoles/ml incubation medium)					
VLDL after incubation with:						
Proteins of d > 1.25 gm/ml[b]	77	64	61	34	146	30.8
Proteins of d > 1.063 gm/ml + PCMPS[c]	70	57	12	63	153	34.4
Proteins of d > 1.063 gm/ml + ME[d]	7	34	5	100	89	33.9
LDL after incubation with:						
Proteins of d > 1.25 gm/ml[b]	7	5	1	4	13	7.7
Proteins of d > 1.063 gm/ml + PCMPS[c]	11	9	2	16	12	8.9
Proteins of d > 1.063 gm/ml + ME[d]	2	14	3	37	22	17.9

[a] VLDL of patient L. G. were isolated by preparative ultracentrifugation and the void volume components removed by filtration through 2% agarose gel (Glomset *et al.*, 1973a). An amount equivalent to that present in 15.3 ml plasma was incubated with the equivalent of 57 ml of normal plasma proteins of d > 1.063 gm/ml or d > 1.25 gm/ml for 24 hours at 37°. Subsequently the proteins of d < 1.006 gm/ml (VLDL) and those of d 1.006–1.063 g/ml (LDL) were reisolated by preparative ultracentrifugation.

[b] Plasma proteins of d > 1.25 gm/ml were heated at 56°C for 30 minutes to inactivate LCAT.

[c] PCMPS (*p*-chloromercuriphenylsulfonate, 2 mM) added to inactivate LCAT.

[d] ME (mercaptoethanol, 0.01 M) added to maintain LCAT activity.

amount of HDL lipid present was very small, the changes in lipid appeared to parallel those in absorbance and protein.

The above findings indicate that LCAT can cause very large changes in the unesterified cholesterol and lecithin of the patients' VLDL, LDL, and HDL, and suggest that these changes are accompanied by partial fragmentation of the lipoproteins of d > 1.006 gm/ml into "small molecular weight" LDL and by formation of HDL. Considered with the descriptive data and the results of the dietary experiments, they support the possibility that a family of large, unesterified cholesterol and lecithinrich particles (mostly of d 1.019–1.063 gm/ml, but also of d 1.006–1.019 gm/ml and d > 1.006 gm/ml) is generated from the surfaces of chylomicrons when the latter are attacked by lipoprotein lipase in the absence of LCAT. They suggest also that the LCAT reaction normally prevents these particles from accumulating by promoting nonenzymatic transfers

Table XI

Effect of Incubation with Normal Plasma Proteins of d > 1.063 gm/ml
or d > 1.25 gm/ml on Isolated LDL Subfractions of a Patient
with Familial LCAT Deficiency[a]

	UC	PC	CE	TG
Subfraction	(mμmoles/mg protein)			
Large LDL after incubation with:				
Proteins of d > 1.25 gm/ml	12.3	6.48	0.61	0.55
Proteins of d > 1.063 gm/ml	8.2	5.45	1.60	0.75
Intermediate LDL after incubation with:				
Proteins of d > 1.25 gm/ml	11.7	7.47	0.54	0.74
Proteins of d > 1.063 gm/ml	7.9	4.35	1.44	0.51
Small LDL after incubation with:				
Proteins of d > 1.25 gm/ml	0.8	0.78	0.78	1.00
Proteins of d > 1.063 gm/ml	0.13	0.30	1.34	0.57
Normal LDL	1.44	0.48	1.77	0.11

[a] LDL of d 1.019–1.063 gm/ml from patient M. R. were subfractionated by filtration through 2% agarose gel columns (see Figs. 3–5). The large, intermediate, and small molecular weight were incubated for 24 hours at 37°C with normal plasma proteins of d > 1.25 gm/ml or d > 1.063 gm/ml. The LCAT activity in the proteins of d > 1.25 gm/ml had previously been heat-inactivated. After the incubation, the lipoproteins of d > 1.063 gm/ml were reisolated by preparative ultracentrifugation.

of unesterified cholesterol and lecithin to HDL. The smaller molecular weight VLDL and LDL also are probably generated by the action of lipoprotein lipase on chylomicrons and larger VLDL. Their abnormal composition is consistent with the possibility that LCAT normally decreases the unesterified cholesterol, lecithin, and triglyceride of VLDL and LDL by promoting nonenzymatic transfers of HDL cholesteryl ester to the VLDL and LDL. Finally, the data suggest that smaller molecular weight HDL also are related to chylomicrons and raise the possibility that apo-A proteins derived from the surfaces of chylomicrons act with LCAT to form HDL cholesteryl ester and dispose of chylomicron polar lipid. Conceivably, further action to the enzyme on the HDL might generate a family comparable to the HDL$_3$ of normal plasma, while the effect of the reaction on the large molecular weight HDL might be to generate a family comparable to the HDL$_2$.

Several of the lipoprotein abnormalities of familial LCAT deficiency remain to be clarified. Although the hyperlipemia seems to be related to renal dysfunction, the mechanisms involved are by no means clear. One possibility is that the action of lipoprotein lipase is blocked in some way,

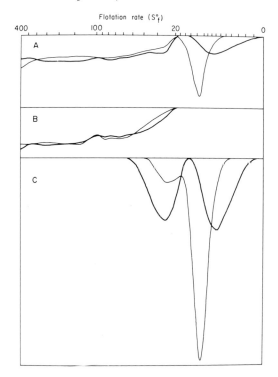

FIG. 19. Effect of incubation on the lipoproteins of d < 1.063 gm/ml of a patient with familial LCAT deficiency. Plasma of patient A. A. incubated for 24 hours at 37°C with normal plasma proteins of d > 1.063 gm/ml. Subsequently, patient's lipoproteins analyzed by analytical ultracentrifugation at d 1.060 gm/ml. A = total lipoproteins of d < 1.063 gm/ml; B = lipoproteins of d < 1.006 gm/ml; C = lipoproteins of d 1.006–1.063 gm/ml. From Norum *et al.* (1973).

even though post heparin lipolytic activity appears to be normal (Norum *et al.*, 1972). One indication of deficient lipoprotein lipase activity is the presence of chylomicrons in the plasma of fasting patients. The apparent effect of the hyperlipemia on the distribution of large and intermediate molecular weight LDL also remains to be explained. Perhaps the relative amount of intermediate LDL formed is dependent on the availability of apo-C so that when apo-C is "trapped" by the hyperchylomicronemia, larger LDL particles that contain less protein are formed. Another question that needs to be explored concerns the large HDL. The "stacked disc" appearance upon electron microscopy is evidently caused by the lack of cholesteryl ester, as indicated by the model recombination experiments of Forte *et al.* (1971b) and by the disappearance of the stacks upon incubation of the patients' plasma with LCAT. However, the site

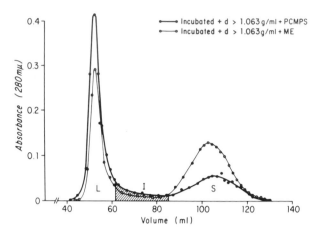

FIG. 20.   Effect of incubation on the lipoproteins of d < 1.063 gm/ml of a patient with familial LCAT deficiency. Same experiment as shown in Fig. 19. LDL of d 1.019–1.063 gm/ml of patient A. A. analyzed by gel filtration on 2% agarose gel. From Norum *et al.* (1973).

Table XII

EFFECT OF INCUBATION WITH NORMAL PLASMA PROTEINS OF d > 1.063 gm/ml
ON LDL SUBFRACTIONS FROM A PATIENT WITH FAMILIAL LCAT
DEFICIENCY[a]

	UC	PC	CE	TG	Protein (μg/ml incubation medium)
	(nmoles/ml incubation medium)				
Large molecular weight					
− LCAT[b]	189.0	98.0	5.5	18.8	9.4
+ LCAT	96.0	54.0	5.1	13.5	8.4
Intermediate molecular weight					
− LCAT[b]	53.0	29.0	2.7	10.6	6.5
+ LCAT	23.0	11.0	4.0	10.1	5.2
Small molecular weight					
− LCAT[b]	61.0	44.0	38.0	46.0	57.0
+ LCAT	62.0	75.0	128.0	142.0	119.0

[a] Normal plasma proteins of d > 1.063 gm/ml corresponding to 17 ml plasma were incubated with 6 ml plasma from patient A. A. for 24 hours at 37°C and LDL subfractions of d 1.019–1.063 gm/ml subsequently isolated by preparative ultracentrifugation and filtration through 2% agarose gel (see Fig. 20).

[b] LCAT activity was inhibited by adding *p*-chloromercuriphenylsulfonate (final concentration 2 mM).

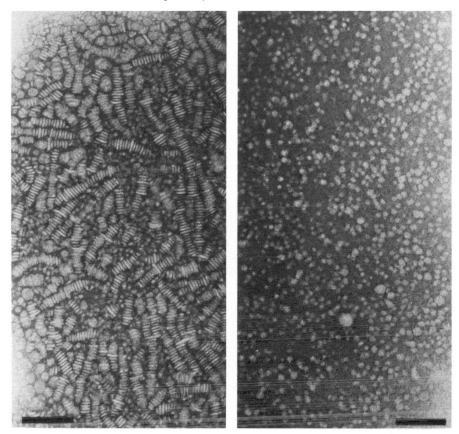

Fɪɢ. 21.   Effect of incubation on the HDL of a patient with familial LCAT deficiency. Plasma of patient L. G. incubated with normal plasma proteins of d > 1.21 gm/ml for 24 hours at 37°C. HDL isolated by preparative ultracentrifugation, negatively stained with phosphotungstic acid, and studied by electron microscopy. Left, before. Right, after. Approx. 135,000 ×. From Norum *et al.* (1973).

of formation of the large HDL and the factors that regulate their secretion are completely unclear. Finally, it is not at all obvious why the total concentrations of small molecular weight LDL protein (total LDL apo-B ?) and HDL protein should be lower than normal although recent unpublished studies (J. Albers) have shown that most of the Apo-A-I of patient I. S. is in the plasma protein fraction of d > 1.25 gm/ml.

Other aspects of familial LCAT deficiency that remain to be clarified are the mechanisms of the anemia and the renal dysfunction. The possibility that these abnormalities may be related to the increased levels of plasma unesterified cholesterol will be discussed in Section V,B.

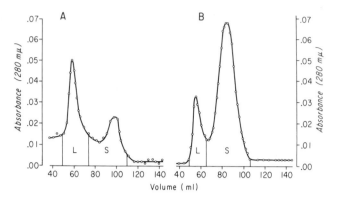

FIG. 22. Effect of incubation on the HDL of a patient with familial LCAT deficiency. Plasma of patient A. A. incubated with normal plasma proteins of d > 1.25 gm/ml for 24 hours at 37°C. HDL isolated by preparative ultracentrifugation and subfractionated by gel filtration on Sephadex G 200. A, incubation in the presence of 2 mM *p*-chloromercuriphenylsulfonate; B, incubation in the presence of 0.01 M mercaptoethanol. From Norum *et al.* (1973).

III. Cholesterol-Fed Guinea Pigs

Several animal species develop anemia when fed cholesterol (Grice *et al.*, 1966), but the phenomenon has been most thoroughly studied in

Table XIII

EFFECT OF INCUBATION WITH NORMAL PLASMA PROTEINS OF d > 1.25 gm/ml
ON HDL SUBFRACTIONS OF A PATIENT WITH FAMILIAL LCAT
DEFICIENCY[a]

	UC	PL	CE	TG	Protein (μg/ml incubation medium)
		(nmoles/ml incubation medium)			
Large HDL					
− LCAT[b]	16	6.0	1.8	1.2	6.5
+ LCAT	3	0.0	1.8	0.0	2.6
Small HDL					
− LCAT[b]	0	0.0	1.8	0.0	2.6
+ LCAT	4	20.4	9.3	1.1	63.5

[a] Incubation conditions as described in Table XII except that 15.5 ml normal plasma proteins of d > 1.25 gm/ml were used and HDL subfractions from patient A. A. were subsequently isolated by preparative ultracentrifugation and filtration through Sephadex G 200.

[b] LCAT inhibited by adding 2 mM *p*-chloromercuriphenylsulfonate.

the guinea pig, and in this species many of the abnormalities induced by the dietary cholesterol resemble those in familial LCAT deficiency. The most striking abnormalities are seen in the plasma lipoproteins (Puppione *et al.*, 1971; Sardet *et al.*, 1972a); but in addition the anemia is associated with increased hemolysis (Yamanaka *et al.*, 1967a) and accompanied by a several-fold increase in erythrocyte unesterified cholesterol and lecithin (Yamanaka *et al.*, 1967b; Ostwald and Shannon, 1964; Ostwald *et al.*, 1970); and proteinuria is present, associated with lipid-filled vacuoles in the glomeruli (French *et al.*, 1967). The lipoprotein abnormalities will be described below; possible causes and effects of the abnormalities will be discussed in Section V,B.

The VLDL of animals fed a 1% cholesterol diet for 10–14 weeks contain increased amounts of unesterified cholesterol compared with those of animals fed a control diet (mass ratio relative to protein 1.7 compared with 0.44) and migrate more slowly on electrophoresis ("β" or "slow pre-β" mobility). These features are reminiscent of those already described for the VLDL of patients with familial LCAT deficiency.

The LDL abnormalities show even more impressive similarities. Not only are the concentrations of LDL unesterified cholesterol and phospholipid increased (Table XIV), but upon being filtered through 2% agarose gel the LDL yield subfractions that are generally similar in size distribution to those of patients with familial LCAT deficiency. The LDL subfractions also resemble those in familial LCAT deficiency in

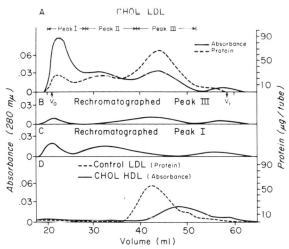

Fig. 23. Gel chromatography of guinea pig LDL and HDL on 2% agarose. A, LDL of d 1.01–1.05 gm/ml from cholesterol-fed guinea pig. B, rechromatography of peak III from experiment shown in A. C, rechromatography of peak I from the experiment shown in A. D, control LDL and HDL from cholesterol-fed guinea pigs. From Sardet *et al.* (1972a).

Table XIV

PLASMA LIPOPROTEIN CONCENTRATION AND COMPOSITION OF GUINEA PIGS
FED DIETS WITH AND WITHOUT 1% CHOLESTEROL[a]

	Concentration (mg lipid/100 ml plasma)	Composition (percent total weight)				
Lipoprotein fraction		CE	PL[b]	TG	UC	FFA[c]
d < 1.006 gm/ml						
Control diet	38	—	—	—	—	—
Cholesterol diet	50	11.8	12.1	65.7	6.5	3.9
d 1.006–1.063 gm/ml						
Control diet	108	53.4	27.0	9.8	8.4	1.3
Cholesterol diet	309	49.2	24.4	2.6	23.1	0.7
d 1.063–1.21 gm/ml						
Control diet	7	—	—	—	—	—
Cholesterol diet	62	20.8	42.2	2.3	33.2	1.5

[a] Data from Puppione *et al.* (1971).
[b] PL = phospholipid.
[c] FFA = free fatty acids.

that those of large and intermediate molecular weight (peaks I and II, Fig. 23) are unusually rich in unesterified cholesterol and phospholipid, whereas the smaller LDL, which emerge in the same position as those of control animals, have a composition more nearly like those of normal LDL (Table XV). Furthermore, electron micrographs (Fig. 24) of the large and intermediate molecular weight subfractions show flat discs, 800 to 1000 Å in diameter, whereas electron micrographs of the small LDL show particles very similar to control LDL; and studies using the analytical ultracentrifuge (Fig. 25) show the presence of fast floating components of S_f 7 to 12 and S_f >12 as well as the component of S_f 7 shown in the control animals. Finally, preliminary studies of the apoproteins by disc gel electrophoresis suggest that the large LDL mainly contain smaller peptides, possibly analogous to apo-C, whereas the small molecular weight LDL, like those of control animals and normal humans, contain apoprotein (apo-B ?) that is too large to enter the gel.

The HDL of cholesterol-fed guinea pigs resemble the large HDL of patients with familial LCAT deficiency in that they are excluded from Sephadex G 200, yield a single component somewhat smaller than normal LDL upon being filtered through agarose gels (Fig. 23), contain large amounts of unesterified cholesterol and phospholipid (Table XVI), and yield stacked discs upon electron microscopy (Fig. 26). The apoproteins of the HDL have not been specifically identified. However, cholesterol

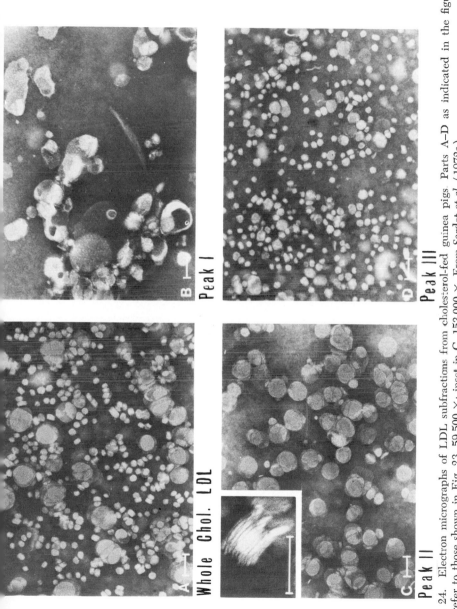

FIG. 24. Electron micrographs of LDL subfractions from cholesterol-fed guinea pigs. Parts A–D as indicated in the figure. Peaks refer to those shown in Fig. 23. 59,500 ×; inset in C, 153,000 ×. From Sardet *et al.* (1972a).

Table XV

COMPOSITION OF LDL SUBFRACTIONS OF CHOLESTEROL-FED GUINEA PIGS[a]

Kind of diet	UC	CE	PL[b]	TG	Percent of total LDL lipids
	(μmoles lipid/mg protein $\pm$ S.D.)				
Cholesterol diet					
Peak I[c]	15.8 ± 4.5	3.9 ± 0.5	8.6 ± 2.0	trace	20
Peak II	13.0 ± 3.4	2.6 ± 0.7	6.3 ± 1.5	0.14 ± 0.03	40
Peak III	3.9 ± 0.2	3.5 ± 0.2	2.3 ± 0.5	0.24 ± 0.06	40
Control diet[d]	0.8 ± 0.4	3.4 ± 1.0	1.4 ± 0.6	0.78 ± 0.31	100

[a] Data from Sardet *et al.* (1972a).
[b] PL = phospholipid.
[c] Peaks correspond to peaks in Fig. 23.
[d] Whole LDL from animals on control diet.

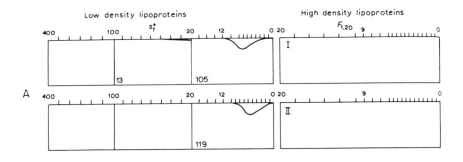

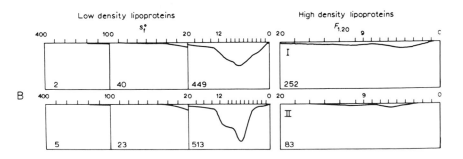

FIG. 25. Analytical ultracentrifugation of guinea pig lipoproteins. A, lipoproteins from a control guinea pig. B, lipoproteins from a cholesterol-fed guinea pig. From Puppione *et al.* (1971).

Table XVI

RELATIVE COMPOSITION OF GUINEA PIG HDL SUBFRACTIONS AS A
FUNCTION OF DIETARY CHOLESTEROL[a]

	UC	CE	PL	TG	Protein
Lipoproteins			(% of total weight)		
d 1.063–1.090 gm/ml					
control diet	6	52	16	2	24
cholesterol diet	31	17	32	2	18
d 1.090–1.21 gm/ml					
control diet	9	25	25	2	39
cholesterol diet	24	15	31	2	28

[a] Data from Sardet *et al.* (1972a).

feeding alters the pattern of bands obtained on disc gel electrophoresis of delipidized HDL, and greatly increases one band (apo-A ?) in particular.

Several important differences between the abnormalities of cholesterol-fed guinea pigs and patients with familial LCAT deficiency must be mentioned. First, LCAT appears to be present in normal guinea pig serum (Felt, 1971), although no measurements of the enzyme activity in the serum of cholesterol-fed guinea pigs have been reported. Possibly because of LCAT activity present, relatively more cholesteryl ester is present in the guinea pig lipoproteins. Also, the LDL contain more sphingomyelin and less triglyceride than those of the patients. Another important difference, possibly related to the presence of LCAT activity, is that the lipoprotein abnormalities are not induced by the triglyceride of the cholesterol-free control diet. Still another difference is that guinea pig plasma normally contains little HDL and cholesterol feeding *increases* the HDL, whereas the HDL of patients with familial LCAT deficiency is decreased compared with that of normal humans. Finally, the livers of cholesterol-fed guinea pigs appear to be damaged since they are greatly enlarged and contain increased amounts of cholesteryl ester, apparently in fat vacuoles. Possibly because of liver damage, the plasma of cholesterol-fed animals contains cholesteryl ester hydrolase activity (R. Ostwald, personal communication), whereas no signs of nonspecific liver dysfunction are observed in familial LCAT deficiency.

IV. Cholestasis

Abnormalities similar to those described in familial LCAT deficiency and in cholesterol-fed guinea pigs have also been observed in humans

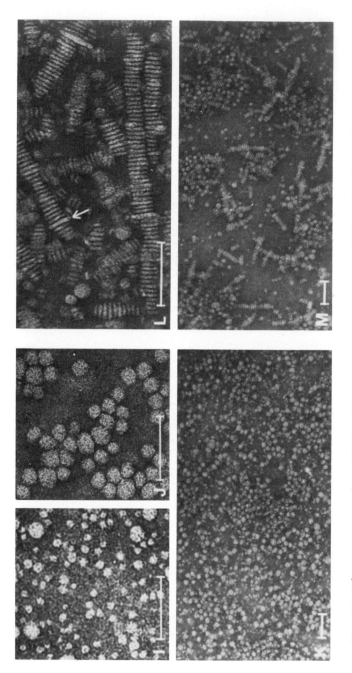

FIG. 26. Electron micrographs of HDL subfractions from guinea pigs. I, HDL of d 1.063–1.090 from control animals. J, HDL of d 1.090–1.21 gm/ml from control animals. K, HDL of d 1.070–1.21 gm/ml from control animals. L and M, HDL of d 1.070–1.21 gm/ml from cholesterol-free guinea pig. K and M, approximate magnification 64,000 ×; I, J, L, 166,000 ×. From Sardet et al. (1972a).

and animals with long-standing cholestasis (obstruction of the bile duct). Increased concentrations of unesterified cholesterol and lecithin are present in the plasma; the content of the same lipids is increased in the erythrocytes; and lipid deposits have been found in the glomeruli. Furthermore, the plasma lipoproteins of human patients with cholestasis have been shown to be abnormal and of particular relevance to the present review since the abnormal LDL are almost identical to the intermediate molecular weight LDL of patients with familial LCAT deficiency. As in earlier sections, we will consider the plasma lipoprotein abnormalities first and then consider possible causes and effects of these abnormalities in Section V,B.

Few systematic studies of VLDL of patients with cholestasis have been performed, but Quarfordt *et al.* (1972) found increased contents of unesterified cholesterol and phospholipid in the VLDL of two of their patients and decreased contents of protein in the VLDL of four of their patients. In addition, the VLDL of all of the patients migrated in the β-position upon electrophoresis, as has been noted for the VLDL of other patients with liver disease with or without cholestasis (Gjone and Norum, 1970; Papadopoulos and Charles, 1970; Seidel *et al.*, 1972a). The cause of this decreased mobility is not known, but Quarfordt *et al.* (1972) report that the content of apo-C is reduced, whereas Seidel *et al.* (1972b) have suggested that apo-A may be lacking. Seidel *et al.* (1972b) state that incubation of the VLDL for 2 hours with normal HDL (0.5 mg HDL protein per milligram VLDL protein) increases the mobility of the VLDL to normal, but they present no experiments to evaluate the effect of the LCAT activity present or to demonstrate whether or not nonenzymatic transfers of lipid or protein occur.

The LDL of patients with cholestasis have been extensively studied since the observation was made (Eder *et al.*, 1955; Furman and Conrad, 1957) that they contain most of the increased unesterified cholesterol and phospholipid long known (Flint, 1862) to be present in the plasma in cholestasis. The first abnormal lipoproteins of d 1.006–1.063 gm/ml were isolated from a patient with biliary cirrhosis by Russ *et al.* (1956); and Switzer (1967) subsequently used a combination of immunoprecipitation and polyanion precipitation, and in some experiments also ultracentrifugation, to purify the pathological lipoprotein ("OLP" = "obstruction lipoprotein"). This lipoprotein contained more than 60% phospholipid by weight (Table XVII), about 25% unesterified cholesterol, and only trace amounts of triglyceride and cholesteryl ester. The protein of purified preparations, only about 5% of the total by weight, did not react with antisera to normal HDL or LDL, but rabbit antisera to the abnormal lipoprotein did react with normal VLDL.

Table XVII

Composition of the Abnormal LDL in Cholestasis, Familial LCAT
Deficiency, and in Cholesterol-Fed Guinea Pigs

	Protein	Phos-pholipids	Cholesterol	Cholesteryl esters	Tri-glycerides
Condition; Reference	(weight % of total lipoprotein)				
Cholestasis					
Switzer (1967)[a]	13.0	61.0	26.0	trace	trace
Seidel et al. (1969)[b]	5.8	66.5	22.4	2.4	2.9
Hamilton et al. (1971)[c]	2.5	65.0	31.0	0.3	0.9
Picard and Veissiere (1970a)[d]	1.3	58.4	17.9	19.4	3.0
LCAT deficiency					
Torsvik et al. (1972)[e]	5.0	60.7	28.3	2.9	3.1
Glomset et al. (1973a)[f]	10.2	50.0	33.0	2.1	5.1
Cholesterol-fed guinea pig					
Sardet et al. (1972a)[g]	7.9	38.5	39.5	13.2	0.9

[a] Mean of values from four patients with extrahepatic biliary obstruction. Purification of lipoprotein fraction by means of ultracentrifugation yielded preparations with protein content of only 5%.

[b] Mean of four preparations from patients with obstructive jaundice.

[c] Highly purified fraction from a patient with obstructive jaundice.

[d] Specific source not given.

[e] Intermediate molecular weight fraction of LDL (d 1.019–1.063) obtained by agarose column chromatograph. Patient with familial LCAT deficiency not designated.

[f] Rechromatographed material from intermediate molecular weight fraction of LDL (d 1.019–1.063) of patient M. R. on ordinary diet.

[g] Recalculated from data given by Sardet et al. (1972a).

More recently, work in other laboratories has confirmed and significantly extended Switzer's observations and in addition provided a basis for comparing the abnormal LDL in cholestasis with those in familial LCAT deficiency. Picard and Veissiere (1970a) showed that the LDL of patients with cholestasis yield several subfractions upon being filtered through 2% agarose gel and that a major subfraction of abnormally large molecular size (peak II, Fig. 27) contains most of the abnormal LDL, whereas a major subfraction of smaller molecular size (peak III, Fig. 27) emerges in the same general position as normal LDL. The composition of the abnormal LDL in peak II (Table XVII, see also Picard and Veissiere, 1970b; Hamilton et al., 1971) is similar to that of the abnormal LDL isolated by the procedure of Switzer (1967) or by a combination of preparative ultracentrifugation, polyanion precipitation, and Cohn fractionation ("LP-X," Seidel et al., 1969), and generally resembles that

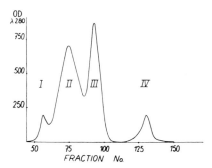

Fɪɢ. 27. Gel chromatography of LDL from a patient with cholestasis. LDL of d 1.019–1.063 gm/ml filtered through 2% agarose gel. From Picard and Veissiere (1970a).

of the intermediate molecular weight LDL of patients with familial LCAT deficiency or cholesterol-fed guinea pigs.[3] Furthermore, additional similarities are revealed by electron microscopy (Fig. 28). Preparations negatively stained with phosphotungstate are coin- or disc-shaped with a major axis of 400 to 600 Å (Hamilton *et al.,* 1971; Seidel *et al.,* 1972b; Quarfordt *et al.,* 1972). However, one apparent difference is that the abnormal LDL of cholestasis readily form rouleaux, whereas the tendency to form rouleaux is much less marked in the other two conditions. It is not yet certain whether this difference is caused by technical aspects of the electron microscopy or by some inherent structural feature of the LDL. Structural studies of the peak II material (Fig. 27) by low angle X-ray diffraction analysis (Hamilton *et al.,* 1971), together with the electron micrographs, suggest that the discs are comprised of bilayer sheets, 50 to 60 Å in thickness and doubled back to form flattened vesicles enclosing a potential water space. However, these studies go considerably beyond those yet done with the intermediate molecular weight LDL of familial LCAT deficiency or cholesterol-fed guinea pigs.

Upon analytical ultracentrifugation, the LDL of patients with cholestasis yield two distinct peaks of S_f approximately 8 and 17 (Mills *et al.,* 1969) or 9–14 and 18–22 (Quarfordt *et al.,* 1972). This is consistent with the gel filtration experiments (Fig. 27) and with the results obtained

[3] Note, however, that Picard and Veissiere (1970a) found much larger quantities of cholesteryl ester than detected by other investigators; the gel filtration procedure in the hands of Picard and Veissiere and of Hamilton *et al.* (1971) yields a smaller content of protein than the precipitation techniques; and the abnormal LDL of cholestasis contain 2–3% bile salts (Seidel *et al.,* 1972b), whereas no reason exists for suspecting such a large content in the LDL of patients with familial LCAT deficiency or cholesterol-fed guinea pigs.

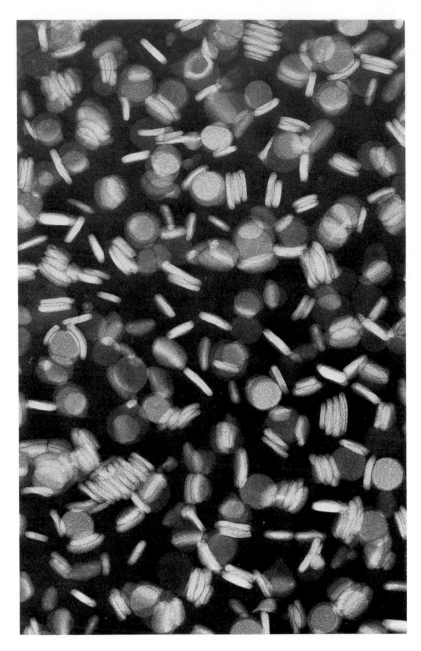

FIG. 28. Electron micrograph of abnormal LDL of cholestasis. LDL corresponding to rechromatographed peak II material (Fig. 27) negatively stained with phosphotungstic acid. Note the presence of single particles, $\sim$100 $\times$ $\sim$500 Å, seen both

with the LDL of patients with familial LCAT deficiency and cholesterol-fed guinea pigs. Very little material of $S_f > 22$ is detectable which also is consistent with the gel filtration experiments in view of the apparently low concentration of larger, molecular weight LDL corresponding to peak I (Fig. 27) or to the large, myelin-like figures seen by Hamilton *et al.* (1971) in unfractionated serum.

The electrophoretic mobility of the abnormal LDL of cholestasis is similar to that of the abnormal LDL of patients with familial LCAT deficiency and cholesterol-fed guinea pigs in that it is only slightly slower than that of normal LDL on agarose, starch gel, or paper. However, in crude agar, where the endosmic effect is large, the abnormal lipoproteins are swept toward the cathode and separated from normal LDL, which have a charge density sufficient to maintain net migration from the origin to the anode (Seidel *et al.*, 1969, 1970). This phenomenon, together with the production of specific antisera, has been used to screen the abnormal lipoprotein in the sera of patients suspected of having obstructive liver disease (Seidel, 1971).

The apoprotein of the abnormal LDL has been studied extensively by Seidel and Alaupovic and their co-workers, fortunately by the same procedures used to study the intermediate molecular weight LDL of patients with familial LCAT deficiency (Torsvik *et al.*, 1972). Only albumin (about 40% of the total protein by weight) and polypeptides of the apo-C family have been found (Alaupovic *et al.*, 1969; Seidel *et al.*, 1970) The albumin is apparently masked and/or located in the interior of the lipoprotein since anti-albumin serum reacts only with material that has been delipidized or attacked by phospholipase (Seidel *et al.*, 1972b). On the other hand, the apo-C is apparently located on the surface of the lipoprotein since specific antisera to apo-C react with both native and delipidized material and since abnormal LDL prepared by gel filtration promote hydrolysis of phospholipid-stabilized emulsions of triglyceride by lipoprotein lipase (Hamilton *et al.*, 1971). The presence of apo-C accounts for the observation of Switzer (1967) that rabbit antisera to the abnormal LDL react with normal VLDL since the antisera would be expected to have contained components sensitive to the apo-C of VLDL.

Whether the HDL of patients with cholestasis are similar to those of

---

on edge and flat. The 100 Å edges of some of these particles are split into approximately 50 Å leaflets. This and other evidence support the interpretation that the particles are lipid bilayer vesicles that collapse during dehydration on the grid of the electron microscope. Note also the presence of rouleaux; more concentrated samples show more rouleaux whereas dilute samples show only the flat round images. 153,000 ×. Courtesy of R. L. Hamilton, Jr.

patients with familial LCAT deficiency or cholesterol-fed guinea pigs is not certain. However, Quarfordt *et al.* (1972) found decreased protein contents and increased contents of unesterified cholesterol and phospholipid in the HDL of three of their patients with cholestasis. Also, the concentration of HDL in the plasma is decreased in long-standing cholestasis as well as in hepatocellular disease without cholestasis. This is true whether the concentration of HDL is evaluated by ultracentrifugation (Havel *et al.*, 1955), electron microscopy (Hamilton *et al.*, 1971), or electrophoresis (Kunkel and Slater, 1952; Nikkilä, 1953; Papadopoulos and Charles, 1970). Seidel *et al.* (1970), without presenting much evidence, report that significant changes in immunologically detectable apo-A do not occur in patients with liver disease. This apparently contradictory finding should be checked by other investigators, especially in view of the report by Torsvik (1969) that appreciable amounts of material that reacts with commercial antisera to HDL are present in lipoprotein fractions other than HDL in the plasma of patients with familial LCAT deficiency.

Comparison of the abnormalities in cholestasis with those in familial LCAT deficiency is complicated not only by the relative lack of information regarding the VLDL and HDL, but also by the variable liver damage usually present. Since both VLDL and HDL are secreted by the liver, abnormalities not *directly* caused by the cholestasis might be present. Furthermore, LCAT activity is diminished in liver disease with or without cholestasis (Gjone and Norum, 1970; Gjone and Blomhoff, 1970; Gjone *et al.*, 1971; Simon and Scheig, 1970; Calandra *et al.*, 1972). This would be expected to exacerbate the LDL abnormalities associated with cholestasis by further increasing the unesterified cholesterol and lecithin of the plasma. Finally, the presence of cholesteryl ester hydrolase activity in the plasma, noted in some patients with liver disease (Jones *et al.*, 1971), might have the same effect. These considerations suggest that future investigators should attempt to define the degree of hepatic dysfunction as rigorously as possible and to select those cases of cholestasis (Simon and Scheig, 1970; Wengeler *et al.*, 1972) in which LCAT activity is not reduced. Probably the best way to study the specific effects of cholestasis is by using experimental animals since the plasma unesterified cholesterol rises within 24 hours following acute obstruction of the bile duct, well before signs of liver damage appear. Detailed descriptions of plasma lipoprotein abnormalities during this initial stage of biliary obstruction would be of great value in distinguishing between the direct effects of cholestasis and effects caused by hepatocellular injury.

V. Discussion

Although several of the abnormalities in familial LCAT deficiency appear to be "explained" by what we now know about the LCAT reaction, the fact that similar abnormalities occur in cholesterol-fed guinea pigs and in cholestasis suggests that the metabolic role of the LCAT reaction should be considered in a broader context. Assuming that the reaction's major effect is to maintain a "physiological" proportion of unesterified cholesterol in the plasma, other factors that influence plasma unesterified cholesterol must be distinguished and the possible effects of pathological levels of plasma unesterified cholesterol explored.

A. Regulation of Plasma Unesterified Cholesterol

Most of the cholesterol of plasma lipoproteins is contributed by the intestinal mucosa and liver (Dietschy and Wilson, 1970), but the quantitative contributions of these organs under different physiological conditions remain to be fully evaluated. The problems involved in this type of evaluation are well illustrated by the case of the intestinal mucosa. This organ contributes chylomicron cholesterol to the blood (via the lymph) in animals fed fat with or without cholesterol, and contributes VLDL cholesterol to the blood also during fasting (Roheim *et al.*, 1965; Ockner *et al.*, 1969a,b; Jones and Ockner, 1971; Tytgat *et al.*, 1971). However, the net efflux of cholesterol from the intestine into the blood is difficult to assess as can be appreciated from the number of potential sources of this cholesterol (Fig. 29) and from the disagreement among investigators (Wilson and Lindsey, 1965; Borgström, 1969) regarding the amount of exogenous cholesterol that can be absorbed in man. Thus, the unesterified cholesterol of chylomicrons and VLDL may be contributed by at least five variable sources: the diet, bile, desquamated mucosal cells, intracellular biosynthesis, and the blood itself. Furthermore, since this unesterified cholesterol is mainly if not solely present on the surfaces of chylomicrons and VLDL (Zilversmit, 1965), its net flow into the lymph and blood probably depends mainly on the rate of formation of triglyceride from dietary and endogenous fatty acids.[4]

Another apparently variable factor that may influence the *total* efflux of cholesterol from mucosal cells is the rate and extent of intracellular cholesterol esterification. Unlike unesterified cholesterol, intestinal cholesteryl ester appears mainly if not solely to contribute to the inner "core" of secreted chylomicrons and VLDL (Zilversmit, 1965; Zilversmit

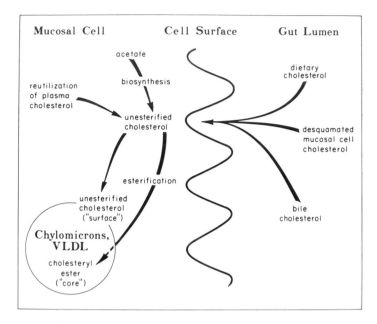

Fig. 29. Schematic diagram showing potential sources of cholesterol utilized in forming chylomicrons and intestinal VLDL.

et al., 1967). In some cases this "core" cholesteryl ester increases in response to dietary cholesterol (Zilversmit *et al.*, 1967; Zilversmit, 1968), and according to one provocative but as yet unconfirmed report (Murthy *et al.*, 1961) the mucosal enzyme that synthesizes the cholesteryl ester increases adaptively in cholesterol-fed rats. Assuming that all cholesterol secreted by mucosal cells is in the form of chylomicrons or VLDL, it might be possible to evaluate the amount secreted by measuring this cholesterol in aliquots of thoracic duct lymph. However, even at this point interpretation would be complicated because of the phenomenon of "secondary particle" formation (Bierman and Strandness, 1966). Thus, chylomicrons undergo changes in mobility and in the content of protein (Bierman and Strandness, 1966; Lossow *et al.*, 1967), unesterified cholesterol, and phospholipid (Minari and Zilversmit, 1963) almost immediately upon being mixed with plasma; and these phenomena may even begin as soon as chylomicrons enter the lymph and interact with the lymph proteins of d > 1.006 gm/ml. Thus, only crude assumptions can be made at present about the daily flow of chylomicron cholesterol

---

[4] Although investigators interested in cholesterol absorption have usually considered this process without relation to chylomicron and VLDL triglyceride formation, evidence of independent absorption of cholesterol has not yet been obtained.

into the blood. If a daily intake of 100 gm dietary triglyceride is assumed (35–40% of the caloric intake of a 70-kg man), and all of this triglyceride is secreted in chylomicrons similar to those analyzed by Kostner and Holasec (1972), then the minimum flow of chylomicron "surface" unesterified cholesterol would be about 1.9 gm/day and that of chylomicron "core" cholesteryl ester would be about 1.0 gm/day.[5]

The amount of plasma lipoprotein cholesterol contributed by the liver is no less difficult to evaluate, and once again the interrelation between triglyceride secretion and cholesterol secretion must be considered. Thus, VLDL secreted by the liver, like those secreted by the intestine, appear to contain "core" triglyceride surrounded by "surface" unesterified cholesterol and lecithin (Sata *et al.*, 1972). Moreover, in animals like the rat (Gidez *et al.*, 1967) hepatic VLDL also contain cholesteryl ester, apparently formed by hepatic acyl CoA:cholesterol acyltransferase activity (Goodman, 1965). However, this enzyme appears to be lacking in man (Stokke, 1972a), and no evidence has yet been adduced that cholesteryl esters are formed by human liver and secreted in hepatic VLDL.

Estimation of the rate of secretion of VLDL unesterified cholesterol is difficult for two principal reasons. First, published values for VLDL triglyceride secretion vary over a wide range for reasons recently reviewed (Nikkilä, 1972). Second, the proportion of unesterified cholesterol secreted relative to triglyceride depends on the size of the VLDL, which in turn appears to be affected by triglyceride fatty acid composition (Heimberg and Wilcox, 1972). Consequently, only crude approximations can be made as in the case of the unesterified cholesterol secreted in chylomicrons. If the average content of unesterified cholesterol in freshly secreted VLDL is of the order of that reported for lipoproteins of S_f 100–400 (Gustafson *et al.*, 1965), and if 13.4 gm of VLDL triglyceride are secreted per day (Nikkilä and Kekki, 1971), then the amount of unesterified cholesterol secreted should be about 0.8 gm/day. On the other hand, this value might be as large as 3.1 gm/day if the amount of triglyceride secreted is 54 gm/day (average value calculated from chemical data for normal subjects given by Boberg *et al.*, 1972).

How much unesterified cholesterol is secreted in lipoproteins other than chylomicrons and VLDL cannot be estimated at present. It is not even certain that *any* LDL are secreted directly into plasma since evidence is accumulating that LDL are formed from VLDL in the bloodstream (Gitlin *et al.*, 1958; Norum *et al.*, 1971b; Eisenberg *et al.*, 1972).

---

[5] These are necessarily minimum values since the relative contents of both unesterified cholesterol and cholesteryl ester compared with triglyceride are higher in VLDL, and the latter have not been considered.

As for HDL, evidence exists (Radding and Steinberg, 1960) that some are directly secreted by the liver, but the daily contribution of this HDL to the total pool of unesterified cholesterol in plasma has not been determined.

The events that occur once chylomicrons and VLDL enter the plasma are not fully clarified, but peripheral tissue LPL appears to play an important role in removing lipoprotein triglyceride (Robinson, 1970), and circulating "remnants" rich in cholesteryl ester appear to be formed in the process (Redgrave, 1970). The esters of these remnants appear to be hydrolyzed by the liver (Goodman, 1965) possibly by an enzyme located on the plasma membrane (Stein et al., 1669),[6] but the fate of the unesterified cholesterol, phospholipid, and peptides is not known. Furthermore, other "remnants" may be formed, possibly depending on the apoproteins of the parent chylomicrons and VLDL. In this way, the apo-A, apo-B, and apo-C lipoprotein "families" whose existence has been emphasized by Alaupovic et al. (1972) might be generated (Fig. 30). This possibility is in line with our own studies of familial LCAT deficiency (Fig. 17) and also with the concept of Schumaker and Adams (1970) since the "excess" unesterified cholesterol which they postulate to be produced during the catabolism of chylomicrons and VLDL might circulate briefly as an apo-C unesterified cholesterol-phospholipid "remnant." However,

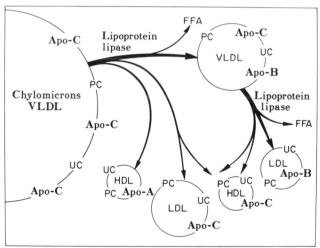

Fig. 30.   Schematic diagram showing possible formation of lipoprotein "families" by the action of lipoprotein lipase on chylomicrons and large VLDL.

---

[6] These studies were performed in rats and may not apply to all species. This is not merely the usual academic disclaimer: the livers of different species appear to metabolize cholesterol differently, and a critical appraisal of these species differences may increase general understanding of cholesterol metabolism.

one problem that complicates evaluation of the concept of Schumaker and Adams (1970) is that of distinguishing between "excess" unesterified cholesterol and that specifically associated with "remnants" such as the LDL of S_f 0–12. If one (a) accepts the chylomicron peptide composition reported by Kostner and Holasec (1972) (7.4% apo-A I, 4.2% apo-A II, 22.5% apo-B, and 65% apo-C), and (b) assumes that apo-A and apo-B can "stabilize" an amount of unesterified cholesterol of the order found in normal HDL and LDL (Norum *et al.*, 1971a), whereas most of the rest is "excess," then the amount of "excess" unesterified cholesterol formed during the daily catabolism of chylomicrons (about 1.6 gm) would not be much lower than the total amount of chylomicron unesterified cholesterol calculated above.[7] However, if the same assumptions are made to obtain the "excess" unesterified cholesterol that might be produced during the catabolism of VLDL, and values of Eisenberg *et al.* (1972) for the distribution of apoproteins in VLDL of S_f 100–400 are employed (apo-B/total protein = 0.26), then the amount of excess cholesterol would be reduced to about 0.7 gm/day or 2.6 gm/day depending on the triglyceride turnover value used. Thus, the total "excess" cholesterol from chylomicrons and VLDL would be approximately 2.3 or 4.2 gm/day. How do these amounts of excess cholesterol compare with the cholesterol that might be esterified by the LCAT reaction? Glomset (1962) and Nestel and Monger (1967) arrived at similar values (0.11 μmoles per ml plasma per hour) from measurements of human plasma cholesteryl ester formation *in vitro* and *in vivo*. Assuming that this value is valid, as much as 2.8 gm of unesterified cholesterol could be esterified in the plasma per day by the LCAT reaction. Furthermore, if LCAT and HDL are distributed between the plasma and extravascular fluid in the same way as albumin (Berson *et al.*, 1953) and 6.6 S gamma globulin (Solomon *et al.*, 1963) appear to be, i.e., if the distribution is approximately 1:1, then the total amount of cholesterol esterified could be as much as 5.6 gm/day.

The purpose of the above exercise in "cumulative assumptions" is not to show that LCAT *is* part of a waste disposal mechanism for "excess" chylomicron and VLDL surface lipid as Schumaker and Adams have suggested, but that it *might* be, and that the possibility is worth testing by careful experimentation. Thus, the amount of "excess" unesterified cholesterol and phospholipid formed during the catabolism of chylomicrons and VLDL, i.e., the potential amount that could contribute to the formation of large, abnormal LDL, will have to be much more carefully defined. Also, attempts will have to be made to correlate rates of

---

[7] Note that this figure does not take into account recirculation of unesterified cholesterol between the plasma and intestine.

triglyceride transport with rates of cholesterol esterification by the LCAT reaction in the *same* subjects under different metabolic conditions and with particular attention to jointly operative regulatory factors. Nestel (1970a,b) has already postulated that triglyceride transport and plasma cholesterol esterification in man may be related on the basis of his observation that the turnover of esterified cholesterol is significantly correlated with the concentration of triglyceride in plasma and with body weight. Akanuma *et al.* (1973) have recently found also that LCAT activity measured *in vitro* is significantly correlated with body weight, serum triglyceride concentration, and serum basal immunoreactive insulin. However, correlations will have to be made on a molar basis in order to determine whether the capacity of the LCAT reaction is fully saturated by the "excess" unesterified cholesterol derived from chylomicrons and VLDL. If it is not, the source or sources of the additional esterified cholesterol will have to be identified, and the degree to which these sources effectively compensate for differences between the unesterified cholesterol provided by chylomicrons and VLDL and that esterified by LCAT will have to be established. The physiological problem can be illustrated by an extreme case. Thus, presumably no "excess" unesterified cholesterol from chylomicrons and VLDL is available in abetalipoproteinemia (Fredrickson *et al.*, 1972), yet LCAT activity is present (Cooper and Gulbrandsen, 1971; J. A. Glomset, unpublished results). Even though the LCAT activity appears to be low compared with that in normal plasma, it is not clear whether unesterified cholesterol provided by sources other than chylomicrons and VLDL is sufficient to adequately balance that esterified by the LCAT reaction. In other words, it is conceivable that some of the tissue abnormalities in this disease might be caused by excessive removal of unesterified cholesterol from plasma membranes by the mechanism suggested in Fig. 1 (see also Glomset, 1968).

Very little is known about the removal of either unesterified cholesterol or cholesteryl ester from plasma, but several possibilities deserve to be explored. The first is that unesterified cholesterol is passively, but selectively, taken up by virtue of exchange reactions between plasma and tissues. Given rapid exchange, *net* uptake would be expected only in cells that convert unesterified cholesterol into nonexchangeable products such as cholesteryl ester (Fig. 31) or steroids at rates that exceed that of cholesterol biosynthesis. Note that experiments designed to test this possibility are valid only if *net* transfer is carefully distinguished from *exchange*, and that the use of radioactive cholesterol alone (Nilsson and Zilversmit, 1972) almost always yields equivocal results since transfer of the *label* is hard to differentiate from transfer of *mass*.

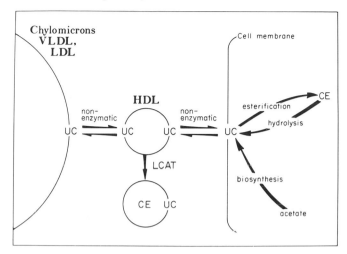

Fɪɢ. 31. Schematic diagram showing equilibria between the unesterified cholesterol of plasma lipoproteins and that of plasma membranes and the effect of the intra- and extracellular formation of cholesteryl esters on these equilibria.

The hydrolysis and subsequent uptake of chylomicron cholesteryl ester by rat liver (Stein *et al.,* 1969) might be a special case of uptake of unesterified cholesterol by exchange if hydrolysis occurs at the plasma membrane surface. Thus, utilization of the unesterified cholesterol released might depend on the subsequent metabolism of unesterified cholesterol within the liver cell, and animals such as rats, which have an active hepatic acylCoA:cholesterol acyltransferase, and animals which do not, might metabolize chylomicron unesterified cholesterol differently.

A second possible mechanism for removal of cholesterol from plasma might involve the specific or nonspecific uptake of intact lipoproteins. This may occur in the case of the liver as suggested by the experiments of Rachmilewitz *et al.* (1972) and a process of this type also has been implicated in atherosclerosis (Wissler and Vesselinovitch, 1968). The uptake and hydrolysis of plasma cholesteryl ester obviously must occur at rates that balance those of lipoprotein cholesteryl ester synthesis in cells and in the plasma. Thus, in man hydrolysis must at least equal 2.8–5.6 gm/day. The reactions that promote this hydrolysis remain to be clarified, but the recent findings of Stokke (1972a,b) suggest that an acid cholesteryl ester hydrolase in lysosomes may be involved.

B. Pᴀᴛʜᴏᴘʜʏsɪᴏʟᴏɢʏ ᴏғ Uɴᴇsᴛᴇʀɪғɪᴇᴅ Cʜᴏʟᴇsᴛᴇʀᴏʟ

In light of the mechanisms discussed above, it seems likely that the abnormal unesterified cholesterol-rich LDL are the "lowest common denominator" in familial LCAT deficiency, cholesterol-fed guinea pigs, and cholestasis. Thus, the metabolic events that promote formation of these LDL probably differ considerably, whereas the effects of the abnormal LDL may be quite similar. As already discussed, the large, abnormal LDL in familial LCAT deficiency appear to be formed largely from "excess" unesterified cholesterol and lecithin produced during the catabolism of chylomicrons. They probably accumulate solely because of the LCAT deficiency, i.e., because of absence of the normal mechanism for converting the "excess" lipid to HDL cholesteryl ester and, indirectly, to VLDL and LDL cholesteryl ester. In contrast to guinea pig studies, no evidence exists that dietary cholesterol contributes significantly to the "excess" polar lipid in familial LCAT deficiency. Thus, the concentration of large LDL in the plasma of patient L. G. was not markedly affected when his diet was changed from one that provided 2 gm of cholesterol per day to one that was cholesterol-free but provided the same amount of triglyceride (Glomset *et al.*, 1973b).

The cause of the increased levels of unesterified cholesterol-rich LDL observed in cholesterol-fed guinea pigs may well be multifactorial. The possibility (mechanism 1, Fig. 32) that dietary cholesterol leads to increased formation and release of chylomicron cholesteryl esters and

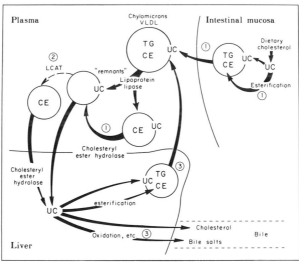

FIG. 32. Schematic diagram showing possible mechanisms that might cause unesterified cholesterol in the plasma of guinea pigs fed cholesterol. (1) Increased absorption through the formation of cholesteryl esters by the intestinal mucosa followed by the subsequent hydrolysis of these esters by the liver. (2) Decreased LCAT activity. (3) Decreased conversion of hepatic cholesterol into VLDL cholesteryl ester or decreased excretion in the bile.

VLDL by guinea pig intestinal mucosa, followed by hydrolysis by a hepatic cholesteryl ester hydrolase and subsequent formation of abnormal particles, needs to be explored. A second possibility (mechanism 2, Fig. 32) is that either a *relative* LCAT deficiency develops due to failure of LCAT to respond to dietary cholesterol or that an *absolute* deficiency develops due to diminished release of LCAT by a damaged liver. In either case, cholesterol derived from both the surfaces and the cores of chylomicrons and VLDL might accumulate. A third possibility (mechanism 3, Fig. 32) is that hepatic uptake of unesterified cholesterol by the exchange mechanism suggested in Fig. 31 is *relatively* reduced due to failure of guinea pig livers to secrete increased amounts of bile acids or biliary cholesterol or to form and secrete VLDL rich in cholesteryl ester. This mechanism may be an important contributing factor since dietary cholesterol increases liver cholesteryl ester (Ostwald and Shannon, 1964), but not the concentration of VLDL cholesterol in plasma (Puppione *et al.*, 1971; Sardet *et al.*, 1972a).

When bile is diverted from the intestine (Saunders and Dawson, 1963; Jones and Ockner, 1971) or its flow is obstructed, mucosal secretion of triglyceride-rich lipoproteins into the lymph diminishes markedly. Consequently, very little if any excess cholesterol produced during the catabolism of chylomicrons or intestinal VLDL is likely to contribute to the abnormal LDL of cholestasis. Furthermore, diminished LCAT activity probably does not contribute *initially* since the activity of the enzyme actually appears to increase during the first few days following experimental biliary obstruction in rats, and does not decrease until later (Castro Mendoza and Jimenez Diaz, 1949; Calandra *et al.*, 1971; Katterman and Wolfrum, 1970). In fact, none of the mechanisms considered above seems to be involved. Instead, the excess unesterified cholesterol is probably derived mainly from increased hepatic biosynthesis. Thus, experimental obstruction of the bile ducts of rats increases hepatic biosynthesis of cholesterol (Fredrickson *et al.*, 1954; Katterman and Creutzfeldt, 1970; Weis and Dietschy, 1971). This increase has been attributed to failure of the hepatic negative feedback control mechanism that normally regulates cholesterol biosynthesis (Katterman and Creutzfeldt, 1970) or its lack of activation due to the diminished flow of chylomicron cholesterol (Weis and Dietschy, 1971). However, recent studies by Cooper and Ockner (1972) have shown that selective biliary occlusion of a single liver lobe increases cholesterol biosynthesis in that lobe compared with biosynthesis in the normal lobes and that this occurs despite equal uptake of lymph cholesterol. Therefore, it seems more likely that the increased hepatic biosynthesis is a local response to the accumulation of bile acids and lecithin. Bile acids normally promote increased formation and biliary secretion of lecithin (Entenman *et al.*, 1968), and bile acids and biliary lecithin together form mixed micelles (Admirand and Small, 1968) which can solubilize about 1 mole of unesterified cholesterol for every 3 moles of lecithin. However, in the absence of bile acids, lecithin spontaneously forms bilayers that can take up unesterified cholesterol in molar proportions of 1:1 (Bangham and Horne, 1964). Therefore, if locally accumulated bile acids promote increased synthesis of lecithin in cholestasis, but mixed micelles formed are unstable because the bile acids become bound to albumin and other proteins, bilayers of lecithin that could take up additional cholesterol might be formed.[8] If this process occurs in the plasma, successive adsorption of albumin (Papahadjopoulos and Miller, 1967) and apo-C peptides might occur spontaneously to form the vesicles or discs observed in cholestasis. An alternative possibility is that lecithin-unesterified cholesterol bilayers formed in the liver might promote formation and secretion of the abnormal lipoproteins. If vesicle formation does take place in the plasma, one might expect transitory mobilization of unesterified cholesterol from other lipoproteins and tissues until a stable phospholipid:cholesterol ratio is achieved. Since rat erythrocytes contain significantly less cholesterol during the first 2 to 4 days following acute biliary obstruction (Calandra *et al.*, 1972), this may indeed occur. However, loss of erythrocyte phospholipid also occurs so that the findings of Calandra *et al.* (1972) might be direct effects of bile acids, related to the observation of Friedman and Byers (1956, 1957) that cholate injections increase the concentrations of both cholesterol and phospholipids in the plasma.

Although it is probable that different mechanisms cause plasma unesterified cholesterol (and phospholipid) to accumulate in familial LCAT deficiency, cholesterol-fed guinea pigs, and cholestasis, the effects of the increased lipid may be similar. Thus, not only are similar, unesterified cholesterol-rich LDL formed, but the "excess" unesterified cholesterol of the large, abnormal lipoproteins appears to equilibrate with and thereby increase the unesterified cholesterol of plasma lipoproteins and plasma membranes. The VLDL may be an example of this since they contain increased amounts of unesterified cholesterol (and have an abnormally slow electrophoretic mobility) in all three conditions, and since the VLDL of normal subjects acquire similar abnormalities upon being incubated with large molecular weight LDL from patients with familial

---

[8] Actually, the molar ratio of unesterified cholesterol to phospholipid in the abnormal LDL of cholestasis, familial LCAT deficiency, and cholesterol-fed guinea pigs is greater than 1. Whether this is an effect of the apoprotein components of these LDL is not yet known.

LCAT deficiency (Norum *et al.*, 1973). Similar experiments with the abnormal LDL of cholesterol-fed guinea pigs and patients with cholestasis have not yet been reported, but clearly would be of interest.

Studies of erythrocytes in the three conditions have provided direct evidence that plasma membranes also are altered in the presence of unesterified cholesterol-rich plasma. Not only do the erythrocytes contain increased amounts of unesterified cholesterol (Table XVIII), but the content of cholesterol diminishes when the erythrocytes are incubated with normal plasma, and the cholesterol of normal erythrocytes increases upon incubation with unesterified cholesterol-rich plasma (Cooper and Jandl, 1968; Norum and Gjone, 1968; Sardet *et al.*, 1972b). In contrast to unesterified cholesterol, the total phospholipid content of the erythrocytes is not markedly increased except in the case of cholesterol-fed guinea pigs, which develop an appreciable reticulocytosis. Nevertheless, the erythrocyte lecithin does increase at the expense of sphingomyelin and phosphatidylethanolamine. This probably occurs because of the slow exchange of erythrocyte and plasma phospholipids *in vivo*.

Whether the plasma membranes of other cells also contain increased amounts of unesterified cholesterol has not been determined, but this would be expected in view of the demonstrated exchange between the unesterified cholesterol of tissues and plasma lipoproteins (Avigan *et al.*,

Table XVIII

ERYTHROCYTE LIPIDS IN FAMILIAL LCAT DEFICIENCY, CHOLESTEROL FED GUINEA PIGS, AND CHOLESTASIS

	Human			Guinea pig	
	Normal[a]	LCAT-def[b]	Cholestasis[a]	Normal[c]	Cholesterol-fed[c]
	(μmoles lipid/10^{10} cells)				
Cholesterol	2.86	5.16	4.80	2.97	11.26
Total phospholipids	3.29	3.10	3.91	2.87	8.40
Phosphatidylethanolamine	0.95	0.66	0.80⎫	0.98[d]⎫	3.30[d]
Phosphatidylserine	0.46	0.37	0.55⎭	⎭	
Phosphatidylcholine	0.90	1.59	1.71	1.42	4.03
Sphingomyelin	0.85	0.44	0.74	0.26	0.44
Lysophosphatidylcholine	0.07	0.03	0.05	0.03	0.18
Phosphatidylinositol	0.05	0.03	0.06	0.18	0.44

[a] Data from Gjone and Norum (1970).
[b] Data from patient M. R. (Norum and Gjone, 1967b).
[c] Recalculated from data of Ostwald and Shannon (1964) and Ostwald *et al.* (1970).
[d] Phosphatidylethanol + -serine.

1962; Chobanian and Hollander, 1962). Furthermore, *in vivo* experiments performed on patients with familial LCAT deficiency (Norum and Gjone, 1967b) have shown that the half-time of plasma cholesterol is approximately doubled, which is compatible with the possibility that the pool of nonexchangeable unesterified cholesterol in plasma membranes is increased.

Whether the increased content of erythrocyte and other plasma membrane unesterified cholesterol is directly deleterious cannot yet be determined. However, hemolytic anemia is present in all of the patients who have familial LCAT deficiency, is very marked in cholesterol-fed guinea pigs, and also occurs in cholestasis (Boon *et al.*, 1969; Cooper, 1970). Furthermore, the volume of the erythrocytes is increased in both familial LCAT deficiency and cholestasis so that they lose their usual biconcave disc appearance and instead are broad, flat, and cup-shaped in wet smears or have the appearance of "target cells" in dried smears. This increase in cell volume probably depends directly on the increased content of unesterified cholesterol (Murphy, 1965); and the erythrocytes tend to regain their normal volume and appearance upon incubation with normal plasma (Cooper and Jandl, 1968; Norum and Gjone, 1968). In the case of cholesterol-fed guinea pigs, the erythrocytes also increase in volume, but "spur" cells rather than "target" cells result (Ostwald and Shannon, 1964). This may depend on a specific structural difference between the erythrocytes of guinea pigs and man,[9] but is certainly caused by interaction between the erythrocytes and the abnormal lipoproteins since "spur" cells are formed when the erythrocytes of normal guinea pigs are incubated with the plasma lipoproteins of cholesterol-fed guinea pigs (Sardet *et al.*, 1972b). In any case, the changes in erythrocyte morphology might increase erythrocyte trapping and destruction by reticuloendothelial cells, especially in the case of the guinea pig "spur" cells. Another possibility is that reticuloendothelial cell dysfunction is involved. One might expect reticuloendothelial cells to take up some of the abnormal LDL particles, and lamellar particles that resemble those seen in plasma have indeed been detected in the spleens of patients with familial LCAT deficiency (Jacobsen *et al.*, 1972; Hovig and Gjone, 1972). Also, fatty deposits (Yamanaka *et al.*, 1967b) and increased quantities of cholesterol (Ostwald and Shannon, 1964) have been found in the spleens of cholesterol-fed guinea pigs. Whether this increased cholesterol contributes to the more rapid hemolysis remains to be explored.

---

[9] Note, however, that "spur" cells or acanthocytes are found in some patients with advanced hepatocellular damage. These cells have an increased content of cholesterol relative to lecithin and a decreased life span (Cooper, 1969).

The most serious and life-threatening defect in familial LCAT deficiency is renal dysfunction. All of the patients have proteinuria, all but one have hyperlipemia apparently of renal origin, and two of the patients have developed edema and renal failure. The cause of this renal dysfunction remains to be determined, but intracellular lipid vacuoles have been observed in the glomerular tufts, and lamellar structures similar to those seen in plasma have been found in capillary basement membranes, mesangial regions, and in pericapsular areas (Hovig and Gjone, 1972). Since Hovig and Gjone also observed endothelial cells partly detached from thickened basement membranes, and since in some capillary loops endothelial cells were actually absent, a direct "toxic" effect of the unesterified cholesterol-rich LDL may be involved. This possibility also is suggested by the renal abnormalities of cholesterol-fed guinea pigs (French *et al.*, 1967) since all cholesterol-fed guinea pigs have lipid inclusions within the glomeruli as well as glomerulosclerosis, i.e., focal or diffuse thickening of the glomerular stalks associated with hyaline deposits at the roots of the glomeruli. Moreover, proteinuria is also present. Finally, glomerular changes also have been observed in cholestasis. Bloodworth and Sommer (1959) reported that about 25% of their patients with cirrhosis had "cirrhotic glomerulosclerosis," and Sakaguchi *et al.* (1965) found the same type of lesion in other forms of human liver disease as well as in experimental cholestasis. They observed several abnormalities upon electron microscopy: osmiophilic, amorphous precipitates and laminated bodies in the endothelial space and mesangial matrix, progressive thickening of the capillary basement membrane accompanied by an increase in the mesangial matrix, and fusion and focal destruction of the foot processes of glomerular cells. Although these abnormalities might conceivably be caused by other factors, the fact that glomerular lesions occur in all three conditions discussed in this review suggests that a direct toxic effect of the abnormal LDL may be a possible common cause. One way to explore this possibility might be to perform time sequence studies of the glomerular changes in guinea pigs fed cholesterol. A second way might be to employ the technique of Quadracci and Striker (1970) for culturing glomerular cells *in vitro* and to include the abnormal LDL in the culture medium.

VI. Conclusions

The argument explored in this review and the assumptions upon which it is based can be summarized as follows. The role of the LCAT reaction is to prevent unesterified cholesterol, derived mainly from the surfaces of chylomicrons and VLDL, from accumulating in the plasma. This is successfully accomplished only when the LCAT reaction balances the mechanisms that increase plasma unesterified cholesterol. A balance does not occur in familial LCAT deficiency because the enzyme is absent. It does not occur in cholesterol-fed guinea pigs because unusually large amounts of dietary unesterified cholesterol enter the plasma through inadequate control in either the intestine or the liver. It does not occur in cholestasis possibly because phospholipid bilayers are formed and promote the accumulation of unesterified cholesterol in plasma through increased hepatic biosynthesis. When unesterified cholesterol accumulates in plasma in the form of abnormal LDL, it equilibrates with and increases the unesterified cholesterol of other plasma lipoproteins and of plasma membranes and directly causes anemia and renal failure. Unesterified cholesterol is the "toxic" factor rather than phospholipid, even though the latter also accumulates in plasma, because the phospholipid of plasma membranes is not markedly increased.

The gaps in this argument are obvious enough. First, we know far too little concerning the mechanisms by which abnormal LDL are generated in familial LCAT deficiency, cholesterol-fed guinea pigs, and cholestasis. Especially in the case of the cholesterol-fed guinea pig, the argument's most positive feature is to suggest additional experiments that should be done. Second, we have failed to emphasize the abnormal HDL, mainly through ignorance regarding their metabolism. Third, the possibility that increased levels of plasma unesterified cholesterol are "toxic" to erythrocytes and/or reticuloendothelial cells and glomeruli is supported by little evidence concerning the possible mechanisms involved; and we still know nothing about the "toxic" effects that cause cholesterol-fed guinea pigs to die! Finally, we have given only the briefest consideration to a question that is fundamental to the whole argument: What is the principal function of unesterified cholesterol in the plasma? Assuming that unesterified cholesterol becomes associated with the surfaces of newly formed lipoproteins by physical equilibration within the cells of the intestinal mucosa and the liver,[10] what effect, if any, does this have on the subsequent metabolism of lipoproteins and/or tissues? Is it possible that the principal role of plasma unesterified cholesterol is to maintain the content of unesterified cholesterol in plasma membranes? In other words, is it pos-

---

[10] Those who believe that unesterified cholesterol functions by filling spaces between the phospholipids of lipoprotein surfaces should consider a proposal made some time ago by Wharton (1656) that the thyroid functions by "filling up of the vacant spaces around the larynx, thus contributing much to the beauty and rotundity of the neck, especially in females."

sible that some cells would be unable to compensate for the loss of plasma membrane unesterified cholesterol which would occur through equilibration with plasma lipoproteins that lacked unesterified cholesterol? In that case we have turned 180 degrees from the possibility suggested earlier (Glomset, 1968) that the function of the LCAT reaction is to transport unesterified cholesterol synthesized in peripheral tissues to the liver.

ACKNOWLEDGMENTS

This review was written while one of the authors (J. C.) was a guest of the Institute for Nutrition Research, University of Oslo, and is a product of many stimulating discussions with the faculty and students there. The authors' research described here was supported by grants HE 10642, RR 00166, HL 10878-07, and HE 12710 from the National Institutes of Health, United States Public Health Service; by the American Heart Association; by the Washington State Heart Association; by the Norwegian Council on Cardiovascular Diseases; by the Norwegian Research Council for Science and the Humanities; and by the Anders Jahre Foundation.

References

Admirand, W. H., and Small, D. M. (1968). *J. Clin. Invest.* **49**, 1043.
Akanuma, Y., Kuzuya, T., Hayashi, M., Ide, T., and Kuzuya, N. (1973). *Eur. J. Clin. Invest.* **3**, 136.
Alaupovic, P. (1971). *Atherosclerosis* **13**, 141.
Alaupovic, P., Seidel, D., McConathy, W. J., and Furman, R. H. (1969). *FEBS Lett.* **4**, 113.
Alaupovic, P., Lee, D. M., and McConathy, W. J. (1972). *Biochim. Biophys. Acta* **260**, 689.
Avigan, J., Steinberg, D., and Berman, M. (1962). *J. Lipid Res.* **3**, 216.
Bangham, A. D., and Horne, R. W. (1964). *J. Mol. Biol.* **8**, 660.
Bierman, E. L., and Strandness, D. E. (1966). *Amer. J. Physiol.* **210**, 13.
Berson, S. A., Yalow, R. S., Schreiber, S. S., and Bost, J. (1953). *J. Clin. Invest.* **32**, 746.
Blomstrand, R., and Dahlbäck, O. (1960). *J. Clin. Invest.* **39**, 1185.
Bloodworth, L. M. B., Jr., and Sommer, S. C. (1959). *Lab. Invest.* **8**, 962.
Boberg, J., Carlson, L. A., Freyschuss, U., Lassers, B. W., and Wahlquist, M. L. (1972). *Eur. J. Clin. Invest.* **2**, 454.
Boon, J., Broekhuyse, R. M., van Munster, P., and Schretlen, E. (1969). *Clin. Chim. Acta* **23**, 453.
Borgström, B. (1969). *J. Lipid Res.* **10**, 331.
Calandra, S., Martin, M. J., and McIntyre, N. (1971). *Eur. J. Clin. Invest.* **1**, 352.
Calandra, S., Martin, M. J., O'Shea, M. J., and McIntyre, N. (1972). *Biochim. Biophys. Acta* **260**, 424.
Castro Mendoza, H., and Jimenez Diaz, C. (1949). *Bull. Inst. Med. Res., Univ. Madrid* **2**, 81.
Chobanian, A. V., and Hollander, W. (1962). *J. Clin. Invest.* **41**, 1732.
Cooper, A. D., and Ockner, R. K. (1972). *Proc. 5th Meet. Int. Asso. Study Liver*, p. 2.

Cooper, R. A. (1969). *J. Clin. Invest.* **48**, 1820.

Cooper, R. A. (1970). *Semin. Hematol.* **7**, 296.

Cooper, R. A., and Gulbrandsen, C. L. (1971). *J. Lab. Clin. Med.* **78**, 323.

Cooper, R. A., and Jandl, J. H. (1968). *J. Clin. Invest.* **47**, 809.

Dietschy, J. M., and Wilson, J. D. (1970). *N. Engl. J. Med.* **282**, 1128, 1179, and 1241.

Eder, H. A. (1957). *Amer. J. Med.* **23**, 269.

Eder, H. A., Russ, E. M., Pritchett, R. A. R., Wilber, M. M., and Barr, D. P. (1955). *J. Clin. Invest.* **34**, 1147.

Eisenberg, S., Bilheimer, D., Lindgren, F., and Levy, R. I. (1972). *Biochim. Biophys. Acta* **260**, 329.

Entenman, C., Holloway, R. J., Albright, M. L., and Leong, G. F. (1968). *Proc. Soc. Exp. Biol. Med.* **127**, 1003.

Felt, V. (1971). *Experientia* **27**, 1158.

Fielding, C. J., and Fielding, P. E. (1971). *FEBS Lett.* **15**, 355.

Fielding, C. J., Shore, V. G., and Fielding, P. E. (1972a). *Biochim. Biophys. Acta* (in press).

Fielding, C. J., Shore, V. G., and Fielding, P. E. (1972b). *Biochim. Biophys. Res. Commun.* **46**, 1493.

Flint, A., Jr. (1862). *Amer. J. Med. Sci.* **44**, 305.

Forte, T. M., and Nichols, A. V. (1972). *Advan. Lipid Res.* **10**, 1.

Forte, T. M., Norum, K. R., Glomset, J. A., and Nichols, A. V. (1971a). *J. Clin. Invest.* **50**, 1141.

Forte, T. M., Nichols, A. V., Gong, E. L., Lux, S., and Levy, R. I. (1971b). *Biochim. Biophys. Acta* **248**, 381.

Fredrickson, D. S., Loud, A. V., Hinkelman, B. T., Schneider, H. S., and Frantz, I. D., Jr. (1954). *J. Exp. Med.* **99**, 43.

Fredrickson, D. S., Gotto, A. M., Jr., and Levy, R. I. (1972). *In* "The Metabolic Basis of Inherited Disease" (J. B. Stanbury, J. B. Wyngaarden, and D. S. Fredrickson, eds.), 3rd ed., p. 493. McGraw-Hill, New York.

French, S. W., Yamanaka, W., and Ostwald, R. (1967). *Arch. Pathol.* **83**, 204.

Friedman, M., and Byers, S. O. (1956). *Amer. J. Physiol.* **186**, 13.

Friedman, M., and Byers, S. O. (1957). *Amer. J. Physiol.* **188**, 337.

Furman, R. H., and Conrad, L. L. (1957). *J. Clin. Invest.* **36**, 713.

Gidez, L. I., Roheim, P. S., and Eder, H. A. (1967). *J. Lipid Res.* **8**, 7.

Gitlin, D., Cornwell, D. G., Nakasato, D., Oncley, J. L., Hughes, W. L., Jr., and Janeway, C. A. (1958). *J. Clin. Invest.* **37**, 172.

Gjone, E., and Blomhoff, J. P. (1970). *Scand. J. Gastroenterol.* **5**, 305.

Gjone, E., and Norum, K. R. (1968). *Acta Med. Scand.* **183**, 107.

Gjone, E., and Norum, K. R. (1970). *Acta Med. Scand.* **187**, 107.

Gjone, E., Torsvik, H., and Norum, K. R. (1968). *Scand. J. Clin. Lab. Invest.* **21**, 327.

Gjone, E., Blomhoff, J. P., and Wienecke, I. (1971). *Scand. J. Gastroenterol.* **6**, 161.

Glomset, J. A. (1962). *Biochim. Biophys. Acta* **65**, 128.

Glomset, J. A. (1968). *J. Lipid Res.* **9**, 155.

Glomset, J. A. (1972). *In* "Blood Lipids and Lipoproteins" (G. Nelson, ed.), p. 745. Wiley, New York.

Glomset, J. A., Janssen, E., Kennedy, R., and Dobbins, J. (1966). *J. Lipid Res.* **7**, 639.

Glomset, J. A., Norum, K. R., and King, W. (1970). *J. Clin. Invest.* **49**, 1827.

Glomset, J. A., Nichols, A. V., Norum, K. R., King, W., and Forte, T. (1973a). *J. Clin. Invest.* **52**.

Glomset, J. A., Norum, K. R., Nichols, A. V., King, W., Mitchell, C. D., Applegate, K., and Gjone, E. (1973b). To be published.

Goodman, D. S. (1965). *Physiol. Rev.* **45**, 747.

Goodman, D. S., and Shiratori, T. (1964). *J. Lipid Res.* **5**, 307.

Grice, H., Zawidzka, A., and Beare, J. (1966). *Can. J. Comp. Med. Vet. Sci.* **30**, 42.

Gustafson, A., Alaupovic, P., and Furman, R. H. (1965). *Biochemistry* **4**, 596.

Hamilton, R. L., Havel, R. J., Kane, J. P., Blaurock, A. E., and Sata, T. (1971). *Science* **172**, 475.

Hamnström, B. (1970). *Acta Med. Scand.* **188**, 55.

Hamnström, B., Gjone, E., and Norum, K. R. (1969). *Brit. Med. J.* **2**, 283.

Havel, R. J., Eder, H. A., and Bragdon, J. H. (1955). *J. Clin. Invest.* **34**, 1345.

Heimberg, M., and Wilcox, H. G. (1972). *J. Biol. Chem.* **247**, 875.

Hovig, T., and Gjone, E. (1972). *Acta Pathol. Scand.* (in press).

Jacobsen, C. D., Gjone, E., and Hovig, T. (1972). *Scand. J. Haematol.* **9**, 106.

Jones, A. L., and Ockner, R. K. (1971). *J. Lipid Res.* **12**, 580.

Jones, D. P., Sosa, F. R., Shartsis, J., Shah, P. T., Skromak, E., and Beher, W. T. (1971). *J. Clin. Invest.* **50**, 259.

Katterman, R., and Creutzfeldt, W. (1970). *Scand. J. Gastroenterol.* **5**, 337.

Katterman, R., and Wolfrum, D. I. (1970). *Z. Clin. Chem. Klin. Biochem.* **8**, 413.

Kayden, H. J., Karmen, A., and Dumont, A. (1963). *J. Clin. Invest.* **42**, 1373.

Kostner, G., and Holasec, A. (1972). *Biochemistry* **11**, 1217.

Kunkel, H. G., and Slater, R. J. (1952). *J. Clin. Invest.* **31**, 677.

Lees, R. S. (1970). *Science* **169**, 493.

Long, C. N. H. (1949). In "The Chemistry and Physiology of Growth" (A. K. Parpart, ed.), p. 266. Princeton Univ. Press, Princeton, New Jersey.

Lossow, W. J., Lindgren, F. T., and Jensen, L. C. (1967). *Biochim. Biophys. Acta* **144**, 670.

Mills, G. L., Seidel, D., and Alaupovic, P. (1969). *Clin. Chim. Acta* **26**, 239.

Minari, O., and Zilversmit, D. B. (1963). *J. Lipid Res.* **5**, 578.

Murphy, J. R. (1965). *J. Lab. Clin. Med.* **65**, 756.

Murthy, S. K., Mahadevan, S., and Ganguly, J. (1961). *Arch. Biochem. Biophys.* **95**, 176.

Nestel, P. J. (1970a). *Advan. Lipid Res.* **8**, 1.

Nestel, P. J. (1970b). *Clin. Sci.* **38**, 593.

Nestel, P. J., and Monger, E. A. (1967). *J. Clin. Invest.* **46**, 967.

Nichols, A. V., and Gong, E. L. (1971). *Biochim. Biophys. Acta* **231**, 175.

Nichols, A. V., and Smith, L. (1965). *J. Lipid Res.* **6**, 206.

Nichols, A. V., Strisower, E. H., Lindgren, F. T., Adamson, G. L., and Coggiola, E. L. (1968). *Clin. Chim. Acta* **20**, 277.

Nikkilä, E. (1953). *Scand. J. Clin. Lab. Invest.* **5**, Suppl. 8.

Nikkilä, E. (1972). *Horm. Metab. Res.* (in press).

Nikkilä, E., and Kekki, M. (1971). *Acta Med. Scand.* **190**, 49.

Nilsson, A., and Zilversmit, D. B. (1972). *Biochim. Biophys. Acta* **260**, 479.

Norum, K. R., and Gjone, E. (1967a). *Biochim. Biophys. Acta* **144**, 698.

Norum, K. R., and Gjone, E. (1967b). *Scand. J. Clin. Lab. Invest.* **20**, 231.

Norum, K. R., and Gjone, E. (1968). *Scand. J. Clin. Lab. Invest.* **22**, 94.

Norum, K. R., Borsting, S., and Grundt, I. (1970). *Acta Med. Scand.* **188**, 323.

Norum, K. R., Glomset, J. A., Nichols, A. V., and Forte, T. (1971a). *J. Clin. Invest.* **50**, 1131.

Norum, K. R., Glomset, J. A., and King, W. (1971b). *Eur. J. Clin. Invest.* **1**, 386.

Norum, K. R., Glomset, J. A., and Gjone, E. (1972). *In* "The Metabolic Basis of Inherited Disease" (J. B. Stanbury, J. B. Wyngaarden, and D. S. Fredrickson, eds.), 3rd ed., p. 531. McGraw-Hill, New York.

Norum, K. R., Glomset, J. A., Nichols, A. V., Forte, T., King, W., Applegate, K., Mitchell, C. D., and Albers, J. (1973). To be published.

Ockner, R. K., Hughes, F. B., and Isselbacher, K. J. (1969a). *J. Clin. Invest.* **48**, 2079.

Ockner, R. K., Hughes, F. B., and Isselbacher, K. J. (1969b). *J. Clin. Invest.* **48**, 2367.

Ostwald, R., and Shannon, A. (1964). *Biochem. J.* **91**, 146.

Ostwald, R., Yamanaka, W., and Light, M. (1970). *Proc. Soc. Exp. Biol. Med.* **134**, 814.

Osuga, T., and Portman, O. W. (1971). *Amer. J. Physiol.* **220**, 735.

Papadopoulos, N. M., and Charles, M. A. (1970). *Proc. Soc. Exp. Biol. Med.* **134**, 797.

Papahadjopoulos, D., and Miller, N. (1967). *Biochim. Biophys. Acta* **135**, 624.

Picard, M. J., and Veissiere, D. (1970a). *Clin. Chim. Acta* **30**, 149.

Picard, M. J., and Veissiere, D. (1970b). *C. R. Acad. Sci.* **270**, 1845.

Puppione, D. L., Sardet, C., Yamanaka, W., Ostwald, R., and Nichols, A. V. (1971). *Biochim. Biophys. Acta* **231**, 295.

Quadracci, L. J., and Striker, G. E. (1970). *Proc. Soc. Exp. Biol. Med.* **135**, 947.

Quarfordt, S. H., Oelschlaeger, H., and Krigbaum, W. R. (1972). *J. Clin. Invest.* **51**, 1979.

Rachmilewitz, D., Stein, O., Roheim, P. S., and Stein, Y. (1972). *Biochim. Biophys. Acta* **270**, 414.

Radding, C. M., and Steinberg, D. (1960). *J. Clin. Invest.* **39**, 1560.

Raz, A. (1971). *Biochim. Biophys. Acta* **239**, 458.

Redgrave, T. G. (1970). *J. Clin. Invest.* **49**, 465.

Rehnborg, C. S., and Nichols, A. V. (1964). *Biochim. Biophys. Acta* **84**, 596.

Robinson, D. S. (1970). *Comp. Biochem.* **18**, 51

Roheim, P. S., Haft, D. E., Gidez, L. I., White, A., and Eder, H. A. (1963). *J. Clin. Invest.* **42**, 1277.

Roheim, P. S., Gidez, L. I., and Eder, H. A. (1965). *J. Clin. Invest.* **45**, 297.

Russ, E. M., Raymunt, J., and Barr, D. P. (1956). *J. Clin. Invest.* **35**, 133.

Sakaguchi, H., Dachs, S., Grishman, E., Paronetto, F., Salomon, M., and Churg, J. (1965). *Lab. Invest.* **14**, 533.

Sardet, C., Hansma, H., and Ostwald, R. (1972a). *J. Lipid Res.* **13**, 624.

Sardet, C., Hansma, H., and Ostwald, R. (1972b). *J. Lipid Res.* **13**, 705.

Sata, T., Havel, R. J., and Jones, A. L. (1972). *J. Lipid Res.* **13**, 757.

Saunders, D. R., and Dawson, A. M. (1963). *Gut* **4**, 254.

Schumaker, V. N., and Adams, G. H. (1970). *J. Theor. Biol.* **26**, 89.

Seidel, D. (1971). *Clin. Chim. Acta* **31**, 225.

Seidel, D., Alaupovic, P., and Furman, R. H. (1969). *J. Clin. Invest.* **48**, 1211.

Seidel, D., Alaupovic, P., Furman, R. H., and McConathy, W. J. (1970). *J. Clin. Invest.* **49**, 2396.

Seidel, D., Greten, J., Geisen, H. P., Wengeler, H., and Wieland, H. (1972a). *Eur. J. Clin. Invest.* **2**, 359.

Seidel, D., Agostini, B., and Muller, P. (1972b). *Biochim. Biophys. Acta* **260**, 146.

Simon, J. B., and Boyer, J. L. (1971). *Biochim. Biophys. Acta* **218**, 549.

Simon, J. B., and Scheig, R. (1970). *N. Engl. J. Med.* **283**, 841.

Solomon, A., Waldman, T. A., and Fahey, J. L. (1963). *J. Lab. Clin. Med.* **62**, 1.

Stein, O., Stein, Y., Goodman, D. S., and Fidge, N. H. (1969). *J. Cell Biol.* **43**, 410.

Stokke, K. T. (1972a). *Biochim. Biophys. Acta* **270**, 156.

Stokke, K. T. (1972b). *Biochim. Biophys. Acta* **280**, 329.

Switzer, S. (1967). *J. Clin. Invest.* **46**, 855.

Torsvik, H. (1969). *Scand. J. Clin. Lab. Invest.* **24**, 187.

Torsvik, H. (1970). *Clin. Genet.* **1**, 310.

Torsvik, H. (1972). *Clin. Genet.* **3**, 188.

Torsvik, H., Gjone, E., and Norum, K. R. (1968). *Acta Med. Scand.* **183**, 387.

Torsvik, H., Solaas, M., and Gjone, E. (1970). *Clin. Genet.* **1**, 139.

Torsvik, H., Berg, H. N., Magnani, H. N., McConathy, W. J., Alaupovic, P., and Gjone, E. (1972). *FEBS Lett.* **24**, 165.

Tytgat, G. N., Rubin, C. E., and Saunders, D. R. (1971). *J. Clin. Invest.* **50**, 2065.

Weis, H. J., and Dietschy, J. M. (1971). *Gastroenterology* **61**, 77.

Wengeler, H., Greten, H., and Seidel, D. (1972). *Eur. J. Clin. Invest.* **2**, 372.

Wharton, T. (1656). Quoted by Long (1949).

Wilson, J. D., and Lindsey, C. A., Jr. (1965). *J. Clin. Invest.* **44**, 1805.

Wissler, R. W., and Vesselinovitch, D. (1968). *Advan. Lipid Res.* **6**, 181.

Yamanaka, W., Winchell, H. S., and Ostwald, R. (1967a). *Amer. J. Physiol.* **213**, 1278.

Yamanaka, W., Ostwald, R., and French, S. W. (1967b). *Proc. Soc. Exp. Biol. Med.* **125**, 303.

Zilversmit, D. B. (1965). *J. Clin. Invest.* **44**, 1610.

Zilversmit, D. B. (1968). *Proc. Soc. Exp. Biol. Med.* **128**, 1116.

Zilversmit, D. B., Courtice, F. C., and Fraser, R (1967). *J. Atheroscler. Res.* **7**, 319.

Lipoprotein-Polyanion-Metal Interactions[1]

M. BURSTEIN

Centre National de Transfusion Sanguine, Paris, France

AND

H. R. SCHOLNICK

Albert Einstein College of Medicine, New York, New York

[1] This investigation was supported in part by U. S. Public Health Service Research Grant HE-02965, and Training Grant TI HE-5273 and PO-AM 13430.

I. Introduction

Virtually all the plasma lipids are combined with specific proteins in the form of lipoproteins. Macheboeuf (1929) was the first to isolate from horse serum a lipoprotein with constant composition. By fractional precipitation with ethanol (Gurd *et al.*, 1949), differential density ultracentrifugation (DeLalla and Gofman, 1954), and electrophoresis (Swahn, 1953), human plasma lipoproteins were divided into two major groups with specific immunological properties: low density lipoproteins (density less than 1.063) found in Cohn fraction III-0, and migrating as β-globulins (β-lipoproteins), and high density lipoproteins (HDL) (density greater than 1.063), found in fraction IV-1, and migrating as α-globulins (α-lipoproteins). The lipoproteins of density less than 1.063 are comprised of low density lipoproteins (LDL), with a density range of 1.006 to 1.063, S_f 0–20, and β-mobility; very low density lipoproteins (VLDL) with density less than 1.006, S_f 20–400, and pre-β-mobility; and chylomicrons, large alimentary particles with S_f greater than 400. LDL and HDL are rich in cholesterol esters and phospholipids while VLDL and chylomicrons are triglyceride-rich. The protein:lipid ratio increases with increasing density from chylomicrons to HDL.

The serum from patients with extrahepatic biliary obstruction or biliary cirrhosis may contain abnormal low density lipoproteins (Eder *et al.*, 1955). These lipoproteins have β-electrophoretic mobility but they do not react with antisera against normal β-lipoprotein. The protein:lipid ratio is low as in VLDL, but they are rich in phospholipids rather than triglycerides (Switzer, 1967; Burstein and Caroli, 1969; Seidel *et al.*, 1969).

Under certain conditions, low density lipoproteins are precipitated from serum by sulfated polysaccharides at neutral pH. This was described independently by several authors (Bernfeld, 1955; Burstein and Samaille, 1955; Oncley *et al.*, 1955). The formation of insoluble complexes was accomplished with high molecular weight compounds such as sulfated amylopectin (Bernfeld) or dextran sulfate (Oncley *et al.*, 1955) and with low molecular weight compounds such as heparin (Burstein and Samaille, 1955); the latter require the addition of divalent cations.

Other serum proteins also interact with sulfated polysaccharides at the pH of serum (above the isoelectric point of the proteins) when both molecules carry a net negative charge. The existence of soluble complexes was demonstrated by Chargaff *et al.* (1941), Jacques (1943), Blasius and Seitz (1952), Hoch and Chanutin (1952), Nikkilä (1952), Clark and Monkhouse (1953), and Gorter and Nanninga (1953). Nevertheless, sulfated polysaccharides have greater affinity for β-lipoproteins than for other proteins; Bernfeld *et al.* (1957b, 1960b) have established that with low concentrations of polysaccharides, in the pH range 7.5–8.6, only complexes with β-lipoproteins are formed. These were either soluble or insoluble, depending on the chemical nature (sulfate content and degree of polymerization) of the polysaccharide used. The electrophoretic mobility of the soluble lipoprotein-sulfated polysaccharide complex is greater than that of the free lipoprotein and by moving boundary electrophoresis, it was shown that certain of the soluble complexes are reversible (dissociate in an electric field) while others are irreversible.

The formation of a soluble β-lipoprotein heparin complex can easily be proven on agarose electrophoresis (Burstein and Morfin, 1969b). In the presence of 0.1% heparin, β-lipoproteins migrate as pre-β (Fig. 1); the mobility of α-lipoproteins and other serum proteins is not altered. The soluble complexes can be precipitated by the addition of divalent cations.

Not only sulfated polysaccharides but also other sulfate-containing compounds such as sodium salt of polyanetholsulfonic acid (Liquoid, Roche), neoarsphenamine, and thioarsphenamine precipitate the low density lipoproteins in the presence of calcium (Burstein and Samaille, 1957b). Further studies have shown that under certain conditions, HDL as well as LDL can be precipitated with sulfated polysaccharides (Burstein, 1962a; Burstein *et al.*, 1970).

In combination with divalent cations, anions other than polysulfates also precipitate serum lipoproteins. Low density (Burstein, 1963) and high density (Burstein *et al.*, 1970) lipoproteins are precipitated by the sodium salt of phosphotungstic acid. The latter, like heparin, is a complex molecule with a relatively high molecular weight and negative charge; has anticoagulant and metachromatic activities; and releases clearing factor (Bragdon and Havel, 1954). The precipitation of lipoproteins can also be accomplished with inorganic polyphosphates (Bur-

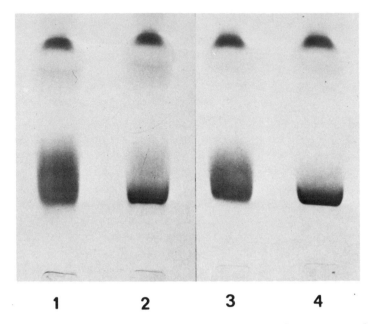

FIG. 1. Electrophoresis on agarose gel; lipid stain. 1 and 3, heparinized human sera, final concentration of 0.1%; 2 and 4, the same sera before heparin.

stein and Morfin, 1968b) and with simple anions such as tetracyclines (Lacko *et al.*, 1959), fatty acids, biliary salts, and sodium lauryl sulfate (Burstein and Morfin, 1971).

Based on the formation of insoluble lipoprotein-polyanion-divalent cation complexes, methods have been developed for the isolation of the major classes of serum lipoproteins, for the turbidimetric estimation of all the low density lipoproteins, for analysis of the lipid distribution between low and high density lipoproteins, and for the preparation of sera specifically devoid of all or certain lipoprotein classes.

The literature on this subject through 1960 was extensively reviewed by Cornwell and Kruger (1961).

II. Precipitation of Serum Lipoproteins with Sulfated Polysaccharides and Sodium Phosphotungstate

All the major classes of serum lipoproteins may be precipitated at neutral pH and room temperature with divalent cations and sulfated polysaccharides or sodium phosphotungstate. Nevertheless, the various lipoproteins do not precipitate under the same conditions; the reagent requirements, i.e., the nature of the polyanion and metal ion as well as the final concentrations, are different for each lipoprotein class. Moreover, the reagent requirements are affected by the ionic strength, by serum proteins, and by the addition of sucrose.

A. Lipoprotein Classes and Reagent Requirements

The reagent requirements for the precipitation of the various lipoprotein classes were analyzed by Burstein *et al.* (1970) and Burstein and Scholnick (1972a). In Table I are summarized the results obtained with different combinations of polyanions and metal ions. All these combinations precipitate chylomicrons plus VLDL; certain of them precipitate, in addition, LDL, and others precipitate LDL and HDL. Thus, the formation of an insoluble lipoprotein-polyanion-metal ion complex is more easily achieved with chylomicrons plus VLDL than with LDL, and in turn more easily with LDL than with HDL. This is confirmed by the data presented in Table II which shows that when the precipitation of all lipoproteins is accomplished with the same polyanion in the presence of the same divalent cation, the minimal final concentration of reagents is higher for HDL than for LDL, and higher for LDL than for chylomicrons plus VLDL. Similarly, in the case of heparin-Mg, less heparin is required to precipitate chylomicrons from lipemic serum than to precipitate VLDL. For these reasons it is possible to isolate the different classes of lipoproteins by the stepwise addition of the same reagents. It can be seen that there is a parallel between the polyanion precipitation

Table I

Lipoproteins Precipitated from Human Serum by Different Combinations of Polyanions and Divalent Cations

| | | Sulfated polysaccharide | | |
| | | | | |
Cation	Heparin	Dextran sulfate (mol. wt. 15×10^3)	Dextran sulfate 2000 (mol. wt. 2×10^6)	Sodium phospho-tungstate
Mg^{++}, Ca^{++}	Chylomicrons VLDL	Chylomicrons VLDL LDL	Chylomicrons VLDL LDL HDL	Chylomicrons VLDL LDL HDL
Mn^{++}, Co^{++}	Chylomicrons VLDL LDL	Chylomicrons VLDL LDL HDL	—	—

Table II

FINAL CONCENTRATIONS OF REAGENTS REQUIRED FOR THE PRECIPITATION
OF LIPOPROTEINS FROM HUMAN SERUM

Reagents	Chylomicrons plus VLDL	LDL	HDL
Heparin	0.25%[a]	No ppt	No ppt
Mg^{++} (Ca^{++})	$0.1\ M$		
Heparin	0.01%	0.1%	No ppt
Mn^{++} (Co^{++})	$0.05\ M$	$0.05\ M$	
Dextran sulfate	0.007%	0.05%	0.65%
Mn^{++} (Co^{++})	$0.025\ M$	$0.025\ M$	$0.2\ M$
Dextran sulfate	0.01% or 0.1%	0.1%	No ppt
Mg^{++} (Ca^{++})	$0.1\ M$ $0.025\ M$	$0.1\ M$	
Dextran sulfate 2000	—	0.05%	0.55%
Ca^{++}		$0.025\ M$	$0.2\ M$
Sodium phosphotungstate	0.05% or 0.1%	0.2% or 0.4%	2.0%
Mg^{++}	$0.1\ M$ $0.05\ M$	$0.1\ M$ $0.05\ M$	$0.2\ M$
Sodium phosphotungstate	—	0.08%	0.6%
Mn^{++}		$0.05\ M$	$0.2\ M$

[a] By lowering the heparin concentration to 0.05% chylomicrons are selectively precipitated.

and the ultracentrifugal methods of isolation of serum lipoproteins; in the former the concentration of reagents is increased stepwise and in the latter it is the solvent density which is increased.

Under the conditions described in Table II, the precipitation of chylomicrons plus VLDL, as well as the precipitation of LDL, is selective. This was demonstrated by performing the precipitations in a VLDL-free 1.006 infranatant and an LDL plus VLDL-free serum prepared by precipitation of the low density lipoproteins with isolated specific antibodies (Burstein and Scholnick, 1970).

In spite of the nonidentity of the composition of the lipid moieties, the abnormal lipoproteins of jaundiced sera (Section I) and VLDL, unlike LDL, are both precipitated by heparin-Mg (Burstein and Caroli, 1969). In addition (Burstein and Scholnick, 1971), in the heparin-Mn precipitation procedure, the minimal final concentration of heparin is practically the same for the abnormal lipoproteins and VLDL (much lower than for LDL).

B. COMPARISONS OF POLYANIONS AND OF DIVALENT CATIONS

In the presence of Mn^{++}, dextran sulfate precipitates LDL and HDL, and heparin precipitates only LDL. With Mg^{++} instead of Mn^{++}, there is neither precipitation of LDL by heparin nor of HDL by dextran sulfate (Table I). Consequently, dextran sulfate is more active than heparin, and Mn^{++} more active than Mg^{++}. This is confirmed by the data in Table II which shows that LDL are precipitated with lower final concentrations of both the polyanion and the divalent cation when dextran sulfate is used instead of heparin or Mn^{++} instead of Mg^{++} (compare heparin-Mn with dextran sulfate-Mn and the latter with dextran sulfate-Mg). The activity of dextran sulfate increases with molecular weight; only the high molecular weight compounds precipitate LDL in the absence of divalent cations (Section I),[1] and, in addition, HDL when Mg^{++} is added (Table I).

These precipitation studies were carried out with Mg^{++}, Ca^{++}, Mn^{++}, and Co^{++}. Mg^{++} has practically the same activity as Ca^{++}, and Mn^{++} has the same as Co^{++}. On the contrary, two other divalent cations, Ba^{++} and Sr^{++}, not only cannot replace the above cations, but in fact inhibit the precipitation of low density lipoproteins by dextran sulfate-Ca (Burstein and Samaille, 1957a), and also by dextran sulfate-Mn and sodium phosphotungstate-Mg. The inhibition by Ba^{++}, but not by Sr^{++}, can be explained by the formation of an insoluble salt with the polyanion. On the other hand, with high molecular weight dextran sulfate, the precipitation of low density lipoproteins is inhibited by Ba^{++} but not by Sr^{++} (Burstein and Scholnick, 1971).

C. Sulfated Polysaccharide-Metal Ion Supernatant

The heparin-Mn and dextran sulfate-Mn supernatants have been analyzed by Burstein *et al.* (1970). The final concentrations used to prepare them were the following: heparin, 0.2% and $MnCl_2$, 0.05 M; and dextran sulfate, 0.65% and $MnCl_2$, 0.2 M (Table II). Mn^{++} was removed by dialysis and the sulfated polysaccharides precipitated as insoluble barium salts; the supernatants were concentrated to their original protein content.

1. *Heparin-Mn Supernatant*

The supernatant is devoid of β- and pre-β-lipoproteins as judged by agarose electrophoresis with lipid stain (Fig. 2). Starch gel electrophoresis with protein stain shows that only the β-lipoprotein band is absent (Fig. 3). There is no immunological reaction with anti-β-lipoprotein (LDL plus VLDL) antibodies, and the immunoelectrophoretic pattern against anti-whole human serum is normal except for the dis-

---

[1] Nevertheless, the quantitative precipitation of the low density lipoproteins with dextran sulfate 2000 requires a certain amount of divalent cations (Burstein and Scholnick, 1971).

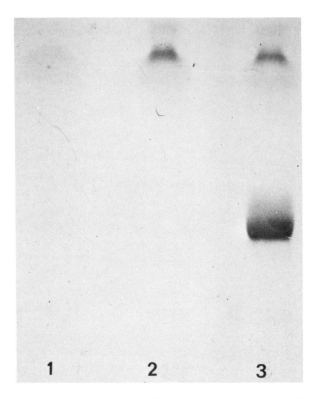

FIG. 2. Electrophoresis an agarose gel; lipid stain. 1, Dextran sulfate-Mn supernatant; 2, heparin-Mn supernatant; 3, normal human serum.

appearance of the β-lipoprotein precipitin line. After adsorption of a rabbit anti-whole human serum with this supernatant, a specific anti-β-lipoprotein serum is obtained (Burstein and Scholnick, 1970). The cholesterol and phospholipid content is the same as that of serum from which LDL and VLDL have been eliminated by the addition of anti-β-lipoprotein antibodies. In the case of a serum of Lp (a+) phenotype the Lp (a) lipoprotein which stays in the 1.063 infranatant is also precipitated. Similar results were also obtained when other combinations of anion and cation were used for the precipitation of LDL (Table II).

2. Dextran Sulfate-Mn Supernatant

There are only traces of HDL on agarose electrophoresis (Fig. 2). The phospholipid content is approximately 30 mg per 100 ml; small amounts of esterified cholesterol can be shown by thin layer chromatography. With a specific anti-HDL serum it is possible to demonstrate by immunodiffusion and immunoelectrophoresis with protein stain (but

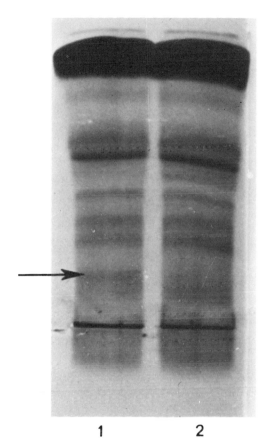

Fig. 3. Electrophoresis on starch gel; protein stain. 1, Normal human serum (arrow indicates β-lipoprotein band); 2, heparin-Mn supernatant.

not with lipid stain) that HDL (approximately 20% of the initial amount) are still present. Immunoelectrophoresis of the supernatant against anti-whole human serum reveals that all the serum antigens, other than lipoproteins, are present in normal concentration. Similar results are obtained after precipitation of HDL with sodium phosphotungstate-Mg (Table II).

As in the case of the dextran sulfate-Mn supernatant, the d 1.21 infranatant also contains immunologically detectable HDL (Levy and Fredrickson, 1965; Alaupovic *et al.*, 1966; Scanu and Granda, 1966), 8–15% of the total serum phospholipids, and small amounts of cholesterol (Havel *et al.*, 1955; Hillyard *et al.*, 1955; Phillips, 1959; Levy and Fredrickson, 1965; Switzer and Eder, 1965; Alaupovic *et al.*, 1966; Scanu and Granda, 1966). Thus, in comparison with preparative ultracentrifugation, the dextran sulfate-Mn supernatant is the equivalent of the d 1.21 infranatant.

D. IONIC STRENGTH

1. *Sulfated Polysaccharides*

Burstein and Samaille (1956, 1957a) have shown that the precipitation of low density lipoproteins by sulfated polysaccharides and metal ions is facilitated by decreasing, and inhibited by increasing, the ionic strength of the serum; the same is true for high density lipoproteins (Burstein *et al.*, 1970). Table III demonstrates that only in a serum dialyzed against buffered distilled water can LDL be precipitated with heparin-Mg and HDL with heparin-Mn (partial) or Mepesulfate-Mn (complete). Furthermore, after dialysis, quantitative precipitation of LDL occurs with lower concentrations of reagents than before dialysis.

Increasing the ionic strength of the serum by the addition of sodium chloride, inhibits the precipitation; this inhibition can be overcome to a certain extent by increasing the concentrations of both the polyanion and the divalent cation.

The effect of ionic strength on the precipitation of lipoproteins can be more or less pronounced depending on the reagents and the lipoprotein class. Table III shows that lower ionic strength is required for the precipitation of LDL when heparin is used rather than dextran sulfate, or

Table III

PRECIPITATION OF LDL AND HDL BEFORE AND AFTER DIALYSIS OF HUMAN SERUM AGAINST TRIS-HCl 0.02 M, pH 7.7. FINAL CONCENTRATIONS OF REAGENTS REQUIRED

Reagents	LDL		HDL	
	Before dialysis	After dialysis	Before dialysis	After dialysis
Heparin Mg^{++} (Ca^{++})	No ppt	0.2% 0.05 M	No ppt	No ppt
Heparin Mn^{++}	0.1% 0.05 M	0.1% 0.025 M	No ppt	0.5%[a] 0.1 M
Dextran sulfate Mg^{++} (Ca^{++})	0.1% 0.1 M	0.05% 0.05 M	No ppt	0.5%[b] 0.1 M
Mepesulfate Mg^{++} (Ca^{++})	0.4% 0.1 M	0.1% 0.05 M	No ppt	No ppt
Mepesulfate Mn^{++}	0.1% 0.05 M	0.05% 0.025 M	0.5%[a] 0.2 M	0.5% 0.1 M

[a] Partial precipitation.
[b] Traces of HDL precipitated.

Mg^{++} used rather than Mn^{++} (compare dextran sulfate-Mg with heparin-Mg and the latter with heparin-Mn). The greater sensitivity to changes in ionic strength of heparin and of Mg^{++} is confirmed by the fact that more sodium chloride is needed to inhibit the precipitation of LDL with dextran sulfate-Mn than with dextran sulfate-Mg or heparin-Mn.

Less sodium chloride is needed to prevent the precipitation of HDL than of LDL and in turn less for LDL than for chylomicrons plus VLDL. The normal sodium chloride content of serum is sufficient to prevent the heparin-Mn precipitation of HDL but not of LDL, and the heparin-Mg precipitation of LDL, but not of chylomicrons plus VLDL; for this reason, selective precipitation of the latter from lipemic serum is possible (Burstein and Samaille, 1955). In addition, the precipitation of VLDL is more easily prevented (smaller increase of ionic strength) than the precipitation of chylomicrons; by adding sodium chloride to a lipemic serum, chylomicrons can be selectively precipitated with heparin-Mg (Burstein *et al.*, 1970).

Like VLDL, the abnormal lipoproteins of jaundiced sera are precipitated by heparin-Mg at the ionic strength of the serum (Section II,A). Consequently, depending on the ionic strength, heparin-Mg precipitates either chylomicrons alone, or chylomicrons plus VLDL and abnormal lipoproteins, or all the above lipoproteins plus LDL.

The control of the ionic strength is important for the selective one-step precipitation of all low density lipoproteins. In normal serum, and in serum diluted tenfold with 1% sodium chloride, this can be accomplished with heparin-Mn, but not with heparin-Mg, for with the latter LDL are not precipitated. In serum dialyzed against distilled water, or diluted tenfold with distilled water, this can be accomplished with heparin-Mg, but not with heparin-Mn, for with the latter HDL are also precipitated. It is worth noting that in a highly diluted serum (1/100) at low ionic strength, heparin-Co also precipitates gamma globulins (Burstein and Fine, 1960).

The precipitation of LDL by high molecular weight sulfated polysaccharides, without addition of divalent cations, is also inhibited by increasing the ionic strength (Oncley *et al.*, 1957; Bernfeld *et al.*, 1960b); more sodium chloride is needed in the presence of calcium (Burstein and Scholnick, 1971).

2. Sodium Phosphotungstate

The precipitation of LDL by sodium phosphotungstate-Mg, unlike that by sulfated polysaccharides, is not inhibited by increasing the ionic strength of the serum (Burstein, 1963). On the contrary, Burstein (1962b) has shown that in the presence of high concentrations of sodium phosphotungstate and sodium chloride, all low density lipoproteins are precipitated at neutral pH without addition of divalent cations.

E. Serum Proteins

The precipitation of LDL and of HDL with sulfated polysaccharides or sodium phosphotungstate is more easily achieved in the absence of other serum proteins. The minimal reagent requirements sufficient for the precipitation of isolated LDL increase when serum free of LDL is added. In the heparin-Mn precipitation of a tenfold diluted serum, the minimal heparin requirement is higher when the diluent is LDL-free serum rather than buffered 0.9% sodium chloride (Burstein et al., 1970). The inhibitory effect of serum proteins is even more pronounced when the precipitation of LDL is accomplished with sodium phosphotungstate-Mg (Burstein, 1963).

In an LDL-free serum dialyzed against distilled water, only traces of HDL are precipitated by dextran sulfate-Ca; the amount of precipitated HDL is much higher when the ionic strength and protein are lowered simultaneously by diluting the serum tenfold with distilled water. Likewise, at low ionic strength, isolated HDL are precipitated by dextran sulfate-Mg; this precipitation is inhibited by the addition of a lipoprotein-free serum dialyzed against distilled water (Burstein et al., 1970).

F. Sucrose

Sucrose also facilitates the precipitation of lipoproteins (Burstein, 1962a,c). The precipitated lipoproteins float on centrifugation due to the high density of the sucrose-rich medium. After addition of sucrose (1 gm/ml) not only chylomicrons plus VLDL but also LDL are quantitatively precipitated by heparin-Mg (final concentration: heparin, 0.025% and $MgCl_2$, 0.02 M); higher reagent concentrations are needed when less sucrose is added (Burstein, 1962c). Table IV shows that sucrose considerably reduces the concentrations of anions necessary for the precipitation of LDL; this is more pronounced in the case of sulfated polysaccharides.

The precipitation of HDL is also facilitated by sucrose; only after addition of sucrose (1 gm/ml serum) is there a partial precipitation of HDL with dextran sulfate-Mg (Burstein, 1962a) and with heparin-Mn (Burstein and Scholnick, 1971). Sucrose has the same effect on the precipitation of LDL and HDL as the simultaneous lowering of the ionic strength and protein content.

Table IV

FINAL CONCENTRATIONS OF POLYANIONS REQUIRED FOR THE PRECIPITATION OF
LDL FROM HUMAN SERUM IN THE PRESENCE OF $0.1 M$ $MgCl_2$—ROLE
OF SUCROSE

Polyanion	Serum	Serum plus sucrose (1 gm/ml)
Heparin	No ppt	0.025%
Dextran sulfate (mol. wt. 15×10^3)	0.1%	0.007%
Mepesulfate	0.4%	0.015%
Sodium polyanetholsulfonate	0.25%	0.05%
Sodium phosphotungstate	0.2%	0.05%

G. pH

At pH below that of serum, heparin, dextran sulfate, sodium phospho-tungstate, and also anions with high negative charge such as ammonium molybdate and sodium tungstate precipitate LDL even in the absence of metal ions (Burstein and Morfin, 1969c; Burstein and Scholnick, 1971). The pH of this almost complete precipitation depends on the reagent used and can be at, above, or below the isoelectric point of LDL (pH 5.7). The data concerning this subject are collected in Table V. The necessary anion concentrations are lower for the sulfated polysaccharides and the pH of precipitation is also lower. The precipitation of LDL is not selective, but in the pH range used, only a small amount of other serum proteins are precipitated. After centrifugation, the supernatants react with anti-β-lipoprotein antibodies and a specific precipitate is formed; the amount of cholesterol precipitated in this manner is approximately 20 mg/100 ml.

The precipitation of LDL at acid pH is not facilitated by addition of sucrose (Section II,F) and is inhibited by increase of the anion concentration. Likewise, Bernfeld *et al.* (1957b), Oncley *et al.* (1957), and Boyle and Moore (1959) have shown that the precipitation of LDL by high molecular weight sulfated polysaccharides is also inhibited by an excess of reagents.

When various preparations of isolated lipoproteins (Section IV) are added to the supernatants obtained under the conditions described in Table V, only LDL are precipitated. Chylomicrons and VLDL isolated from lipemic serum as well as HDL and the abnormal lipoproteins of jaundiced sera stay in solution, unless the pH is lowered.

Consequently, in regard to the precipitation of the different classes of

Table V

PRECIPITATION OF LDL FROM HUMAN SERUM BY ANIONS WITHOUT
ADDITION OF DIVALENT CATIONS

Reagent	Heparin	Dextran sulfate	Sodium phospho-tungstate	Sodium tungstate or Sodium molybdate	Ammonium molybdate
Final concentration	0.2%	0.1%	1%	1.5%	1.2%
pH	5.0[a]	5.3[b]	6.5[c]	5.7[d]	5.7[d]

[a] Traces precipitated at pH 5.6.
[b] Most of LDL precipitated at pH 5.6.
[c] Partial precipitation at pH 7.5.
[d] No precipitation at pH 6.1 even in the presence of Ca^{++}.

low density lipoproteins by polyanions, the results are quite different depending on whether the precipitation is carried out at neutral pH in the presence of Mg^{++} or at acid pH in the absence of metal ions; with heparin-Mg, abnormal lipoproteins, chylomicrons, and VLDL precipitate but LDL form soluble complexes; at pH 5.0 only LDL precipitate.

In addition, Burstein and Scholnick (1971) analyzed the pH requirements for the heparin precipitation of the various classes of isolated lipoproteins in a sodium veronal/sodium acetate ($0.0286\,M/0.0286\,M$) buffer containing 0.02% heparin and no sodium chloride. The precipitation of each class occurs in the following pH ranges (pH of onset of precipitation–pH of complete precipitation): LDL, 6.30–5.50; VLDL, 5.70–5.20; chylomicrons, 5.40–5.00; abnormal lipoproteins, 5.00–4.30; HDL, 4.70–3.90. Lower pH was required when the ionic strength was higher (addition of 1% NaCl) or when the heparin content was higher (0.1% instead of 0.02%). These results confirm that LDL are more easily precipitated by heparin (higher pH) than the other lipoproteins; they show also that VLDL are more easily precipitated than chylomicrons, chylomicrons more easily than abnormal lipoproteins, and the latter more easily than HDL.

A similarity exists between the precipitation of low density lipoproteins by heparin at acid pH and the precipitation by high molecular weight sulfated polysaccharides at neutral pH. In fact, according to Bernfeld et al. (1960a), lipoproteins with low flotation rates (S_f 2–12) have the highest affinity for amylopectin sulfate; the affinity slowly diminishes as the S_f increases, while chylomicrons are not precipitated at all. Boyle and Moore (1959) have found that only lipoproteins with flotation rates between S_f 2 and 16 (d 1.006–1.063) form insoluble complexes with K-agar; lipoproteins $S_f > 17$ (d < 1.006) are not precipitated.

H. Nature of the Lipoprotein-Polyanion-Metal Ion Interaction

After delipidation of HDL, or of the abnormal lipoprotein of jaundiced sera, with ethanol-diethylether, the soluble apoproteins are not precipitable by polyanions under the same conditions as the nondelipidated compounds (Burstein *et al.*, 1970). Furthermore (Section II,A and D) the formation of an insoluble lipoprotein-polyanion-metal ion complex is more easily achieved, the lower the protein:lipid ratio; more easily with chylomicrons than with VLDL, more easily with VLDL than with LDL, and more easily with LDL than with HDL (i.e., precipitation with a lower concentration of reagents, in a medium with a higher ionic strength, with Mg^{++} instead of Mn^{++}, with heparin instead of dextran sulfate). Table VI shows that the ease of precipitation depends on the protein:lipid ratio, but does not depend on the nature of the lipid moiety; indeed, abnormal lipoproteins of jaundiced sera and VLDL precipitate under the same conditions despite the fact that the lipid moieties are quite different. The abnormal lipoproteins are high in phospholipids and very low in triglycerides, while VLDL are rich in triglycerides; however, in both cases the protein:lipid ratio is approximately the same.

The above can be explained by the assumption that the polyanions combine with the protein moiety of the lipoproteins and form a soluble complex (by electrostatic interaction between the positive charges of the protein and the negative charges of the polyanion) which is precipitated by divalent cations; this precipitation requires the presence of lipid and is facilitated by a low protein:lipid ratio, but is independent of the chemical composition of the lipid moiety (Burstein *et al.*, 1970). On the contrary, there is a possibility that the nature of the protein moiety may be important. In fact, in the absence of divalent cations, the difference in the pH requirements for the heparin precipitation of the various classes of lipoproteins (Section II,G) cannot be explained either by the protein:lipid ratio or by the composition of the lipid moiety. By using succinylated or acetylated LDL, Nishida and Cogan (1970) have shown that the protein polar groups are responsible for the dextran sulfate-LDL interaction; the conversion of soluble complexes to insoluble ones in the presence of divalent cations is the result of additional cross-linking involving negative charges of both dextran sulfate and LDL.

On the other hand, Bernfeld and Kelley (1964) and Canal and Girard (1968) concluded that sulfated polysaccharides combine with the positive charged groups of LDL phospholipids and that the protein moiety is not essential.

It is worthy of note that there is a similarity in the precipitation of lipoproteins by polyanion-metal ion combinations and by a neutral poly-

Table VI

Composition of Lipoproteins and Their Precipitation by Different Combinations of Sulfated Polysaccharides and Divalent Cations from Human Serum

Lipoprotein	Protein (%)	Cholesterol: protein ratio (mg/mg)	Phospholipid: protein ratio (mg/mg)	Triglyceride: protein ratio (mg/mg)	Precipitation by heparin- Mg^{++}	(Mn^{++})	Precipitation by dextran sulfate- Mg^{++}	(Mn^{++})
Abn-LP[a]	4–6	4.5–6	9–13	0.5	+	(+)	+	(+)
VLDL	5–7	1.8–2.6	2–2.8	9–11	+	(+)	+	(+)
LDL	19–21.5	1.4–1.6	0.9–1.1	0.55–0.65	–	(+)	+	(+)
HDL	44–47	0.29–0.32	0.50–0.55	0.08	–	(–)	–	(+)

[a] Abnormal lipoprotein of jaundiced serum.

mer, polyvinylpyrrolidone (PVP). At neutral pH and in a hypertonic sodium chloride medium, PVP selectively precipitates chylomicrons, VLDL, and LDL. The concentrations of PVP required are lower for chylomicrons than for VLDL (Burstein and Prawerman, 1959) and lower for VLDL than for LDL (Burstein and Berlinski, 1960; Bierman *et al.*, 1962). The precipitation of the abnormal lipoproteins of jaundiced sera occurs under the same conditions as the precipitation of VLDL (Burstein and Caroli, 1969). For both PVP and polyanions, the precipitation occurs more readily when the protein:lipid ratio is low; and it is independent of the composition of the lipid moiety.

III. Precipitation of Serum Lipoproteins with Polyphosphates, Tetracyclines, and Detergents

A one-step precipitation of lipoproteins can also be accomplished with the following associations of reagents: (1) polyphosphates and divalent cations, (2) tetracyclines and divalent cations, (3) anionic detergents and divalent cations, (4) anionic detergents and protamine, (5) cationic detergents and heparin. With certain combinations of reagents (chlortetracycline-Ca, sodium deoxycholate-Mg, anionic detergent-protamine, cationic detergent-heparin) the precipitation of lipoproteins is complete and a lipoprotein-free supernatant is obtained after centrifugation. This supernatant, concentrated to the original protein content, contains less phospholipids (10–20 mg per 100 ml) and less esterified cholesterol (as shown by thin layer chromatography) than the dextran sulfate-Mn supernatant (Section II,C,2); in addition no HDL can be detected by immunodiffusion (Burstein and Scholnick, 1971). This supernatant appears to approximate the 1.25 infranatant as described by Alaupovic *et al.* (1966), while the dextran sulfate-Mn supernatant is the equivalent of the 1.21 infranatant (Section II,C,2). The precipitated lipoproteins are poorly soluble.

All the associations of reagents mentioned above form insoluble salts, and the precipitation of lipoproteins seems to be related to this formation. On the contrary, sulfated polysaccharides and sodium phosphotungstate do not form insoluble salts with the divalent cations used for precipitation of lipoproteins.

A. POLYPHOSPHATES

Polyphosphates are a mixture of phosphoric acid molecules, predominantly linear but of variable degrees of polymerization $(HPO_3^-)_n$. Long-chain polyphosphates have heparin-like activity: strongly negative charge at neutral pH, metachromatic reaction with toluidine blue (Tewari and Krishnan, 1959), precipitation by protamine (Singh, 1964), release of lipoprotein lipase in the rat (Havel and Bragdon, 1954) and rabbit (Brignon and Wolff, 1958), antithrombin activity (Burstein and Morfin, 1968b).

Burstein and Morfin (1968b) have shown that at neutral pH and in the presence of calcium chloride, polyphosphates with a mean degree of polymerization of 15, the same described by Nitschman et al. (1960) for the fractionation of plasma proteins at acid pH, precipitate selectively all the lipoproteins of density <1.063. The precipitation is complete after the addition to 100 ml of normal human serum of 6 ml of a freshly prepared 5% polyphosphate solution alkalinized to pH 8.00, and of 5 ml of $1 M$ $CaCl_2$ (the pH of the mixture is 7.3, but precipitation occurs even after alkalinization to pH 8.2). The precipitate is removed by centrifugation (6000g, 10 minutes) and the clear supernatant is dialyzed against buffered saline to eliminate the excess of Ca^{++}. As shown by electrophoretic and immunological studies of the supernatant, the precipitation of LDL and VLDL is complete and selective; HDL remain in solution. In a lipemic serum, chylomicrons are also precipitated but the minimal requirement of reagents is higher than in a normal serum.

As mentioned above (Section II,A), for polysulfates and sodium phosphotungstate, lower concentrations are required for the precipitation of chylomicrons than for LDL; this is not the case for polyphosphates where the minimal concentration depends only on the amount of lipoprotein in the serum and not on the lipoprotein class (chylomicrons or LDL). Moreover, the minimal reagent requirement is not reduced by the addition of sucrose.

Ca^{++} can be replaced by Mn^{++}, Ba^{++}, and Sr^{++} but not by Mg^{++}; this is related to the fact that the first four but not Mg^{++} form insoluble salts with polyphosphates at neutral pH. It should also be noted that in the presence of calcium a naturally occurring organic phosphorus compound, phytic acid (inositol hexaphosphoric acid), also precipitates LDL from human serum but only at pH 4.5 (Barre and Labat, 1960).

B. TETRACYCLINES

Tetracyclines are amphoteric compounds with an isoelectric point of approximately pH 5.0. When added to serum, chlortetracycline HCl forms soluble complexes with both LDL and HDL; these complexes remain close to the origin after electrophoresis on paper (Searcy et al., 1963). At neutral pH the soluble complexes are precipitated by divalent cations.

Lacko *et al.* (1959) have demonstrated that after adding chlortetracycline HCl and Ca^{++} to human serum, LDL precipitate quantitatively
and HDL partially. Burstein and Morfin (1968b) have further shown
that, under certain conditions, HDL can also be completely precipitated.
The conditions were the following: 100 mg chlortetracycline HCl and 50
mg sodium glycinate (content of one ampoule of Aureomycin) are dissolved in 20 ml of serum and 1 ml of $1\,M$ CaCl$_2$ is added. After 10
minutes, the mixture is centrifuged for 10 minutes at 20,000g. The clear
supernatant is separated from the yellow precipitate by decanting, dialyzed against buffered saline to remove CaCl$_2$, and concentrated to the
original protein content. The phospholipid content of the supernatant is
15–20 mg/100 ml; and zonal electrophoresis, immunoelectrophoresis, and
immunodiffusion show normal patterns with the exception of the absence
of lipoproteins.

Calcium can be replaced by Mg^{++}, Mn^{++}, Sr^{++}, or Ba^{++}. All these cations
form insoluble salts with chlortetracycline at pH above the isoelectric
point.

C. Detergents

1. *Anionic Detergents and Divalent Cations*

The interaction of serum lipoproteins with anionic detergents, espe
cially fatty acids, is well known (Macheboeuf, 1953; Gordon, 1955,
Laurell, 1955; Goodman and Shafrir, 1959; Burstein and Morfin, 1968c).
Figure 4 demonstrates that sodium lauryl sulfate combines with lipoproteins and increases the net negative charge; with small amounts of
detergent the electrophoretic mobility (agarose) of LDL and HDL, but
not of the other serum proteins is increased.

Burstein and Morfin (1971) have shown that in the presence of divalent
cations lipoproteins can be precipitated from human serum by anionic
detergents such as sodium oleate, sodium lauryl sulfate, and biliary salts
(sodium deoxycholate, sodium glycocholate, and sodium cholate). The
precipitation occurs at neutral pH and can be complete or partial, selective or not selective, depending on the detergent and cation used. Results
are summarized in Table VII. Only with sodium deoxycholate associated
with Mg^{++}, Sr^{++}, or Ba^{++} can a complete and selective precipitation of
lipoproteins be achieved (with Ca^{++} and Mn^{++} the precipitation is less
selective). Sodium lauryl sulfate-Ca^{++} precipitates only LDL; with Mn^{++}
instead of Ca^{++} HDL are also precipitated but this precipitation is not
selective. Associated with Mg^{++} (but not Ca^{++} or Mn^{++}), sodium oleate
precipitates LDL completely and HDL only partially. In combination

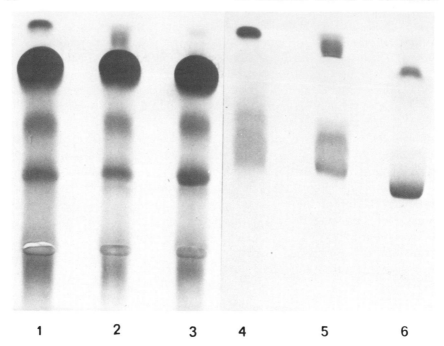

1   2   3   4   5   6

Fig. 4. Electrophoresis on agarose gel. 1, 2, and 3, Protein stain; 4, 5, and 6, lipid stain. 3 and 6, Normal human serum; 1, 2, 4, and 5, the same serum with sodium lauryl sulfate added; 2 and 5, 0.1%; 1 and 4, 0.2%.

with Mn^{++} (but not with Ca^{++} or Mg^{++}), sodium cholate and sodium glycocholate precipitate LDL but not HDL.

2. Anionic Detergents and Protamine

Laurell (1959) has shown that the addition of oleate and protamine to human serum flocculates β-lipoproteins as well as some α-lipoproteins.

Table VII

PRECIPITATION OF LIPOPROTEINS FROM HUMAN SERUM BY ANIONIC
DETERGENTS IN THE PRESENCE OF DIVALENT CATIONS

Detergent	Final concentration	Divalent cation	Final concentration	Lipoproteins precipitated
Sodium deoxycholate	2%	Mg^{++}	$0.2\,M$	LDL + HDL
Sodium oleate	1.5%	Mg^{++}	$0.1\,M$	LDL + HDL (partial)
Sodium lauryl sulfate	1%	Ca^{++}	$0.1\,M$	LDL
	2%	Mn^{++}	$0.1\,M$	LDL + HDL
Sodium glycocholate	2%	Mn^{++}	$0.1\,M$	LDL
Sodium cholate	2%	Mn^{++}	$0.1\,M$	LDL

Burstein and Morfin (1968d, 1971) have demonstrated that with higher concentration of both reagents a complete precipitation of VLDL, LDL, and HDL can be obtained. Anionic detergents other than sodium oleate (sodium lauryl sulfate, biliary salts) can also be used. In the case of sodium deoxycholate, sodium glycocholate, and sodium cholate the final concentrations needed are 1.0% for the detergents and 0.8% for protamine. With sodium oleate, the precipitation occurs with lower concentrations (0.5% oleate and 0.5% protamine) and with sodium lauryl sulfate it occurs with higher concentrations (1.2% sodium lauryl sulfate and 1.0% protamine). The precipitation is selective except with sodium lauryl sulfate in which case α_1-antitrypsin is also partially precipitated.

3. Cationic Detergents and Heparin

Lipoproteins can also be completely eliminated from human serum using a cationic detergent, cetyltrimethylammonium bromide (CTAB), together with heparin. The final concentrations needed are: detergent 0.3% and heparin 0.125% (Burstein and Morfin, 1968d). As with sodium lauryl sulfate-protamine, α_1-antitrypsin is also precipitated.

It is noteworthy that CTAB and protamine combine with lipoproteins and decrease their net negative charge. Figure 5 shows that both reagents decrease the electrophoretic mobility of LDL and HDL on agarose.

In summary, the soluble lipoprotein-detergent complexes are precipitated by polyelectrolytes of opposite charge which form insoluble salts

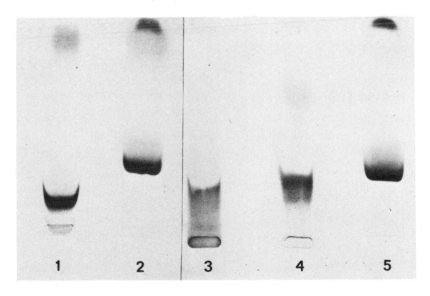

Fig. 5. Electrophoresis on agarose gel; lipid stain. 2 and 5, Normal human sera. 1, Serum plus protamine 0.5%. 3 and 4, Serum plus CTAB. 3, 0.1%; 4, 0.05%.

with the detergent. Thus, with certain reagent concentrations, the combination of an anionic detergent and a polycation (protamine) or a cationic detergent and a polyanion (heparin) completely precipitates VLDL, LDL, and HDL from human serum. There is no precipitation of the serum lipoproteins when one uses either two detergents or two polyelectrolytes of opposite charges (sodium deoxycholate-CTAB or heparin-protamine).

4. Anionic Detergents at Acid pH

Precipitation of lipoproteins by anionic detergents can also be achieved by lowering the pH. At final concentrations of 0.5%, sodium oleate, sodium deoxycholate, and sodium lauryl sulfate bring about the precipitation of lipoproteins from human serum after the mixture is acidified to pH 4.5. Sodium lauryl sulfate precipitates only β-lipoproteins and the other two detergents precipitate in addition a fraction of α-lipoprotein (Burstein and Morfin, 1971). All detergents precipitate a small amount of other serum proteins.

5. Sodium Lauryl Sulfate

Burstein and Scholnick (1972b) have shown that even without addition of either divalent cations or protamine, sodium lauryl sulfate (SLS) can selectively precipitate VLDL and chylomicrons from normal and abnormal sera. This precipitation requires an appropriate concentration of SLS, incubation at 35°C, and the presence of a thermolabile serum factor.

D. Detergents and Precipitation of Serum Lipoproteins with Polyanions

1. Anionic Detergents

Anionic detergents not only precipitate serum lipoproteins, but also, under certain conditions, inhibit the precipitation of LDL by polyanions. Nishida (1968) and Cogan and Nishida (1969) have shown that fatty acids prevent the precipitation of LDL by high molecular weight dextran sulfate and that an insoluble complex is formed only after addition of magnesium sulfate. Burstein and Morfin (1971) have further demonstrated that not only fatty acids but also other anionic detergents, such as sodium lauryl sulfate and biliary salts prevent the precipitation of LDL by dextran sulfate 2000; however, none of the detergents used inhibit the precipitation of LDL by the combination of dextran sulfate 2000 and Ca^{++} or Mg^{++}.

On the contrary, the precipitation of LDL by low molecular weight dextran sulfate and Ca^{++} or sodium phosphotungstate and Mg^{++} is inhibited by sodium lauryl sulfate (but not by sodium oleate or biliary salts); the concentration of detergents (0.5%) used for the inhibition studies was below that required for the precipitation of lipoproteins in the presence of Ca^{++} or Mg^{++} (Section III,C,1).

2. Nonionic Detergents

Burstein and Scholnick (1971) have shown that the nonionic detergent, Tween 80, has a strong inhibitory effect on the precipitation of lipoproteins by polyanions. The detergent was added to clear human serum (final concentration 1%) and the mixture was incubated for 3 hours at 20°C; the precipitation of VLDL, LDL, and HDL with all the combinations of polyanion and divalent cation described in Table II was completely inhibited. Precipitation of LDL by polyphosphate-Ca^{++}, and by polyanions without addition of divalent cations as described in Table V was also inhibited. Another nonionic detergent, Triton WR 1339, was also active but higher concentration (2%) was required.

It is known that nonionic detergents combine with serum lipoproteins and alter their electrophoretic mobility (Mora *et al.*, 1955; Scanu and Oriente, 1961; Burstein and Morfin, 1968c). The detergent-lipoprotein complex is not precipitated by polyanions.

IV. Isolation of Serum Lipoproteins by Precipitation with Polyanions

The isolation of the major classes of serum lipoproteins is generally accomplished by flotation in a preparative ultracentrifuge with progressive increase of the solvent density (DeLalla and Gofman, 1954; Havel *et al.*, 1955; Ewing *et al.*, 1965). The precipitation methods described in Section II can also be used for the isolation of lipoproteins from small or large volumes of serum. Various techniques utilizing polyanions and divalent cations have been described for the isolation of VLDL, LDL, and HDL from clear human sera (Burstein *et al.*, 1970), chylomicrons and VLDL from lipemic sera (Burstein and Gouzi, 1969), and abnormal lipoproteins from jaundiced sera (Burstein and Caroli, 1969). The precipitated HDL are further purified by ultracentrifugation and the other lipoproteins by several reprecipitations.

Procedures have also been developed for the isolation of LDL (but not HDL) with high molecular weight (10^6 or more) sulfated polysaccharides without the addition of divalent cations. The polysaccharides used were dextran sulfate (Oncley *et al.*, 1957; Briner *et al.*, 1959;

Margolis and Langdon, 1966) and sulfated amylopectin (Bernfeld *et al.*, 1960b; Bernfeld and Kelley, 1964; Levy *et al.*, 1967).

The methods for the isolation of serum lipoproteins using divalent cations and low molecular weight sulfated polysaccharides or sodium phosphotungstate will be presented in this section.

The reagents required are the following:

Sodium salt of heparin, 5% in 0.15 M NaCl.

Dextran sulfate (molecular weight approximately 15,000), Sochibo, Boulogne, France, 10% in 0.15 M NaCl.

Dextran sulfate 2000 (molecular weight 2×10^6), Pharmacia, Uppsala, Sweden, 5% in 0.15 M NaCl.

Sodium phosphotungstate, 4%, pH 7.6. To prepare this solution, 40 gm of phosphotungstic acid (Merck) are dissolved in 500 ml of distilled water, and 160 ml of 1 N NaOH are then added with stirring; the volume is made up to 1000 ml with distilled water.

Tris buffers: tris-HCl, 0.02 M, pH 7.7; tris-HCl-NaCl, the same buffer containing 1% NaCl.

All precipitations are carried out at room temperature (the precipitation can be less selective in the cold). Centrifugation, if not otherwise indicated, is performed at 20°C. All dialyses are conducted at 4°C.

A. Isolation of LDL and VLDL by Precipitation with Heparin, MgCl₂, and Sucrose[2]

A solution is prepared by dissolving 1000 gm of sucrose in 1 liter of serum, increasing the volume to 1600 ml. To this solution, 16 ml of 5% heparin and 80 ml of 2 M MgCl₂ are added; precipitation occurs immediately and after 15 minutes at room temperature the mixture is centrifuged in stoppered tubes at 6000g for 30 minutes. The high density of the solution (sucrose) causes the precipitated lipoproteins to float to the top and form a pellicle on the surface of the clear subnatant. The latter is removed by aspiration with a syringe and needle; the tubes are then centrifuged for 1 minute to sediment the pellicles and the precipitates are combined and dissolved in 20 ml of 5% NaCl by incubation for 30 minutes at 37°C. The lipoproteins are precipitated again by adding 1 liter of the tris-HCl buffer and 25 ml of 2 M MgCl₂ in order to remove contaminating serum proteins. The precipitate sediments on centrifugation (10 minutes at 6000g) and is dissolved in 20 ml of 5% NaCl; the lipo-

---

[2] This procedure is preferred when the object is only to obtain pure LDL and VLDL.

proteins are precipitated once again as above to eliminate the last traces of protein impurities.

The washed precipitate is dissolved in 5 ml of 10% sodium citrate and the lipoprotein solution is dialyzed for 24 hours against the tris-HCl-NaCl buffer to remove the citrate and the Mg^{++}. The heparin is eliminated by dialysis against 5% $BaCl_2$ at 4°C; after 24 hours the insoluble heparin-barium salts are separated by centrifugation in the cold and the Ba^{++} is removed by a further dialysis against tris-HCl-NaCl buffer (highly concentrated solutions of lipoproteins are not denatured by prolonged dialysis). The resultant is a clear yellow solution of concentrated lipoproteins (15 gm/100 ml or more) with a protein-free density of approximately 1.006. The LDL and VLDL isolated in this way may be separated from each other by ultracentrifugation (24 hours at 100,000g).

In this procedure, sucrose must be added to precipitate the lipoproteins with heparin and Mg^{++} from native serum, but in the reprecipitation steps the ionic strength is low and the addition of sucrose is therefore not necessary. It is worthy of note that when dextran sulfate is added to the sucrose-containing subnatant, a fraction of HDL precipitates; immunologically pure HDL can be isolated from this precipitate without ultracentrifugation (Burstein, 1962b).

B. Isolation of LDL and VLDL by Precipitation[3] with Heparin and $MnCl_2$

To 1000 ml of serum 40 ml of 5% heparin and 50 ml of 1 M $MnCl_2$ are added. Opacification appears immediately and the mixture is centrifuged for 10 minutes at 6000g; the precipitated lipoproteins sediment; the supernatant is clear but there is a white pellicle of manganese oxide which floats on the surface. The supernatant is decanted, and the precipitates are combined and dissolved in 10 ml of 10% sodium bicarbonate. The manganese ions precipitate as carbonate salts and these are removed by centrifugation. One liter of tris-HCl buffer is added to the solution of lipoproteins, and a second precipitation is achieved by the addition of 25 ml of 2 M $MgCl_2$. This precipitate is separated by centrifugation (10 minutes at 6000g) and redissolved in 20 ml of 5% NaCl. The lipoproteins are reprecipitated by the addition of 1 liter of the tris-HCl buffer and 25 ml of 2 M $MgCl_2$; recovered by centrifugation; and again dissolved in 20 ml of 5% NaCl. This reprecipitation is repeated once more and the precipitate is then dissolved in 5 ml of 10% sodium citrate. This is fol-

---

[3] This method is preferred when one wishes to obtain an LDL- and VLDL-free serum in addition to the isolated lipoproteins.

lowed by the dialysis procedures as described in the heparin-Mg-sucrose method (Section IV,A).

In this method, Mg^{++} is substituted for Mn^{++} in the reprecipitation steps because there is some coprecipitation of serum proteins in the case of Mn^{++}.

C. Stepwise Isolation of LDL plus VLDL and HDL by Precipitation with Dextran Sulfate and $MnCl_2$

1. Isolation of LDL plus VLDL

In this procedure 5 ml of 10% dextran sulfate and 50 ml of $1\ M\ MnCl_2$ are added to 1 liter of human serum; the LDL and VLDL are completely and selectively precipitated. The precipitate is separated by centrifugation for 10 minutes at 6000g and the lipoproteins purified by a procedure similar to that used in the heparin-Mn method. The precipitate is dissolved in 20 ml of 10% sodium bicarbonate and after removing the $MnCO_3$ by centrifugation, the lipoproteins are reprecipitated by adding 1 liter of tris-HCl buffer and 25 ml of $2\ M\ MgCl_2$. The precipitate is redissolved in 20 ml of 5% NaCl, and the lipoproteins are precipitated again by addition of 1 liter of 0.5% NaCl buffered with tris-HCl ($0.02\ M$, pH 7.7) and 50 ml of $2\ M\ MgCl_2$; this procedure is repeated. The washed precipitate is handled in the same way as in the heparin-Mg-sucrose method (Section IV,A) except that the dextran sulfate is precipitated as dextran sulfate-barium salts by dialysis against 1% $BaCl_2$ in 1% NaCl (instead of 5% $BaCl_2$ in distilled water for removal of heparin).

2. Isolation of HDL

For the isolation of HDL, 60 ml of 10% dextran sulfate and 150 ml of $1\ M\ MnCl_2$ are added to the LDL- and VLDL-free supernatant; precipitation begins immediately and is complete in 2 hours at room temperature. After centrifugation at 20,000g for 30 minutes, the supernatant is decanted, and the precipitate is washed in 500 ml of the tris-HCl-NaCl buffer containing 0.1% dextran sulfate and $0.1\ M\ MnCl_2$. The washed precipitate which contains the HDL, some other proteins, and manganese oxide, is recovered by centrifugation (10 minutes, 6000g) and is suspended in 80 ml of 2% sodium citrate in 1% NaCl. Solubilization is achieved by stirring the suspension (magnetic stirrer) for 30 minutes and adjusting the pH to 8.0 with $1\ N$ NaOH. The turbid mixture is centrifuged at 6000g for 10 minutes to remove the white precipitate of manganese oxide and this results in a clear yellow solution of HDL contaminated by small amounts of serum proteins. To purify the HDL it is necessary to perform one ultracentrifugation at the appropriate solvent density (approximately 1.22). In this hypertonic medium, dextran sulfate precipitates and is removed by low speed centrifugation. After ultracentrifugation of the supernatant (Spinco model L-2, rotor 50-Ti, 105,000g, 18°C, 24 hours), the HDL float to the top and are removed. The yellow-green color of the subnatant is due to Mn^{++}. The clear yellow solution of concentrated HDL obtained (8 gm/100 ml or more) is dialyzed against the tris-HCl-NaCl buffer.

The combination of high molecular weight dextran sulfate and $CaCl_2$ can also be used to isolate HDL. After precipitation of LDL plus VLDL (dextran sulfate 2000, 0.5%; $CaCl_2$, 0.1 M)[4] and removal of the precipitate by centrifugation, HDL are precipitated by adding to the supernatant sufficient dextran sulfate 2000 and $CaCl_2$ to raise the concentrations to 0.55% and 0.2 M. The precipitated HDL are soluble in 0.5 M potassium oxalate (40 ml for the HDL from 1000 ml of serum) and can then be purified by ultracentrifugation.

D. Stepwise Isolation of LDL plus VLDL and HDL by Precipitation with Sodium Phosphotungstate and $MgCl_2$

1. *Isolation of LDL plus VLDL*

To 1 liter of serum 100 ml of 4% sodium phosphotungstate and 25 ml of 2 M $MgCl_2$ are added; LDL and VLDL are completely and selectively precipitated. The mixture is immediately centrifuged at 6000g for 10 minutes, and the precipitate is dissolved in 1 liter of nonbuffered 0.2% sodium citrate with the use of a magnetic stirrer; 10 gm of sodium chloride are added producing some turbidity. The LDL and VLDL are reprecipitated by the addition of 30 ml of 2 M $MgCl_2$. The precipitate is recovered by centrifugation and this washing procedure is repeated once to eliminate the protein impurities. The washed precipitate is then dissolved at 37°C in 10 ml of 10% sodium citrate by adding crystals of ammonium chloride. The solubilized lipoproteins are dialyzed against a solution containing 5% sodium citrate and 10% ammonium chloride; with this combination the phosphotungstate is removed. The concentrated polyanion-free lipoprotein solution is finally dialyzed against the tris-HCl-NaCl buffer to eliminate the citrate and ammonium.

---

[4] Procedures for isolation of low density lipoproteins with dextran sulfate 2000-Ca precipitation have been described; the precipitation is followed by further purification either by chromatography on DEAE Sephadex (Stokes *et al.*, 1967) or by ultracentrifugation (Hatch and Lees, 1968).

2. Isolation of HDL

To the clear LDL-free supernatant from the above procedure is added 900 ml of 4% sodium phosphotungstate; a lipid-free precipitate composed mostly of gamma globulin appears immediately and is removed by centrifugation (10 minutes, 6000g). To this supernatant is added 175 ml of 2 M MgCl$_2$; after 2 hours at room temperature the precipitation of HDL is complete and the mixture is centrifuged for 30 minutes at 20,000g. The supernatant is decanted and the precipitate washed with 500 ml of a solution containing 1% NaCl, 0.4% sodium phosphotungstate, and 0.1 M MgCl$_2$. The washed precipitate is recovered by centrifugation at 6000g for 10 minutes and it is suspended in 70 ml of 1% NaCl. Solubilization is achieved by the dropwise addition of 10% sodium carbonate (approximately 20 ml) with stirring on a magnetic stirrer. The concentrated neutral solution of HDL obtained is contaminated by small amounts of serum protein and must be further purified by ultracentrifugation in the same manner as in the method with dextran sulfate and MnCl$_2$ (Section IV,C,2).

E. ANALYSES OF ISOLATED SERUM LIPOPROTEINS

The chemical composition of the lipoproteins isolated from clear human serum by polyanion precipitation is given in Table VIII. These data are in agreement with those for the lipoproteins isolated by other methods (Oncley, 1963; Hatch and Lees, 1968).

Electrophoretic and immunological studies have shown that the isolated LDL are free of HDL and vice versa; in addition both LDL and HDL are free of other serum proteins.

Zonal electrophoresis with protein and lipid stains (agarose gel, starch gel, cellulose acetate, paper) of concentrated solutions of HDL and LDL reveals only one component with normal electrophoretic mobility (Figs. 6, 7, and 8).

Table VIII

COMPOSITION OF LIPOPROTEINS ISOLATED FROM NONLIPEMIC HUMAN SERUM BY POLYANIONS

Lipoprotein	Protein (%)	Lipid (%)	Cholesterol: lipid ratio (mg/mg)	Phospholipid: lipid ratio (mg/mg)	Cholesterol: phospholipid ratio (mg/mg)
VLDL	5–7	93–95	0.12–0.17	0.15–0.20	0.8–1.0
LDL	19–21.5	78.5–81	0.37–0.39	0.24–0.26	1.45–1.55
HDL	44–47	53–56	0.27–0.30	0.44–0.48	0.57–0.61

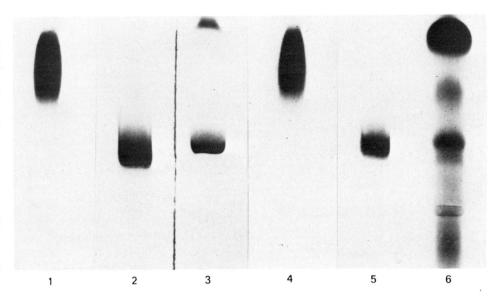

Fig. 6. Electrophoresis on agarose gel; 1, 2, and 3, Lipid stain; 4, 5, and 6, protein stain. 3 and 6, Normal human serum; 2 and 5, isolated LDL; 1 and 4, isolated HDL.

Immunoelectrophoretic studies with anti-whole human serum revealed only one precipitation arc and similarly, no protein impurities could be demonstrated by using the Oudin or Ouchterlony immunodiffusion methods. When rabbit or horse anti-whole human serum adsorbed by poly-

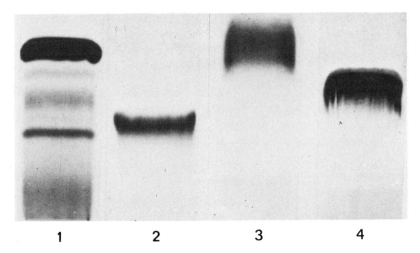

Fig. 7. Electrophoresis on cellulose acetate, protein stain. 1, Normal human serum; 2, isolated LDL; 3, isolated HDL; 4, VLDL isolated from lipemic serum.

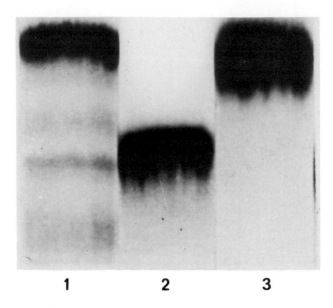

Fig. 8. Paper electrophoresis, protein stain. 1, Normal human serum; 2, isolated LDL; 3, isolated HDL.

anion-isolated LDL or HDL is reacted on immunodiffusion against human serum, all the normal precipitation arcs are found except that of the adsorbant used. Ultracentrifugal analysis of isolated HDL demonstrated the presence of one sharp peak with the sedimentation constant of this single component being 4.9–5.0 Svedberg units.

These isolated lipoprotein preparations are essentially free of polyanions; there is no precipitation when divalent cations are added even at low ionic strength, and no metachromatic reaction with toluidine blue. The amount of LDL isolated by these methods is about 0.40 gm/100 ml and that of HDL, 0.25 gm/100 ml of serum.

F. Isolation of Chylomicrons and VLDL from Lipemic Serum by Precipitation with Heparin and $MgCl_2$

To 100 ml of lipemic serum are added 5 ml of 5% heparin and 5 ml of 2 M $MgCl_2$. Flocculation begins immediately and after 30 minutes at room temperature the mixture is centrifuged for 15 minutes at 6000g in stoppered tubes. The lipoprotein-Mg-heparin complexes float and form a creamy layer at the tops of the tubes. The clear subnatant is removed by aspiration with needle and syringe (LDL can be precipitated from the chylomicron and VLDL-free subnatant by adding sucrose) and the creamy layer is suspended in 50 ml of 0.02 M tris-HCl, pH 7.7, containing 0.6% NaCl and 0.5% sodium citrate. A stable emulsion is obtained by stirring on a magnetic stirrer. Reprecipitation is performed by the addition of 2.5 ml of 2 M MgCl$_2$; the precipitate again floats on centrifugation; this washing procedure is repeated twice. The precipitate is suspended in 3% sodium citrate (the volume is dependent on the extent of the lipemia of the serum); with stirring, a stable emulsion is formed. This emulsion is first dialyzed against tris-HCl-NaCl buffer to remove the citrate and Mg^{++}, and then against 5% BaCl$_2$ to precipitate the heparin; the heparin-barium salts are removed by centrifugation and the supernatant is subjected to a final dialysis against the tris-HCl-NaCl buffer.

The concentrated preparation (20% lipids or more) contains chylomicrons and VLDL and may be subdivided by centrifugation at 40,000g for 2 hours. The chylomicrons and a part of VLDL float and form a creamy layer (fraction I); the remaining VLDL stay in the subnatant and may be concentrated by precipitation with heparin-Mg^{++} (fraction II). Neither fraction contains protein impurities detectable by electrophoretic or immunological techniques. On cellulose acetate electrophoresis, fraction I remains at the origin and fraction II migrates in the α_1-α_2 area (Fig. 7). The protein:lipid ratio in fraction I varies between 0.018 and 0.03 and in fraction II between 0.04 and 0.06. It is known that both chylomicrons and VLDL are very heterogeneous and that the protein percentage decreases with increase in the size of the particles (Gustafson *et al.*, 1965, Yokoyama and Zilversmit, 1965; Lossow *et al.*, 1969).

G. Isolation of HDL and LDL Components from Partially Delipidated Chylomicrons and VLDL by Precipitation with Heparin and MgCl$_2$

It is known that HDL is present in VLDL and that partial delipidation dissociates the α- and β-components of VLDL (Levy *et al.*, 1966a; Gustafson *et al.*, 1966; Granda and Scanu, 1966). Burstein and Scholnick (1971) have shown that after partial delipidation of the chylomicron plus VLDL emulsion by diethylether extraction only the β-component is precipitated by heparin-Mg. The precipitate can be eliminated by centrifugation and the supernatant is concentrated by dialysis against PVP. Figure 9 shows that the supernatant contains a lipoprotein with α-mobility on paper electrophoresis. In other words the HDL component is precipitated by heparin-Mg before but not after delipidation. Somewhat different results were obtained by Kook *et al.* (1970) with VLDL isolated by ultracentrifugation from the pooled human serum of normal volunteers and with

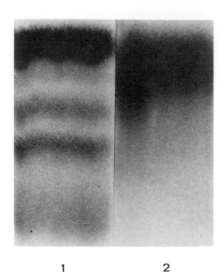

1   2

FIG. 9.   Paper electrophoresis; protein stain; 1, Normal human serum; 2, α-component isolated from a chylomicron + VLDL emulsion partially delipidated by diethyl-ether extraction.

rat VLDL. These authors have demonstrated that by use of heparin and Ca^{++} the α-component (heparin supernatant) can be separated from the β-component (heparin precipitate) even without delipidation. The difference in the behavior of the α-component in these two studies may be due to the fact that in one, lipemic sera but in the other, normal sera were used.

H. ISOLATION OF THE ABNORMAL LIPOPROTEINS FROM JAUNDICED SERUM BY PRECIPITATION WITH HEPARIN AND MgCl$_2$

In this method 30 ml of jaundiced serum (obstructive jaundice, biliary cirrhosis) are diluted with 300 ml of 0.7% NaCl containing 0.1 M MgCl$_2$; 6 ml of 5% heparin solution are added. The precipitate, consisting of the abnormal lipoproteins and some lipoproteins which are immunologically LDL, is separated by centrifugation (6000g for 10 minutes) and redissolved in 5 ml of 1% NaCl containing 0.5% sodium citrate. The lipoproteins with LDL component are eliminated by adding anti-LDL antibodies. The specific precipitate is removed by centrifugation and the volume of the supernatant is brought to 50 ml with the tris-HCl buffer. The abnormal lipoproteins are reprecipitated by adding 2.5 ml of 1 M MgCl$_2$. The precipitate is recovered by centrifugation dissolved in 2 ml of 5%

sodium citrate, and treated in the same way as in the heparin-Mg-sucrose procedure (Section IV,A) to remove the citrate, Mg^{++}, and heparin.

The isolated abnormal lipoproteins have β-mobility on zonal electrophoresis and are free of protein impurities; their chemical composition is given in Table VI. After delipidation with ethanol/diethyl ether (3/1), the protein moiety is water soluble and migrates on paper and agarose electrophoresis in the α_1-globulin region.

Polyanion precipitation has also been employed in other procedures for the isolation of the abnormal lipoproteins. Switzer (1967) combined immunoprecipitation, Mepesulfate-Ca precipitation, and ultracentrifugation. Seidel *et al.* (1969) used ultracentrifugation, heparin-Mn precipitation, and ethanol fractionation. Isolation by PVP precipitation is also possible (Burstein and Caroli, 1969).

V. Determination of Serum Low Density Lipoproteins

Based on polyanion precipitation, procedures have been developed both for the turbidimetric estimation of human low density lipoproteins and for the analysis of the lipid distribution between low and high density lipoproteins.

A. Turbidimetric Estimation

The procedure developed by Burstein and Samaille (1956, 1959) is based on the selective and quantitative one-step precipitation of all low density lipoproteins (triglyceride-rich chylomicrons and VLDL, cholesterol-rich LDL, and phospholipid-rich abnormal lipoproteins of jaundiced serum) with heparin-Ca (or -Mg) at low ionic strength and at room temperature. The turbidimetric determination is performed in the following way: 0.2 ml of fasting serum (or less depending on the spectrophotometer used) is added to 2 ml of $0.025\ M$ $CaCl_2$ is a calibrated cuvette; the optical density is read (serum blank) at 700 nm and 0.04 ml of 1% heparin is added. After 4 minutes, the optical density is measured again. The blank is subtracted and the turbidity values are expressed as optical density units $\times 100$; the results are reproducible, independent of the source of heparin, of the temperature between 20 and 30°C, and of the pH between 6.5 and 8.5. In the case of hyperlipidemic serum, the sample must be diluted with saline prior to turbidity determination. In normal fasting sera the blank is low, but in lipemic sera it may be very high; the high blank is due to the inherent turbidity of the triglyceride-rich lipoproteins; in this case the blank is not subtracted.

The precipitate can be separated by centrifugation; and analysis of the precipitate has shown that in nonlipemic sera there is a linear relationship between the turbidity values and the total lipid content. Turbidimetric results may also be expressed as total low density lipoprotein lipids (mg/100 ml serum) by multiplying the turbidity measurement by a conversion factor (mg lipid/O.D. unit) which must be calculated for each spectrophotometer used. This factor is not exactly the same for chylomicrons and LDL and is much higher for the abnormal lipoprotein of jaundiced sera (Burstein and Caroli, 1969).

In similar experiments with clear sera, Srinivasan *et al.* (1970) and Lopez-S. *et al.* (1971) found a linear correlation between turbidity and cholesterol values of the precipitates. The precipitation is selective; there is no increase in turbidity over blank value in the case of low density lipoprotein-free serum: abetalipoproteinemia, dialyzed d 1.063 infranate, or serum from which β-lipoprotein was removed by addition of specific antibodies (Burstein and Scholnick, 1971).

After turbidimetric estimation, low density lipoprotein cholesterol (Fried and Hoeflmayr, 1963) or cholesterol and phospholipids (Burstein and Caroli, 1969) can be measured in the precipitate recovered by centrifugation. These values are identical to those obtained after precipitation of low density lipoproteins with isolated anti-β-lipoprotein antibodies (Burstein and Scholnick, 1971).

Since chylomicrons precipitate at higher ionic strength than VLDL, and in turn VLDL higher than LDL (Section II,D,1), differential precipitation followed by turbidimetric estimation of these lipoproteins can be accomplished by varying the ionic strength (Scholnick *et al.*, 1970, 1972).

For each serum studied three turbidimetric measurements are made in a manner similar to that of Burstein and Samaille described above; for chylomicrons, 0.2 ml serum, 0.04 ml 5% heparin, 2 ml 0.1 M MgCl$_2$ in 1.0% saline; for chylomicrons plus VLDL, 0.2 ml serum, 0.04 ml 5% heparin, 2 ml 0.1 M MgCl$_2$ in 0.7% saline; for chylomicrons, VLDL plus LDL, 0.2 ml serum, 0.04 ml 1% heparin, 2 ml 0.025 M CaCl$_2$. The differential precipitation of these lipoprotein fractions is quite dependent on the source of heparin. With certain heparins it may be necessary to use different saline concentrations, i.e., 0.6% instead of 0.7% and 0.9% instead of 1.0%. Normal ranges were determined by studying subjects with normal triglycerides, cholesterol, and paper electrophoresis. Analysis of these three turbidimetric determinations yields an estimation of the levels of LDL, VLDL, and chylomicrons. This provides a simple and rapid method for the detection and typing of the various hyperlipoproteinemias.

The heparin-calcium turbidimetric method, as described above, or with some modifications, has been used by many investigators (Ledvina *et al.*, 1960; Ledvina and Lukastik, 1961; Juret and Chouly, 1961; Hartmann *et al.*, 1962; Dangerfield and Faulkner, 1964; Kellen, 1964; Link and Fassati, 1964; Farstad, 1966; Hartmann, 1966; Klimov *et al.*, 1966; Switzer, 1967; Daver *et al.*, 1969; Srinivasan *et al.*, 1970; Lopez-S. *et al.*, 1971). Similar procedures have been described using calcium and dextran sulfate of low molecular weight (Badin and Schmitt, 1957; Castaigne and Amselem, 1959; Groulade and Jacqueline, 1959; Badin *et al.*, 1960; Dangerfield and Faulkner, 1964; Badin, 1965; Daver *et al.*, 1969) or high molecular weight (Walton and Scott, 1964).

High molecular weight sulfated polysaccharides without addition of divalent cations have also been employed for the nephelometric or turbidimetric estimation of β-lipoproteins; Antoniades *et al.* (1958) used dextran sulfate, Bernfeld *et al.* (1957a, 1960a) used sulfated amylopectin, and Boyle and Moore (1959), K-agar. Turbidimetric determination can also be accomplished with sodium phosphotungstate in a concentrated sodium chloride medium (Burstein and Berlinski, 1961), or with poly-vinyl-pyrrolidone (Burstein and Berlinski, 1960).

B. Lipid Distribution in Man

Studies of lipid distribution by polyanion precipitation in normal and disease states are based on the assumption that the polyanion precipitate contains all the low density lipoproteins and the supernatant all the high density lipoproteins. In fact there is good agreement between cholesterol precipitated by polyanions and the cholesterol content of the lipoprotein fraction isolated by ultracentrifugation at density 1.063 from the same sera. This has been shown for Mepesulfate-Ca (Florsheim and Gonzales, 1960), dextran sulfate-Ca (Kritchevsky *et al.*, 1963), heparin-Mn (Levy *et al.*, 1966a) and heparin-Ca (Jordan *et al.*, 1966). It is worthy of note that the paraprotein lipid fraction in patients with plasmacytoma is not precipitated by polyanions (Keler-Bacoka, 1967).[5]

1. Dextran Sulfate-Calcium Precipitation

Polonovski *et al.* (1958) have analyzed the total lipid, cholesterol, and phospholipid distribution in the dextran sulfate precipitate and super-

---

[5] Polyanion precipitation of β-lipoproteins has been used not only for lipid distribution studies, but also to remove nonspecific serum inhibitors of streptolysin O (Hallen, 1963; Cabau and Badin, 1965; Winblad, 1966) and of virus hemagglutination (Mann *et al.*, 1967; Feldman, 1968).

natant of normal and hyperlipemic sera. Total serum cholesterol and cholesterol in the dextran sulfate supernatant (HDL cholesterol) have been measured in normal men and in patients with hypercholesterolemia; LDL plus VLDL cholesterol was calculated by subtracting the HDL cholesterol from the serum cholesterol (Burstein and Samaille, 1956, 1958; Azerad et al., 1958; Castaigne and Amselem, 1959; Kritchevsky et al., 1963). A method for the analysis of lipid phosphorus in the dextran sulfate precipitate has been described by Henry and Chatelain (1965).

In the case of lipemic sera magnesium must be used in place of calcium; after centrifugation the precipitate floats instead of sedimenting, and a well-defined creamy layer at the top of the clear infranatant is obtained with Mg^{++} but not with Ca^{++} (Burstein and Samaille, 1958). In all these studies, low molecular weight dextran sulfate was used, but dextran sulfate 2000 can also be employed (Hatch and Lees, 1968); however, under certain conditions, high molecular weight dextran sulfate also precipitates HDL (Jordan, 1968).

2. Heparin-Manganese Precipitation

In the procedure described by Burstein and Samaille (1960), LDL plus VLDL are precipitated by heparin-Mn. To 1 ml of serum are added 0.04 ml of 5% heparin solution and 0.05 ml of 1 M $MnCl_2$. After 15 minutes at room temperature, the clear supernatant is separated from the precipitate by centrifugation. The difference between the serum cholesterol and the HDL cholesterol (supernatant cholesterol multiplied by 1.09 to correct for dilution) represents the LDL plus VLDL cholesterol. This method has been used by several authors (Franzini and Schivi, 1964; Franzini, 1965; Pries et al., 1968). Under these conditions, chylomicrons are also precipitated; in a highly lipemic serum, the insolubilized lipoproteins float, and cholesterol analysis can be done on the clear subnatant; but in a slightly lipemic serum, the separation of the precipitate by centrifugation can only be effected after twofold dilution of the serum with distilled water (the precipitate sediments). LDL plus VLDL cholesterol can also be measured directly on the precipitate obtained by adding 0.1 ml of serum to 2 ml of 0.05 M $MnCl_2$ solution containing 1% NaCl and 0.02% heparin (Burstein and Scholnick, 1971). VLDL and LDL cholesterol can also be estimated separately by measuring (a) serum cholesterol (VLDL + LDL + HDL), (b) ultracentrifugation infranatant d 1.006 cholesterol (LDL + HDL), and (c) heparin-Mn supernatant cholesterol (HDL); (a) minus (b) represents the VLDL cholesterol, and (b) minus (c), the LDL cholesterol (Levy et al., 1966a,b; Frederickson et al., 1967, 1968).

C. Polyanion Precipitation and Lipid Distribution
   in Various Species

Combined with divalent cations, sulfated polysaccharides of low
molecular weight also precipitate lipoproteins from different animal sera
(dog, baboon, rat, chicken, etc.). Low density lipoproteins can be removed by precipitation with dextran sulfate-Ca (Burstein and Samaille,
1957b; Castaigne and Amselem, 1959; Sakagami and Zilversmit, 1961,
1962; Kritchevsky *et al.*, 1965; Hill and Dvornik, 1969), Mepesulfate-Ca
(Florsheim and Gonzales, 1960; Leveille *et al.*, 1961), and heparin-Mn
(Burstein and Samaille, 1960). In several of these studies, the complete-
ness of precipitation was confirmed by ultracentrifugal analysis. Burstein
and Morfin (1969a) have analyzed the lipid distribution in low and high
density lipoproteins in various mammals by cholesterol and phospholipid
determinations before and after heparin-Mn precipitation (Table IX).
There is a predominance of LDL in human, pig, rabbit, and guinea pig
sera, whereas, HDL is the major component in horse, beef, dog, cat, rat,
and sheep sera. This is in agreement with results obtained by analytical
ultracentrifugation (Lewis *et al.*, 1952) and by preparative ultracentrifugation (Havel *et al.*, 1955; Hillyard *et al.*, 1955). The high density lipo-

Table IX

Cholesterol and Phospholipid Determinations before and after
Heparin-Mn and Dextran Sulfate-Mn Precipitation in
Various Species

	Cholesterol (mg %)			Phospholipids (mg %)		
Species	Normal serum	Super-natant, heparin-Mn[a]	Super-natant, dextran sulfate-Mn[a]	Normal serum	Super-natant, heparin-Mn[a]	Super-natant, dextran sulfate
Man	230	70	Traces	240	125	30
Horse	135	85	Traces	145	120	10
Sheep	85	45	Traces	100	70	25
Beef	100	70	Traces	90	70	12
Pig	150	40	Traces	120	55	25
Rabbit	80	20	Traces	105	55	20
Guinea pig	75	0	0	65	15	12
Rat	110	70	Traces	170	135	30
Cat	140	100	Traces	240	190	25
Dog	300	210	Traces	435	315	25

[a] Values corrected for dilution.

proteins can also be removed from these sera by polyanion precipitation; this is accomplished with dextran sulfate-Mn (Burstein and Morfin, 1969a). Table IX shows that dextran sulfate-Mn supernatant from different species is poor in phospholipids and contains only traces of cholesterol. Recently pure HDL were prepared from rat plasma by the dextran sulfate-$MnCl_2$ precipitation method (Roheim et al., 1971).

VI. Summary

    In the presence of divalent cations, sulfated polysaccharides and sodium phosphotungstate can precipitate at neutral pH all the lipoprotein classes: chylomicrons, VLDL, LDL, and HDL. This precipitation is dependent on the nature of the anion and cation, the concentration of reagents, and the ionic strength. The formation of an insoluble complex (lipoprotein-polyanion-cation) is more easily achieved with chylomicrons and VLDL than with LDL, and in turn more easily with LDL than with HDL. This is related to the protein:lipid ratio and not to the composition of the lipid moiety of the individual lipoproteins. Though certain combinations of anion and cation precipitate all the lipoproteins, the reagent requirements are not the same (chylomicrons < VLDL < LDL < HDL). For this reason, it is possible to isolate the different classes of serum lipoproteins by the stepwise increase of the reagent concentrations; a similarity is apparent between this method and the fractionation method by flotation in the preparative ultracentrifuge which requires a stepwise increase of solvent density.

    Procedures have been described for the isolation from large volumes of human serum of the major classes of lipoproteins by polyanion precipitation followed by, at most, only a single preparative ultracentrifugation. The highly concentrated solutions of isolated lipoproteins are uncontaminated by other serum proteins as judged by immunological and electrophoretic methods. The same procedures can also be applied to small volumes of individual sera (normal and abnormal).

    Under certain conditions the precipitation of low density lipoproteins is complete and selective. Based on this, methods have been developed for the turbidimetric estimation of all the low density lipoprotein fractions, and for the analysis of the lipid distribution between the high and low density lipoproteins. By varying the ionic strength, differential precipitation of chylomicrons, VLDL, and LDL, followed by turbidimetric estimation of these lipoproteins, can be accomplished.

    Serum lipoproteins are also precipitated by divalent cations and polyphosphates, tetracyclines, or anionic detergents. In addition, a lipoprotein-free serum can be prepared by using either an anionic detergent and protamine, or a cationic detergent and heparin.

References

Alaupovic, P., Sanbar, S. S., Furman, R. H., Sullivan, M. L., and Valraven, S. L. (1966). *Biochemistry* **5**, 4044.

Antoniades, H. N., Tullis, J. L., Sargeant, L. H., Pennel, R. B., and Oncley, J. L. (1958). *J. Lab. Clin. Med.* **51**, 630.

Azerad, E., Lewin, J., and Ghata, J. (1958). *Bull. Mem. Soc. Med. Hop. Paris* **74**, 703.

Badin, J. (1965). *Presse Med.* **73**, 2659.

Badin, J., and Schmitt, F. (1957). *Ann. Biol. Clin. (Paris)* **15**, 469.

Badin, J., Martin, J., and Schmitt, F. (1960). *Ann. Biol. Clin. (Paris)* **18**, 341.

Barre, R., and Labat, J. (1960). *Ann. Biol. Clin. (Paris)* **18**, 420.

Bernfeld, P. (1955). *Fed. Proc., Fed. Amer. Soc. Exp. Biol.* **14**, 182.

Bernfeld, P., and Kelley, T. F. (1964). *J. Biol. Chem.* **239**, 3341.

Bernfeld, P., Berkowitz, M. E., and Donahue, V. M. (1957a). *J. Clin. Invest.* **36**, 1363.

Bernfeld, P., Donahue, V. M., and Berkowitz, M. E. (1957b). *J. Biol. Chem.* **226**, 51.

Bernfeld, P., Bonner, C. D., and Berkeley, B. J. (1960a). *J. Clin. Invest.* **39**, 1864.

Bernfeld, P., Nisselbaum, J. S., Berkeley, B. J., and Hanson, R. W. (1960b). *J. Biol. Chem.* **235**, 2852.

Bierman, E. L., Gordis, E., and Hamlin, J. T. (1962). *J. Clin. Invest.* **41**, 2254.

Blasius, R., and Seitz, W. (1952). *Klin. Wochenschr.* **30**, 905.

Boyle, E., and Moore, R. V. (1959). *J. Lab. Clin. Med.* **53**, 272.

Bragdon, J. H., and Havel, R. J. (1954). *Science* **120**, 113.

Brignon, H. J., and Wolff, R. (1958). *Bull. Soc. Chim. Biol.* **40**, 1567.

Briner, W. W., Riddle, J. W., and Cornwell, D. C. (1959). *J. Exp. Med.* **110**, 113.

Burstein, M. (1962a). *Life Sci.* **1**, 739.

Burstein, M. (1962b). *J. Physiol. (Paris)* **54**, 647.

Burstein, M. (1962c). *C. R. Acad. Sci.* **255**, 605.

Burstein, M. (1963). *Nouv. Rev. Fr. Hematol.* **3**, 139.

Burstein, M., and Berlinski, M. (1960). *Rev. Fr. Etud. Clin. Biol.* **5**, 193.

Burstein, M., and Berlinski, M. (1961). *Rev. Fr. Etud. Clin. Biol.* **6**, 479.

Burstein, M., and Caroli, J. (1969). *Rev. Med. Chir. Mal. Foie, Rate Pancreas* **44**, 125.

Burstein, M., and Fine, J. M. (1960). *Rev. Fr. Etud. Clin. Biol.* **5**, 612.

Burstein, M., and Gouzi, M. (1969). *Rev. Fr. Transfus.* **12**, 271.

Burstein, M., and Morfin, R. (1968a). *Nouv. Rev. Fr. Hematol.* **8**, 45.

Burstein, M., and Morfin, R. (1968b). *Nouv. Rev. Fr. Hematol.* **8**, 65.

Burstein, M., and Morfin, R. (1968c). *Nouv. Rev. Fr. Hematol.* **8**, 793.

Burstein, M., and Morfin, R. (1968d). *Rev. Fr. Etud. Clin. Biol.* **13**, 274.

Burstein, M., and Morfin, R. (1969a). *Nouv. Rev. Fr. Hematol.* **9**, 231.

Burstein, M., and Morfin, R. (1969b). *Nouv. Rev. Fr. Hematol.* **9**, 365.

Burstein, M., and Morfin, R. (1969c). *Nouv. Rev. Fr. Hematol.* **9**, 645.

Burstein, M., and Morfin, R. (1971). *Nouv. Rev. Fr. Hematol.* **11**, 173.

Burstein, M., and Prawerman, A. (1959). *Pathol. Biol.* **7**, 1035.

Burstein, M., and Samaille, J. (1955). *C. R. Acad. Sci.* **241**, 664.

Burstein, M., and Samaille, J. (1956). *C. R. Acad. Sci.* **243**, 2185.

Burstein, M., and Samaille, J. (1957a). *J. Physiol.* (*Paris*) **49**, 83.

Burstein, M., and Samaille, J. (1957b). *Rev. Hematol.* **5**, 679.

Burstein, M., and Samaille, J. (1958). *Clin. Chim. Acta* **3**, 320.

Burstein, M., and Samaille, J. (1959). *Ann. Biol. Clin.* (*Paris*) **17**, 23.

Burstein, M., and Samaille, J. (1960). *Clin. Chim. Acta* **5**, 609.

Burstein, M., and Scholnick, H. R. (1970). *Nouv. Rev. Fr. Hematol.* **10**, 181.

Burstein, M., and Scholnick, H. R. (1971). In preparation.

Burstein, M., and Scholnick, H. R. (1972a). *Protides Biol. Fluids, Proc. 19th Colloq.* p. 21

Burstein, M., and Scholnick, H. R. (1972b). *Life Sci.* **II**(**pt 2**), 177.

Burstein, M., Scholnick, H. R., and Morfin, R. (1970). *J. Lipid Res.* **11**, 583.

Cabau, M., and Badin, J. (1965). *Clin. Chim. Acta* **12**, 508.

Canal, J., and Girard, M. L. (1968). *Bull. Soc. Chim. Biol.* **50**, 1523.

Castaigne, A., and Amselem, A. (1959). *Ann. Biol. Clin.* (*Paris*) **17**, 336.

Chargaff, E., Ziff, M., and Moore, D. (1941). *J. Biol. Chem.* **139**, 383.

Clark, D. W., and Monkhouse, F. C. (1953). *Can. J. Med. Sci.* **31**, 394.

Cogan, M., and Nishida, T. (1969). *Biochim. Biophys. Acta* **187**, 444.

Cornwell, D. G., and Kruger, F. A. (1961). *J. Lipid Res.* **2**, 110.

Dangerfield, W. G., and Faulkner, G. (1964). *Clin. Chim. Acta* **10**, 123.

Daver, J., Daver, M., Ferrand, J. C., Dupasquier, J. P., and Ricoeur, M. (1969). *Rev. Fr. Etud. Clin. Biol.* **14**, 241.

DeLalla, O. F., and Gofman, J. W. (1954). *Methods Biochem. Anal.* **1**, 459.

Eder, H. A., Russ, E. M., Pritchett, R. A., Wilber, M. M., and Barr, D. P. (1955). *J. Clin. Invest.* **34**, 1147.

Ewing, A. M., Freeman, N. K., and Lindgren, F. T. (1965). *Advan. Lipid Res.* **3**, 25.

Farstad, M. (1966). *Clin. Chim. Acta* **14**, 341.

Feldman, H. A. (1968). *Proc. Soc. Exp. Biol. Med.* **127**, 570.

Florsheim, W. H., and Gonzales, C. (1960). *Proc. Soc. Exp. Biol. Med.* **104**, 618.

Franzini, C. (1965). *Clin. Chim. Acta* **12**, 33.

Franzini, C., and Schivi, T. (1964). *Clin. Chim. Acta* **9**, 87.

Fredrickson, D. S., Levy, R. I., and Lees, R. S. (1967). *N. Engl. J. Med.* **276**, 148.

Fredrickson, D. S., Levy, R. I., and Lindgren, F. T. (1968). *J. Clin. Invest.* **37**, 2446.

Fried, R., and Hoeflmayr, J. (1963). *Klin. Wochenschr.* **41**, 246.

Goodman, D. S., and Shafrir, E. (1959). *J. Amer. Chem. Soc.* **81**, 364.

Gordon, R. S. (1955). *J. Clin. Invest.* **34**, 477.

Gorter, E., and Nanninga, L. (1953). *Discuss. Faraday Soc.* **13**, 205.

Granda, J. L., and Scanu, A. (1966). *Biochemistry* **5**, 3301.

Groulade, J., and Jacqueline, F. (1959). *Ann. Biol. Clin.* (*Paris*) **17**, 377.

Gurd, F. R. N., Oncley, J. L., Edsall, J. T., and Cohn, E. J. (1949). *Discuss. Faraday Soc.* **6**, 70.

Gustafson, A., Alaupovic, P., and Furman, R. H. (1965). *Biochemistry* **4**, 596.

Gustafson, A., Alaupovic, P., and Furman, R. H. (1966). *Biochemistry* **5**, 632.

Hallen, J. (1963). *Acta Pathol. Microbiol. Scand.* **57**, 301.

Hartmann, G. (1966). *Triangle* **6**, 230.

Hartmann, G., Creux, G., Widmer, L. K., and Staub, H. (1962). *Helv. Med. Acta* **29**, 515.

Hatch, F. T., and Lees, R. S. (1968). *Advan. Lipid Res.* **6**, 1.

Havel, R. J., and Bragdon, J. H. (1954). *Circulation* **10**, 591.

Havel, R. J., Eder, H. A., and Bragdon, J. H. (1955). *J. Clin. Invest.* **34**, 1345.
Henry, J., and Chatelain, S. (1965). *Ann. Biol. Clin. (Paris)* **23**, 275.
Hill, P., and Dvornik, D. (1969). *Can. J. Biochem.* **47**, 1043.
Hillyard, L. A., Entenman, C., Feinberg, M., and Chaikoff, I. L. (1955). *J. Biol. Chem.* **214**, 79.
Hoch, M., and Chanutin, A. (1952). *J. Biol. Chem.* **197**, 503.
Jacques, L. B. (1943). *Biochem. J.* **37**, 189.
Jordan, W. J. (1968). *Clin. Chem.* **14**, 31.
Jordan, W. J., Faulkner, A. G., and Knoblock, E. C. (1966). *Anal. Biochem.* **14**, 91.
Juret, P., and Chouly, J. P. (1961). *Rev. Fr. Etud. Clin. Biol.* **6**, 1051.
Keler-Bacoka, M. (1967). *Clin. Chim. Acta* **16**, 365.
Kellen, J. A. (1964). *Clin. Chim. Acta* **9**, 138.
Klimov, A. N., Lovyagina, T. N., and Bankovskaya, E. B. (1966). *Lab. Delo* **5**, 276.
Kook, A. I., Eckhaus, A. S., and Rubinstein, D. (1970). *Can. J. Biochem.* **48**, 712.
Kritchevsky, D., Tepper, S. A., Alaupovic, P., and Furman, R. H. (1963). *Proc. Soc. Exp. Biol. Med.* **112**, 259.
Kritchevsky, D., Werthessen, N. T., and Shapiro, I. L. (1965). *Clin. Chim. Acta* **11**, 44.
Lacko, L., Korinek, J., and Burger, M. (1959). *Clin. Chim. Acta* **4**, 800.
Laurell, S. (1955). *Scand. J. Clin. Lab. Invest.* **7**, 28.
Laurell, S. (1959). *Scand. J. Clin. Lab. Invest.* **11**, 97.
Ledvina, M., and Lukastik, R. (1961). *Z. Gesamte Inn. Med. Ihre Grenzgeb.* **16**, 272.
Ledvina, M., Confalova, S., and Saucek, V. (1960). *Clin. Chim. Acta* **5**, 818.
Leveille, G. A., Schockley, J. W., and Sauberlich, E. (1961). *Proc. Soc. Exp. Biol. Med.* **108**, 544.
Levy, R. I., and Fredrickson, D. S. (1965). *J. Clin. Invest.* **44**, 426.
Levy, R. I., Lees, R. S., and Fredrickson, D. S. (1966a). *J. Clin. Invest.* **45**, 63.
Levy, R. I., Fredrickson, D. S., and Laster, L. (1966b). *J. Clin. Invest.* **45**, 531.
Levy, R. S., Lynch, A. C., McGee, E. D., and Mehl, J. W. (1967). *J. Lipid Res.* **8**, 463.
Lewis, L. A., Green, A. A., and Page, I. M. (1952). *Amer. J. Physiol.* **171**, 391.
Link, J., and Fassati, P. (1964). *Z. Gesamte Inn. Med. Ihre Grenzgeb.* **19**, 400.
Lopez-S., A., Srinivasan, S. R., Dugan, F. A., Radhakrishnamurthy, B., and Berenson, G. S. (1971). *Clin. Chim. Acta* **31**, 123.
Lossow, W. J., Lindgren, F. T., Murchio, J. C., Stevens, G. R., and Jensen, L. C. (1969). *J. Lipid Res.* **10**, 68.
Macheboeuf, M. (1929). *Bull. Soc. Chim. Biol.* **11**, 268.
Macheboeuf, M. (1953). *In* "Blood Cells and Plasma Proteins. Their State in Nature" (J. L. Tullis, eds.), p. 358. Academic Press, New York.
Mann, J. J., Rossen, R. D., Lehrich, J. R., and Kasel, J. A. (1967). *J. Immunol.* **98**, 1136.
Margolis, S., and Langdon, R. C. (1966). *J. Biol. Chem.* **251**, 469.
Mora, R., Rebeyrotte, P., and Polonovski, J. (1955). *Bull. Soc. Chim. Biol.* **37**, 957.
Nikkilä, E. (1952). *Scand. J. Clin. Lab. Invest.* **4**, 369.
Nishida, T. J., and Cogan, U. (1970). *J. Biol. Chem.* **245**, 4689.
Nishida, T. J. (1968). *J. Lipid Res.* **9**, 627.
Nitschman, H. S., Rickli, E., and Kistler, P. (1960). *Vox Sang.* **5**, 232.
Oncley, J. L. (1963). *In* "Brain Lipids and Lipoproteins and Leucodystrophies" (J. Folch-Pi and H. Bauer, eds.), p. 1. Elsevier, Amsterdam.

Oncley, J. L., Walton, K. W., and Cornwell, D. G. (1955). *128th Meet. Amer. Chem. Soc., Minneapolis,* p. 41c.

Oncley, J. L., Walton, K. W., and Cornwell, D. G. (1957). *J. Amer. Chem. Soc.* **79,** 4666.

Phillips, G. B. (1959). *Proc. Soc. Exp. Biol. Med.* **100,** 9.

Polonovski, J., Jarrier, M., Petit, M., and Dupuy, C. (1958). *Ann. Biol. Clin. (Paris)* **16,** 69.

Pries, C., van Gent, C. M., Baes, H., Polono, M. K., Hulsman, H. A. M., and Quarido, A. (1968). *Clin. Chim. Acta* **19,** 81.

Roheim, P. S., Rachmilewitz, D., Stein, O., and Stein, J. (1971). *Biochim. Biophys. Acta* **248,** 315.

Sakagami, T., and Zilversmit, D. B. (1961). *J. Lipid Res.* **2,** 271.

Sakagami, T., and Zilversmit, D. B. (1962). *J. Lipid Res.* **3,** 111.

Scanu, A., and Granda, J. L. (1966). *Biochemistry* **5,** 446.

Scanu, A., and Oriente, P. (1961). *J. Exp. Med.* **113,** 735.

Scholnick, H. R., Burstein, M., and Eder, H. A. (1970). *Circulation* **42,** Suppl. III, 54.

Scholnick, H. R., Burstein, M., and Eder, H. A. (1972). *Protides Biol. Fluids, Proc. 19th Colloq.* p. 289.

Searcy, R. L., Foreman, J. A., and Bergquist, L. M. (1963). *Clin. Chem.* **9,** 463.

Seidel, D., Alaupovic, P., and Furman, R. H. (1969). *J. Clin. Invest.* **48,** 1211.

Singh, C. (1964). *Indian J. Chem.* **2,** 67.

Srinivasan, S. R., Lopez-S., A., Radhakrishnamurthy, B., and Berenson, G. S. (1970). *J. Atheroscler. Res.* **12,** 321.

Stokes, R. P., Jacobsson, A., and Walton, K. W. (1967). *J. Atheroscler. Res.* **7,** 187.

Swahn, B. (1953). *Scand. J. Clin. Lab. Invest.* Suppl. **5,** 9.

Switzer, S. (1967). *J. Clin. Invest.* **46,** 1855.

Switzer, S., and Eder, H. A. (1965). *J. Lipid Res.* **6,** 506.

Tewari, K., and Krishnan, P. S. (1959). *Arch. Biochem. Biophys.* **82,** 99.

Walton, K. W., and Scott, P. J. (1964). *J. Clin. Pathol.* **17,** 627.

Winblad, S. (1966). *Acta Pathol. Microbiol. Scand.* **66,** 93.

Yokoyama, H., and Zilversmit, D. B. (1965). *J. Lipid Res.* **6,** 241.

Uptake and Transport of Fatty Acids into the Brain and the Role of the Blood–Brain Barrier System

GOVIND A. DHOPESHWARKAR

Laboratory of Nuclear Medicine and Radiation Biology, and Department of Nutrition, School of Public Health, University of California at Los Angeles, Los Angeles, California

AND

JAMES F. MEAD

Laboratory of Nuclear Medicine and Radiation Biology, and Department of Biological Chemistry, School of Medicine, University of California at Los Angeles, Los Angeles, California

I. Introduction

The restriction posed by the central nervous system on the uptake of intravenously administered dyes has been known since the early work by

Ehrlich (1882). Goldmann (1909) showed that after an intravenous injection of trypan blue, the brain was not stained, although the choroid plexus and the meninges were. Later, in another experiment, Goldmann (1913) injected the same dye into the cerebrospinal fluid (CSF) and was surprised to find that the whole brain was heavily stained. Since the time of these publications, the term "blood–brain barrier" (BBB) emerged and has persisted in the literature on this subject. Although the concept originated in relation to dyes, it soon was widened to include many compounds, ions, metabolites, nonmetabolites, etc. A similar barrier has been proposed for the retina (Blotevogel, 1924) but has not received as much attention.

In this communication it is not our intention to present a critical review of the arguments, either pro or con, on this controversial subject since many such reviews have appeared in the literature in recent years. The following list, although not complete, includes some very comprehensive reviews: Friedemann (1942), Bakay (1956), Dobbing (1961), Edstrom (1964), Davson, (1967), Lajtha and Ford (1968), Oldendorf (1971b), and Dhopeshwarkar and Bawa (1971). Our intention is to discuss the uptake and transport of fatty acids into the brain and to examine the role of the BBB system as it applies to this phenomenon.

II. Blood–Brain Barrier (BBB) and Lipids

A. EARLY WORK USING NONRADIOACTIVE MARKERS

Soon after Schoenheimer and Rittenberg (1936) pioneered the use of the stable isotope, deuterium, to study the dynamics of body lipids, Waelsch and co-workers (1940, 1941; Waelsch, 1955) using heavy water as a tracer, found that fatty acids of the growing as well as the adult brain were synthesized in the brain itself and that there was no necessity to assume that the BBB was penetrable by fatty acids or cholesterol even in growing animals. McConnell and Sinclair (1937) used a nonradioactive but easily identifiable fatty acid, elaidic acid, in the diet of pregnant rats and their offspring and found that when they had reached maturity, their brain phospholipids had only one-fourth as high a proportion of elaidic acid as the liver phospholipids. Bloch et al. (1943) found that when deuterium-labeled cholesterol was fed to adult dogs, all tissues except the brain and the spinal cord incorporated labeled cholesterol from the circulation. Thus, these early studies strongly indicated the restriction posed by the BBB in limiting penetration of lipids into the brain.

B. STUDIES WITH RADIOACTIVE MARKERS

Soon after ^{14}C-labeled fatty acids and precursors were available for biochemical research, Sperry *et al.* (1953) found that a short-chain fatty acid such as octanoate-1-^{14}C was readily incorporated into the brain lipids. Similarly, Laurell (1959) found that a small amount of radioactivity was incorporated into the brain lipids of rats given an intrajugular injection of palmitate-1-[14]C.

Carroll (1962), using a series of carboxy-labeled fatty acids, came to the conclusion that only a small amount of radioactivity was incorporated into brain total lipids. However, when the same tracer was administered to young weanling rats (12–13 days old), there was greater uptake of radioactivity in the brain as compared to adult (2- to 3-month-old) rats.

Such studies of brain uptake with isotopically labeled compounds, although useful, have been difficult to interpret because of factors such as different metabolic rates, exchange without net accumulation, etc. Moreover, it is necessary to bear in mind that the mere presence of radioactivity in brain fatty acids following ingestion cannot be taken as a proof of passage from the blood into the brain, since the radioactivity in the brain fatty acids could be the result of synthesis from acetate derived by oxidation of the administered fatty acid.

C. EFFECT OF AGE

Increased uptake of radioactivity by the brain of 8- to 13-day-old rats as compared to adult rats, 2–6 months old, was noted by many workers (Fries *et al.*, 1940; Bakay, 1953) and thus, much of the work done during the last decade has been performed by administering tracers to baby rats. For example, Fulco and Mead (1961) injected acetate-1-^{14}C into 13-day-old rats and determined the biosynthetic pathway of lignoceric, cerebronic, and nervonic acids. Kishimoto *et al.* (1965a) injected labeled acetate into 7-day-old rats to study lipid changes and turnover in the developing rat brain.

Whether age has some definite relationship to the development of the BBB, and in turn, myelination or whether the differential uptake is simply a reflection of metabolic requirement and turnover associated with growth, is still a debatable question. Dobbing (1968), who favors the latter view, has discussed the subject exhaustively.

D. ROUTES OF ENTRY

When a radioactive tracer is injected intracranially to study biosynthesis of nervonic acid (Kishimoto and Radin, 1963), or to study half-life and turnover of palmitate 1-[14]C (Sun and Horrocks, 1969, 1971), the route of entry can be described as "bypassing the BBB." On the other hand, perfusion via a carotid artery (Sperry *et al.*, 1953) using the Geiger-Magnes brain perfusion technique, although not bypassing the BBB, undoubtedly presents a rather large localized dose to the brain, thereby introducing another unknown variable. The same argument applies to the single intracarotid injection used by Oldendorf (1970) and in our own studies (Dhopeshwarkar *et al.*, 1971c). However, in these studies the mass injected was negligible.

Another variation is introduced by the concept of "sink-action" of the CSF proposed by Davson *et al.* (1961). These authors point out that if the tracer concentration in the CSF is low, it could act as a drain or sink, continuously draining the tissue of the tracer that the tissue originally acquired by way of the blood. If the tracer is introduced into the CSF, the same phenomenon occurs with the only difference, that now, it is the sink-action of the blood instead of the CSF. To circumvent this factor, Levin and Kleeman (1970) have described a technique for introducing the tracer simultaneously into the blood and the CSF.

That the route of entry is an important factor in determining and comparing the uptake of compounds by the brain and for the evaluation of the concept of the BBB, is discussed by Levin and Scicli (1969) and by Levin and Kleeman (1970).

Oldendorf (1970), by injecting a mixture of a test substance labeled with ^{14}C and water-^{3}H into the carotid artery followed by decapitation within the short interval of 15 seconds, was able to compare the uptake of many compounds. This technique uses only the ratio of ^{14}C to ^{3}H in the brain relative to the ratio of ^{14}C to ^{3}H in the original mixture and thereby eliminates both elaborate experimental procedure and complex calculations.

III. BBB and Fatty Acids

A. NATURE OF THE BRAIN FATTY ACIDS

In addition to the usual saturated and unsaturated fatty acids such as palmitic, stearic, and oleic acids, the brain contains a rather large amount of polyunsaturated fatty acids (PUFA) with four, five, and six double bonds (Biran and Bartley, 1961; Johnston *et al.*, 1961; Kishimoto *et al.*, 1965b; Miyamoto *et al.*, 1967; Rouser and Yamamoto, 1969; O'Brien *et al.*, 1964; Dhopeshwarkar *et al.*, 1969). Another class of fatty acids found largely in the brain is that of the α-hydroxy long-chain fatty acids (Klenk, 1928; Kishimoto and Radin, 1959). The formation of the long-chain α-hydroxy fatty acids and the odd-chain fatty acids by α-oxidation was first described by Mead and Levis (1962, 1963). Finally, the occurrence of very long-chain fatty acids, up to 35 carbon atoms, has been reported by Pakkala *et al.* (1966).

B. Synthesis of Fatty Acids in the Brain

That the brain is capable of synthesizing fatty acids as efficiently as other organs, such as liver, was demonstrated by Brady (1960). The major fatty acid synthesized by the brain synthetase was palmitic acid. Recently, a brain "microsomal" chain elongation system responsible for stearate and longer chain saturated fatty acids as well as the chain elongation-desaturation system has been characterized by Aeberhard and Menkes (1968). A brain mitochondrial system, which elongates 16:0 as well as 22:0 and 22:1, has been recently described by Boone and Wakil (1970). As mentioned above, the α-oxidation system producing hydroxy and odd-chain fatty acids was first demonstrated *in vivo* by Mead and Levis (1963) and later demonstrated in the brain "microsomal" system *in vitro* (Levis and Mead, 1964; McDonald and Mead, 1968; Davies *et al.*, 1966). In a recent report, Mead and Hare (1971) have implicated ascorbic acid as a cofactor in the α-oxidation system.

The brain has the necessary enzymes for synthesis (either by *de novo* or chain elongation-desaturation processes) of the required fatty acids, thus reducing the demand on transport of fatty acids synthesized elsewhere or ingested in the diet. Obviously, the essential fatty acids 18:2ω6 and 18:3ω3, which cannot be synthesized by the mammalian systems, must come from the diet and be transported into the brain by the circulating blood.[1] Both of these fatty acids are found in trace amounts in the rat brain but their polyunsaturated products occur abundantly.

C. Nutritional Studies

Several years before the actual nutritional studies designed to ascertain whether dietary fatty acids penetrated the BBB and were taken up by the adult brain were undertaken, Klenk (1955) has postulated that 20:4ω6 and 22:6ω3, occurring in rather large amounts in the brain can be formed only from dietary sources of 18:2ω6 and 18:3ω3. Thus, at least these essential fatty acids must pass from the blood into the brain through the BBB.

Following this prediction, Mohrhauer and Holman (1963) found that increasing amounts of dietary linoleate and arachidonate fed to weanling

---

[1] 18:2ω6 denotes octadecadienoic acid with the first double bond at the sixth carbon starting from the methyl end.

rats led to increased deposition of arachidonate and docosapentaenoate, 22:5ω6, in the brain. Similarly, dietary linolenate gave rise to brain polyunsaturated fatty acids of the ω3 family. Rathbone (1965), starting with animals that were a little older (8–12 weeks instead of weanling), came to similar conclusions.

Thus it was clearly established that dietary fatty acids could influence the composition of brain lipids. This is possible only if we assume that at least some fatty acids pass into the brain by way of circulating blood.

D. Uptake of Labeled Fatty Acid Precursors

The uptake of fatty acid precursor by the brain has, for the most part, centered around uptake and incorporation of radioactivity from acetate-1-[14]C. Since earlier experiments failed to show any appreciable uptake of long-chain fatty acids by the adult brain (Laurell, 1959; Carroll, 1962) fatty acid precursors such as acetate-1-^{14}C were used extensively to study uptake and incorporation into brain fatty acids. Thus, acetate-1-^{14}C was injected into rats to study uptake and incorporation of radioactivity in brain fatty acids (Waelsch et al., 1941; Van Bruggen et al., 1953). Much metabolic information on the biosynthesis and transformation of brain fatty acids was obtained from the radioactivity distribution pattern obtained after administration of acetate-1-[14]C (Fulco and Mead, 1961; Kishimoto and Radin, 1966). More recently, uniformly labeled glucose has been used as a fatty acid precursor by Smith (1968) in the study of myelin turnover in the adult rat. Although use of ^{14}C-labeled glucose resulted in 4–6 times higher uptake of radioactivity in the brain than did acetate-1-[14]C (Smith, 1967), the nonlipid fractions of the brain also were labeled to an appreciable extent. The main advantage of using a labeled precursor such as glucose, is that the tracer permeates freely into the brain and thus overcomes the influence of the BBB. However, the use of labeled glucose does not permit the facile prediction of metabolic pathways of fatty acids in a manner that labeled acetate can provide. This point is discussed in detail in Section III,E,1,a,b, and c.

E. Uptake of Long-Chain Fatty Acids

1. Nonessential, Palmitic and Oleic Acids

Although Miyamoto et al. (1967) found ready incorporation of linoleic acid-1-^{14}C as well as linolenic acid-1-^{14}C into the embryonic chick brain, the route of entry was via the yolk sac, bypassing the BBB. On the other hand, Gatt (1963) found practically no radioactivity in the brains of rats after intravenous administration of lignoceric acid-1-[14]C (24:0).

With such varied and often conflicting data reported in the literature, we decided to reexamine the uptake of saturated and unsaturated as well as essential fatty acids. The main object was to determine whether long-chain fatty acids, administered either by mouth or injected into the bloodstream, would be taken up by the brain directly as intact molecules rather than after oxidative degradation to acetate elsewhere in the body. In order to determine the direct uptake of a carboxy-labeled fatty acid and distinguish it from the uptake of acetate derived by degradation of the administered tracer and resynthesis, we resorted to comparing the labeling pattern of fatty acids isolated from the brain after administration of labeled fatty acid (Dhopeshwarkar *et al.*, 1971a,b; Dhopeshwarkar and Mead, 1969, 1970) with that obtained after administration of acetate-1-^{14}C (Dhopeshwarkar *et al.*, 1969). The label distribution was obtained by decarboxylating the fatty acids isolated from the brain using the Schmidt decarboxylation procedure as described by Brady *et al.* (1960). The activity in the carboxyl carbon compared to the total activity of the intact fatty acid gave the percent relative carboxyl activity (%RCA).[2]

The following three possible pathways can be detected by this procedure:

a. De Novo Synthesis from Acetate. Alternate carbon atoms are labeled; in the case of palmitic acid, for example, all odd carbon atoms (8 out of 16) will be labeled and theoretically the carboxyl carbon will have 1/8 or 12:5% of the total radioactivity of palmitic acid. Thus, by determining %RCA and comparing it with the theoretical value for that particular chain length, one can postulate whether the fatty acid was synthesized *de novo* from acetate.

b. Synthesis by Chain Elongation. (1) One molecule of radioactive acetate adds to a preexisting nonradioactive precursor; this will result in 100% RCA. (2) A radioactive acetate adds to a radioactive precursor, which may have been formed by *de novo* synthesis. In this case the %RCA will vary considerably depending on the relative radioactivity of the precursor and the acetate. This in turn, will depend upon the time interval between dose and sacrifice (Kishimoto and Radin, 1966).

c. Direct Uptake. Obviously, when a fatty acid is taken up directly, it will have a %RCA that is very close to that of the starting material.

Since the possibility that radioactivity will be largely confined to the carboxyl carbon can theoretically be realized both in the case of direct uptake and in chain elongation, it is advisable to determine the label distribution at two or more intervals between dose and sacrifice, thus elimi-

---

[2] Relative carboxyl activity $= \dfrac{\text{Radioactivity in } -COOH}{\text{Radioactivity in total FA}} \times 100$.

nating a coincidental RCA characteristic of direct uptake when it could as well be by chain elongation. Similarly the variable %RCA value in the chain elongation process can theoretically (by coincidence) be very close to the *de novo* synthesis value. Again, by choosing two or more intervals, this coincidence can be avoided (Kishimoto and Radin, 1966).

This reasoning has been extensively used by Mead (1961) and Klenk (1961) to establish biosynthetic pathways.

The first experiments (Dhopeshwarkar *et al.*, 1969) were carried out on a group of weanling 13-day-old rats, and for comparison a group of adult rats approximately 90 days old was included. Sodium acetate-1-^{14}C (5 μCi/gm body wt) was injected intraperitoneally and the animals were killed after 4 hours. The results are shown in Table I.

From these data it can be observed that the total lipid content per gram of brain had almost doubled in the adult animals as compared to weanling rats, which agrees with earlier work by Wells and Dittmer (1967). No such profound change was found in the liver total lipids. The radioactivity in the brain was higher than that in the liver in young animals, whereas the opposite was true in the case of adult animals. In the earlier literature, this reduced uptake by adult animals was linked to the development of the BBB. However, as early as 1955, Folch-Pi suggested caution in such interpretations, emphasizing that during the weanling period the brain is building new tissue at a high rate thus giving apparent high uptakes, which could be mistakenly interpreted as related to the BBB. This point has been exhaustively discussed by Dobbing (1968). After separation of cholesterol and traces of neutral lipids on a SiO$_2$ column, the polar lipid fraction, phospholipids + sphingolipids (PL + SphL), was subjected to methanolysis and the methyl esters were separated on a SiO$_2$-AgNO$_3$ column (Stein and Slawson, 1968) into classes according to degree of unsaturation. Further separation was performed by preparative gas–liquid chromatography (GLC) and the fatty acids were obtained by alkali hydrolysis of the methyl esters. The fatty acids were then decarboxylated to obtain %RCA data. Table II shows the specific activities and %RCA of the various brain fatty acids.

Palmitic acid, the major product of the extramitochondrial fatty acid synthetase in the brain (Brady, 1960), had the maximum specific activity in both weanling and adult rats. The %RCA was very close to the theoretical value of 12.5% for *de novo* synthesis. The polyunsaturated fatty acids, 20:4 and 22:6, had a very high %RCA. Thus, this would be the pattern of labeling if any 1-^{14}C-labeled fatty acid administered to the animals was first degraded to radioactive acetate which would be used for resynthesis of 16:0 or to chain elongate 18:2 and 18:3 in the brain itself.

With this basic information, we proceeded to determine the uptake of

Table I

INCORPORATION OF SODIUM ACETATE-1-^{14}C INTO BRAIN AND LIVER LIPIDS OF WEANLING (13 DAYS OLD) AND ADULT RATS (3 MONTHS OLD), 4 HOURS AFTER INTRAPERITONEAL INJECTION

	Rats			Weight per gm wet wt of tissue (mg/gm)	Total lipids		Percent incorporation
No.	Body wt (av; gm)	Dose given μCi/gm body wt			Specific activity (cpm/mg)	Radioactivity per gm wet wt of tissue	Radioactivity per gm tissue / Radioactivity administered[a] × 100
Brain lipids							
Weanling	10	30	5	51.8	27,752	1.44×10^6	12.9
Adult	6	310	5	107.5	4,744	5.1×10^5	4.6
Liver lipids							
Weanling	10	30	5	43.2	7,972	3.4×10^5	3.1
Adult	6	310	5	43.9	50,621	2.22×10^6	20.0

[a] μCi/gm body weight.

Table II

INCORPORATION OF SODIUM ACETATE-1-^{14}C INTO BRAIN FATTY ACIDS
OF WEANLING AND ADULT RATS

Fatty acid	Percent composition of total methyl esters by GLC		Specific activity (cpm/mg)		Radioactivity in the carboxyl carbon (% of total)	
	Weanling	Adult	Weanling	Adult	Weanling	Adult
16:0	17.1	13.2	79,395	20,480	12.5	13.5
18:0	14.7	15.8	40,586	7,133	20.7	25.6
18:1	14.1	18.4	37,324	1,879	28.1	30.4
20:4	18.0	14.8	3,223	815	87.8	84.1
22:6	21.3	21.1	775	318	89.6	70.2

two fatty acids, palmitic and oleic, that are present in substantial amounts in the brain (Dhopeshwarkar and Mead, 1969, 1970). We restricted our work to adult animals to reduce the influence of rapid growth and consequent high rate of lipid synthesis in the brain during the myelinating period. Carboxy-labeled palmitic acid was dissolved in corn oil and fed by mouth to 3-month-old rats, whereas oleic acid-1-^{14}C was complexed with bovine fatty acid-poor albumin and injected into the tail vein. Animals were sacrificed 4 and 24 hours after administration of the dose. Table III shows the uptake of radioactivity in the blood, brain, and liver total lipids.

It is important to note that the radioactivity of the blood in all cases dropped considerably between the 4- and 24-hour periods, but that the radioactivity in brain lipids did not show a comparable decrease. The radioactivity in brain total lipids cannot be attributed to a small amount of blood that is trapped in any dissected brain tissue. It may also be pointed out that previously the actual amount of blood left in the brain was determined using ^{51}Cr-labeled erythrocytes. It was found that it amounted to 0.1 to 1.5% of the fresh weight of the brain or 1.2 ml of blood per 100-gm brain (Davson and Spaziani, 1959; Lajtha et al., 1957; Bito et al., 1966; Kabara, 1967). Thus a maximum amount of blood (equivalent to 6 μliters of plasma) trapped in the brain could contribute 363 counts out of 13,287 cpm/gm fresh weight of the brain, in the 4-hour experiment. Contribution of radioactivity by the blood to the brain in the 24-hour experiment is only 0.35% of the total brain radioactivity per gram and hence negligible. Evidence that the radioactivity in the brain was associated with all polar lipid components including myelin lipids is shown in Table X (and discussed in Section V) giving conclusive proof of true uptake and incorporation.

Table III

INCORPORATION OF RADIOACTIVITY FROM PALMITIC ACID-1-¹⁴C AND OLEIC ACID-1-¹⁴C INTO BLOOD, BRAIN, AND LIVER TOTAL LIPIDS

| Fatty acid administered | Route of entry | Interval between dose and sacrifice (hours) | Blood total lipids | | Brain total lipids | | Percent incorporation Radioactivity gm wet tissue / Radioactivity administered[a] × 100 | |
			Specific activity (cpm/mg)	Plasma radioactivity (cpm/ml)	Specific activity (cpm/mg)	Total radioactivity (cpm/gm wet wt)	Brain	Liver
Palmitic acid-1-¹⁴C								
	Oral feeding	4	21,688	60,509	125	13,287	2.39	—
	As oil emulsion	24	2510	7003	111	11,799	2.12	39.0
Oleic acid-1-¹⁴C								
	IV injection as albumin complex	4	4941	13,794	124	13,181	2.37	69.1
	Oral feeding	24	1703	4751	80	8504	1.53	12.5

[a] 0.25 μCi/gm body weight.

The uptake of radioactivity by the brain does not seem to be different whether the route of entry was oral feeding of palmitic acid or intravenous injection of albumin-bound oleic acid.

The radioactivity distribution in fatty acids isolated from the brain polar lipid fraction 4 and 24 hours after a tracer dose of palmitate-1-^{14}C and oleate was compared with data obtained from a tracer dose of acetate-1-^{14}C.

Comparing the specific activities of brain fatty acids, one can see from the data presented in Table IV that even 24 hours after administration of palmitic acid-1-^{14}C, the brain palmitic acid was still the most active component. However, this was not the case in the oleic acid experiment. The brain oleic acid, which was the most active component 4 hours after injection of the tracer, had lost its activity at 24 hours, but 20:1 had gained in radioactivity making it the most active component. This suggests a precursor–product relationship, 18:1 → 20:1. Furthermore, the experiment suggests direct uptake of both palmitic and oleic acids. The proof that this is actually the case comes from the label distribution data.

When palmitic acid-1-^{14}C was administered, irrespective of the interval between dose and sacrifice, the brain palmitate had most of the radioactivity in the carboxyl carbon, showing direct uptake of the tracer. If the fed palmitate had been extensively degraded to acetate, which was then taken up by the brain, the labeling pattern would have been similar to that obtained with acetate-1-^{14}C as tracer. That this was not the case, can be concluded from distinct differences in the label distribution (%RCA). By the same token, it was concluded that oleic acid injected intravenously was taken up by the brain directly without extensive oxidation to acetate and resynthesis in the brain.

The gain in radioactivity by eicosenoic acid (20:1) and its low %RCA shows a definite precursor-product relationship. C_3 of eicosenoic acid corresponds to C_1 of oleic acid, which had high radioactivity. On the other hand, the acetate derived by oxidative degradation of the tracer would be low in radioactivity, contributing only a small amount to C_1 of eicosenoic acid resulting in a low %RCA. This agrees with the general conclusion of Fulco and Mead (1961) and Kishimoto and Radin (1963) that oleic acid is the precursor of eicosenoic acid and nervonic acid (24:1). However, Kishimoto and Radin found that very little oleate entered the cells that make sphingolipids and that much was degraded to acetate. These differences between their study and ours (Dhopeshwarkar and Mead, 1970) might be due to variation in age and route of entry of the tracer.

The differences in both the specific activities and %RCA of oleic acid as against stearic acid indicate that biohydrogenation must be at best a

Table IV

Distribution of Radioactivity in Fatty Acids Isolated from Brain Polar Lipids 4 and 24 Hours after Administration of Tracer

| Tracer | Interval between dose and sacrifice (hours) | Fatty acid isolated from brain polar lipids (PL + SphL)[a] | | | | | | | |
| | | 16:0 | | 18:0 | | 18:1 | | 20:1 | |
		Specific activity (cpm/mg)	%RCA	Specific activity (cpm/mg)	%RCA	Specific activity (cpm/mg)	%RCA	Specific activity (cpm/mg)	%RCA
Sodium acetate-1-14C	4	—	13.5	—	25.6	—	30.4	—	49.8
Palmitic acid-1-14C	4	2057	86.9	132	26.6	—	—	—	—
Oleic acid-1-14C	4	—	—	40	53.5	1221	84.3	306	14.1
Sodium acetate-1-14C	24	—	14.1	—	20.3	—	23.3	—	38.6
Palmitic acid-1-14C	24	1805	85.1	243	21.6	—	—	—	—
Oleic acid-1-14C	24	—	—	93	23.2	911	58.1	3145	10.1

[a] PL = Phospholipids; SphL = sphingolipids.

minor pathway, although biohydrogenation of palmitoleate (Mead and Nevenzel, 1960) and elaidate (Dhopeshwarkar and Mead, 1962), even in the absence of intestinal flora (Blomstrand et al., 1963), may have been demonstrated in the whole animals. It was interesting to note that the palmitic and oleic acids taken up by the brain were incorporated into all the major brain lipid components, phosphatidyl choline (PC) being the most and sphingomyelin the least radioactive component. This is in general agreement with the observations by Sun and Horrocks (1969, 1971). Cholesterol was relatively less radioactive, indicating that its precursor, acetate (itself a breakdown product of the administered labeled fatty acid) had relatively low radioactivity.

F. Uptake of Essential Fatty Acids

1. Linoleic and Linolenic Acid

One could argue that since the brain has most of the necessary enzymes for synthesis of fatty acids, it may not require fatty acids synthesized elsewhere in the body or from dietary sources. However, it is now a well established fact that essential fatty acids comprising $18:2\omega6$ and $18:3\omega3$, cannot be synthesized by mammalian systems; hence, they must be provided by the diet. Moreover, Bernsohn and Stephanides (1967) have discussed a possible connection between dietary deficiency of essential fatty acids and multiple sclerosis, based on an earlier hypothesis by Sinclair (1956). Although no such definite relationship has been established, the question of whether the essential fatty acids can pass from the blood into adult brain had remained cloudy. The reason for this was that much of the earlier work that dealt with uptake of labeled essential fatty acids was done when the BBB was poorly developed (Miyamoto et al., 1967). Nutrition studies by Mohrhauer and Holman (1963) made use of young rats, although Rathbone (1965) had used slightly older rats. These studies in animals of premyelination age were not acceptable to those who believed in the concept of BBB and who argued that there was no restriction whatsoever from BBB at that early age. If this argument is taken to be valid and the assumption made that in older animals there is a restriction to the uptake of fatty acids, one would have to conclude that the animal must depend upon the supply of essential fatty acids it received during the early or premyelination period of life. Further, in these circumstances the recycling hypothesis (Sun and Horrocks, 1969) would be very useful to conserve the limited supply.

We therefore used rats 3 months of age or older and administered carboxy-labeled linoleic acid to one group and linolenic acid-1-^{14}C to another, to determine whether these essential fatty acids could be taken up by the brain as intact molecules (Dhopeshwarkar *et al.*, 1971a,b). As in earlier experiments, animals were sacrificed 4 and 24 hours after the dose. Data on uptake into the blood, brain, and liver lipids are presented in Table V.

Animals that were sacrificed after 24 hours received a slightly higher dose per gram of body weight than animals that were sacrificed 4 hours after the dose. However, in spite of this higher dose, the radioactivity per milliliter of plasma had dropped considerably between the 4- and 24-hour periods. However, during this interval, radioactivity of brain total lipids had actually increased. That this increase was not due to the higher dose, is borne out by the data on percent incorporation. In calculating this figure, the dose given per gram of tissue is taken into consideration and as can be observed in Table V, the percent uptake of radioactivity by the brain between 4 and 24 hours after tracer administration increased almost 80%. During the same interval, there was a drop in percent incorporation in the liver that was more pronounced with linoleate than with linolenate-1-^{14}C feeding.

The specific activity and label distribution data after administration of linoleic and linolenic acid are given in Table VI.

Although the amount of 18:2ω6, in the brain is of the order of 1–1.5% of the total fatty acids (Rathbone, 1965; Dhopeshwarkar *et al.*, 1969), use of argentation column chromatography (Stein and Slawson, 1968), followed by preparative GLC permitted the isolation of very pure 18:2 from brain total fatty acids. Since there is virtually no 18:3, we added carrier material to isolate traces of 18:3. In this manner it was possible to determine label distribution in 18:3 but not the specific activity.

As can be seen in Table VI, the 18:2 isolated from brains of rats given linoleate-1-^{14}C was the most active component, indicating a direct uptake. Since the mammalian system cannot make 18:2ω6 from small molecular weight precursors, the high activity of linoleic acid isolated from brain polar lipids must be derived by direct uptake from circulating blood. Further, it is known that linoleate is converted into arachidonate (Mead, 1961) and the label distribution in brain arachidonate clearly shows this to be true. C_3 of arachidonate corresponds to C_1 of the administered linoleate. Thus, C_3 is expected to have high activity and the carboxyl carbon coming from an acetate would have relatively lower activity. This is borne out in the 4-hour experiment and, more dramatically, in the 24-hour experiment. One also can observe an increase in specific activity of arachidonic acid between the 4- and 24-hour periods during which time more of the tracer was taken up and converted into arachidonate. It may be pointed out here that Steinberg *et al.* (1956), who were the first to

Table V

INCORPORATION OF RADIOACTIVITY FROM LINOLEIC ACID-1-^{14}C AND LINOLENIC ACID-1-^{14}C INTO BLOOD, BRAIN, AND LIVER TOTAL LIPIDS

Fatty acid administered	Dose fed (μCi/gm body wt)	Interval between dose and sacrifice (hours)	Blood total lipids		Brain total lipids		Percent incorporation Radioactivity/gm wet tissue Radioactivity administered × 100	
			Specific activity (cpm/mg)	Plasma radio-activity (cpm/ml)	Specific activity (cpm/mg)	Total activity (cpm/gm wet wt)	Brain	Liver
Linoleic acid-1-^{14}C	0.16	4	32,504	90,686	50	5315	1.5	81.4
	0.21	24	6703	18,701	120	12,756	2.7	47.8
Linolenic acid-1-^{14}C	0.16	4	15,818	44,132	41	4358	1.2	44.7
	0.21	24	3984	11,115	108	11,480	2.5	38.1

Table VI

DISTRIBUTION OF RADIOACTIVITY IN FATTY ACIDS ISOLATED FROM BRAIN POLAR LIPIDS 4 AND 24 HOURS AFTER ADMINISTRATION OF TRACER

| Tracer | Interval (hours) | Fatty acid isolated from brain polar lipids (PL + SphL) | | | | | | |
| | | 18:2 | | 18:3 | 20:4 | | 22:6 | |
		Specific activity (cpm/mg)	%RCA	%RCA	Specific activity (cpm/mg)	%RCA	Specific activity (cpm/mg)	%RCA
Sodium acetate-1-^{14}C	4	—	—	—	—	84.1	—	70.2
Linoleic acid-1-^{14}C	4	1439	92.0	—	99	28.1	52	68.4
Linolenic acid-1-^{14}C	4	—	—	91.0	—	—	42	23.0
Sodium acetate-1-^{14}C	24	—	—	—	—	83.3	—	81.9
Linoleic acid-1-^{14}C	24	6857	88.0	—	870	3.5	51	72.4
Linolenic acid-1-^{14}C	24	—	—	92.4	39	81.7	765	12.4

show the transformation of 18:2 to 20:4 had noted that C_1 and C_3 comprised all the activity of the arachidonic acid with no activity at all in the rest of the molecule. However, they found a rather high activity in the carboxyl carbon, unlike the findings in our studies of the brain (Dhopeshwarkar et al., 1971a), which they attributed to acetate formed by oxidative degradation of the fed material and a reflection of relative pool size for acetate and linoleate at the site of elongation. This oxidative process, however, seems to be a very slow reaction in the brain resulting in a low activity in acetate and in the derived carboxyl carbon.

Linolenic acid isolated from the brain polar lipids, even 24 hours after feeding still had most of the activity in the carboxyl carbon, indicating direct uptake. The label distribution in docosahexaenoic acid ($22:6\omega3$) is exactly what one would predict from the precursor–product relationship. The carboxyl carbon, derived from acetate formed by oxidation of the fed material, has low radioactivity as compared to the hydrocarbon chain comprising carbons 5 to 22; carbon 5, being derived from the carboxyl carbon of linolenic acid, was high in radioactivity. Thus, the observation by Miyamoto et al. (1967), in which linolenic acid-1-^{14}C was injected into the yolk sac to demonstrate uptake and conversion to $22:6\omega3$ in the chick embryonic brain, is true in the adult rat brain as well.

Thus the rat brain does not have to depend on the supply of essential fatty acids (EFA) it received during very early periods of development and growth, but can take up these essential nutrients throughout adult life. Since the brain has no mechanism for storage of fatty acids, it seems likely that after the period of active myelination, when the need for rapid lipid synthesis is reduced, although essential fatty acids would still gain access to the brain, only a portion would be retained. This agrees with the observation by White et al. (1971) that the return to normal of EFA-deficient animals, after shifting to a balanced diet, is quite rapid. If the BBB had prevented or severely restricted the uptake of EFA, full-grown animals that were EFA deficient would not return to normal even if dietary corrections were made.

IV. Specificity of Fatty Acid Uptake

A. PREFERENTIAL UPTAKE OF LINOLENIC OVER LINOLEIC ACID

A careful look at the percent composition of fatty acids of brain total lipids shows one predominant feature. The brain fatty acids are rich in polyunsaturated fatty acids and in particular the fatty acids of the linolenic acid ($\omega3$) family (Biran and Bartley, 1961; Johnston et al., 1961;

Table VII

INCORPORATION OF RADIOACTIVITY FROM CARBOXY-LABELED FATTY ACIDS INTO BRAIN LIPIDS 4 HOURS AFTER THE DOSE

Fatty acid	Tracer	Percent composition of total fatty acids by GLC (average)	Amount administered (μCi/gm body wt)	Brain lipids		Ratio[b]	
				Radioactivity (per gm wet wt of tissue) (cpm/gm)	Percent incorporation[a]	Radioactivity (per gm tissue) $\dfrac{\text{Liver}}{\text{Brain}}$	Radioactivity $\dfrac{\text{Plasma/ml}}{\text{Brain/gm}}$
16:0	Acetate-1-^{14}C	13.2	5	5.1×10^5	4.6	4.0	—
18:0	Palmitic acid-1-^{14}C	15.8	0.25	13.3×10^3	2.4	48.0	4.5
18:1	Oleic acid-1-^{14}C	18.4	0.25	13.2×10^3	2.4	29.2	1.0
20:4	Linoleic acid-1-^{14}C	14.8	0.16	5.3×10^3	1.5	53.0	16.6
22:6	Linolenic acid-1-^{14}C	21.1	0.16	4.4×10^3	1.2	36.7	9.8

[a] Percent of administered dose incorporated $= \dfrac{\text{Radioactivity per gm tissue}}{\text{Radioactivity administered } (\mu\text{Ci/gm body wt})} \times 100.$

[b] Distribution of radioactivity between liver, blood plasma, and brain.

Miyamoto *et al.*, 1967; Dhopeshwarkar *et al.*, 1969; Rouser and Yama-moto, 1969). In liver fatty acids, for example, there is an appreciable amount of linoleic acid, but very small amounts of linolenic acid. Thus, even if there were equal amounts of $20:4\omega6$ and $22:6\omega3$ in the brain and the liver, the overall composition in the liver would be made up predominantly of the $\omega6$ family. This feature of brain fatty acids poses a question of whether there is any specific uptake of $18:3$ over $18:2$ in the brain. We already had the data on the uptake of various fatty acids by the brain and decided to evaluate the data with respect to this question, as shown in Table VII.

Looking at the percent incorporation data (ratio of radioactivity per gram of tissue to that of radioactivity administered per gram body weight $\times 100$) it does not seem to indicate any preferential uptake of linolenic acid over linoleic acid. However, if one compares the radioactivity per gram of tissue in the liver to that in the brain it is found that the ratio is higher for $18:2\omega6$ than for $18:3\omega3$. This decreased ratio indicates that there is greater uptake of radioactivity from $18:3\omega3$ in the brain than in the liver and the opposite was true in the case of $18:2\omega6$. Similar conclusions can be drawn from the ratio of radioactivity in the plasma (per milliliter) to that in brain.

In another study, uptake of radioactivity in the brain following 1 hour continuous infusion of carboxy-labeled fatty acid-albumin complex via the carotid artery was studied in rabbits (G. A. Dhopeshwarkar and E. Levin, unpublished data). The results are shown in Table VIII.

In this experiment, the gray matter comprising the first two $400\text{-}\mu$ slices of the dissected brain and the white matter made up of the fourth and fifth slices (Levin and Kleeman, 1970) were used for lipid extraction and radioactivity determination. It was found that in all cases, the ratio of radioactivity of brain tissue per gram to plasma per milliliter was higher when linolenic acid-1-^{14}C was infused than it was with linoleic acid. Thus it appears that there is a selective uptake of $18:3\omega3$ by the brain tissue *in vivo*. It is well to remember here, that neither of the two EFA occurs in the brain in any appreciable amounts, but their products $20:4\omega6$ and $22:6\omega3$ are major unsaturated fatty acids.

B. Rapid Uptake via the Intracarotid Route

In most of the studies cited so far, the interval between administration of tracer dose and sacrifice of the animals has been hours or days. The main reason for this was a general belief that brain lipid metabolism, at least in adult animals, is rather slow and that a shorter time interval would not be adequate to obtain all data regarding uptake, metabolic

Table VIII

COMPARISON OF UPTAKE OF RADIOACTIVITY FROM CARBOXY-LABELED FATTY ACIDS INFUSED VIA CAROTID ARTERY IN RABBITS

Tracer (infused over a period of 1 hour)	Blood plasma (cpm/ml)	Whole brain			Gray matter			White matter		
		cpm/gm	Percent uptake[a]	Ratio (cpm/gm) tissue/plasma	cpm/gm	Percent uptake[a]	Ratio (cpm/gm) tissue/plasma	cpm/gm	Percent uptake	Ratio (cpm/gm) tissue/plasma
10 μCi Palmitate-1-^{14}C	2608	6939	0.95	2.66	11,116	1.5	4.26	7673	1.05	2.94
10 μCi Linoleate-1-^{14}C	3156	676	0.09	0.21	743	0.1	0.23	547	0.07	0.17
10 μCi Linolenate-1-^{14}C	1239	955	0.13	0.77	1049	0.14	0.85	903	0.12	0.73

[a] Percent uptake = Radioactivity per gram tissue × 100/Radioactivity administered (0.33 μCi/100 gm body wt).

transformations, and biosynthesis. Our attention was drawn to a study by Oldendorf (1970, 1971a) who had used a single carotid injection of a mixture of tritiated water and ^{14}C-labeled test compound to determine brain uptake. The animals were decapitated in 15 seconds, just enough time for one complete pass through cerebral circulation. We used this method (Dhopeshwarkar et al., 1971c) to determine the uptake and incorporation of acetate-1-^{14}C into the brain. The data are shown in Table IX.

Within this short interval of only 15 seconds after injection, there was considerable uptake of radioactivity resulting in a specific activity of brain lipids 10 times greater than that of the liver lipids. This was the first time that brain did not come out second best in uptake of radioactivity after a tracer dose to an adult animal. It was interesting to note that the radioactivity of blood plasma per milliliter was very low, thus eliminating the possibility of any appreciable contribution from trapped blood. Moreover the radioactivity of the brain was in the form of complex lipids.

Three conclusions can be drawn from these data. First, considerable radioactivity in the brain cholesterol must mean rapid metabolic conversion of acetate to cholesterol. Second, the label distribution of palmitic acid isolated from the purified polar lipid fraction (PL + SphL) sug-

Table IX

INCORPORATION OF RADIOACTIVITY FROM ACETATE-1-^{14}C INTO BRAIN, LIVER, AND PLASMA LIPIDS 15 SECONDS AFTER CAROTID ARTERIAL INJECTION

	Total lipids		
	Brain	Liver	Plasma
Specific activity (cpm/mg)	326	31	168
cpm/gm tissue	35×10^3	1.2×10^3	467

	Brain	
	Cholesterol	Polar lipids
cpm/mg	86	294

	Total fatty acids	
	Palmitic acid	Stearic acid
Specific activity (cpm/mg)	595	91
%RCA	13.4	43.1

gested total *de novo* synthesis from acetate. Third, all major polar lipid components were radioactive, indicating incorporation of newly synthesized fatty acids into complex lipids.

Thus most of the major lipid metabolism reactions occurred very rapidly, within 15 seconds of dose administration plus less than 50 seconds between decapitation and tissue dispersion in chloroform:methanol. This rapid uptake raises many questions, one of which is how can there be a rapid synthesis of complex molecules such as cholesterol and polar phospho- and sphingolipids and also at the same time a very long stable half-life of these brain lipids? For example, radioactivity in brain cholesterol has been shown by Davison *et al.* (1958) to be persistent up to 220 days. We have shown evidence of rapid *de novo* synthesis of cholesterol from acetate. In the light of present knowledge, the only possible explanation for this apparent contradiction is that the brain cholesterol has more than one compartment: one turning over very rapidly and the other, very slowly (Kabara, 1967).

The earlier findings that the BBB causes the brain to come out second best to the liver (Kishimoto and Radin, 1966) is not true in all cases. For example, when the brain is presented with the tracer via a carotid injection, there is greater uptake by the brain than by the liver, at least in the case of acetate; the opposite is true when tracer is injected intravenously or intraperitoneally. Whether this is true for all compounds is not known. However, the carotid injection does not bypass the BBB and so the dramatic uptake shows that the BBB plays a minor role, if any, under these circumstances.

V. Incorporation of Radioactivity into Brain Polar Lipids

The radioactivity from carboxy-labeled fatty acids and acetate was completely incorporated into brain complex lipids and there was no radioactive free fatty acid fraction detectable in the brain. The results are shown in Table X.

Examination of the first two columns in Table X shows quite a remarkable difference between specific activities of various components when acetate was injected intraperitoneally followed by sacrifice after 24 hours, and when it was administered by the intracarotid route and the animals were killed just 15 seconds later. In the former case PC (phosphatidyl choline) was the most active component, whereas, in the latter case PS (phosphatidyl serine) had the highest specific activity. Thus, the route of entry as well as the interval between dose and sacrifice seem to influence the label distribution. From the earlier work of Borkenhagen *et al.*

Table X

INCORPORATION OF RADIOACTIVITY FROM CARBOXY-LABELED FATTY ACIDS INTO VARIOUS POLAR LIPIDS OF THE RAT BRAIN

Fatty acid administered	Route of entry	Period between dose and sacrifice	Specific activity (cpm/mg)[a]				
			PC	PE	PS	Sph	Cereb
Acetate-1-^{14}C	Intraperitoneal	24 hours	130	75	46	30	51
Acetate-1-^{14}C	Intracarotid	15 seconds	86	45	239	59	138
Palmitic acid-1-^{14}C	Intracarotid	15 seconds	181	122	83	63	26
Palmitic acid-1-^{14}C	Oral feeding	24 hours	304	116	83	14	22
Oleic acid-1-^{14}C	Oral feeding	24 hours	266	156	71	42	67
Linoleic acid-1-^{14}C	Oral feeding	24 hours	179	79	79	38	71
Linolenic acid-1-^{14}C	Oral feeding	24 hours	101	84	76	23	100

[a] PC = Phosphatidyl choline; PE = phosphatidyl ethanolamine; PS = phosphatidyl serine; Sph = sphingomyelin; Cereb = cerebroside.

(1961), it is known that liver mitochondria can decarboxylate PS to PE (phosphatidyl ethanolamine). Wilson *et al.* (1960) had shown that brain slices could decarboxylate L serine to ethanolamine. However, Ansell and Spanner (1962) reported that decarboxylation and stepwise methylation to form PC was not a major pathway in the brain. This would explain a rather low activity of PE; another reason could be that although PS could lead to the formation of PE via decarboxylation, the PE, having a rapid turnover (Ansell and Spanner, 1968), might have lost a portion of the activity, although 15 seconds seems to be too short an interval for this to happen.

That the route of entry could be the sole influence is ruled out, because palmitate-1-^{14}C irrespective of the type of administration gave rise to the highest radioactivity in the same component, PC. Wright and Green (1971) found that when palmitate-1-^{14}C was injected into the femoral vein and the liver dissected out after 1 minute, PC was the most active component. They also found that this radioactive component was predominantly in the plasma membrane fraction. The high activity in PC following intracarotid injection of palmitic acid-1-^{14}C and decapitation in 15 seconds might be similarly associated with the plasma membrane fraction. However, in our studies, PC was the most radioactive component even at longer intervals, contrary to the experiments reported by Wright and Green wherein the high activity of PC was lost to the liver triglyceride fraction. In the brain, triglycerides form a very minor component and this may be one of the reasons for the observed differences, in addition to organ specificity and experimental conditions. Sun and Horrocks (1969) also found that PC was the most active component after an intracerebral injection in 4-month-old mice. However, when the time interval was shortened to 6–10 minutes, they observed high activity in diacylglycerols (Sun and Horrocks, 1971).

The high radioactivity of PC was observed in all experiments except when linolenic acid-1-^{14}C was administered. In this experiment the radioactivity distribution was very unusual in that the cerebroside fraction (which was rather poorly labeled in all other cases, except with 18:2) appears to have an increased proportion of the radioactivity, resulting in specific activities of the cerebroside fraction almost equal to that of lecithin. Unfortunately, there was not enough material to characterize this fraction and identify the most active component of the complex cerebroside mixture. This highly active cerebroside gave two spots on TLC similar to the authentic standard. The lower spot, presumably containing hydroxy fatty acids (Hooghwinkel *et al.*, 1964; Svennerholm and Svennerholm, 1963), was the one that had most radioactivity. Further characterization and confirmation is being pursued in our laboratory.

VI. Fatty Acid Transport into the Brain

PREFERRED FORM OF FATTY ACID TRANSPORT

Although it had been conclusively demonstrated that long-chain fatty acids both saturated and unsaturated, including essential fatty acids, are readily taken up by the adult rat brain *in vivo*, a question remained as to the preferred form in which fatty acids are transported into the brain.

It was already known from the early work by Fredrickson and Gordon (1958) that although free fatty acids (FFA) make up only 1 to 5% of plasma lipids, they have a very rapid turnover that can account for most of the net lipid transport in the blood. The myocardium of man and dog, for example, is known to extract free fatty acids from the circulating plasma (Gordon, 1957; Rothlin and Bing, 1961). The circulating fatty acids are associated with plasma albumin (Gordon, 1957; Goodman, 1958) forming the fatty acid albumin complex. These complexes are formed immediately after FFA release into the bloodstream and are transported to the sites of utilization where the fatty acids are transferred from binding sites on the albumin to sites on the cell surface. There has been considerable discussion as to whether the brain should be included among "all other tissues" in which fatty acids are utilized. For example, Bragdon and Gordon (1958) found that when ^{14}C-labeled FFA or chylomicra were administered intravenously, virtually all the tissues of the rat became labeled except those of the brain. This was then attributed to the existence of the BBB. The other reason for considering brain to be different from other tissues, was the fact that lipid metabolism in the brain was considered to be rather slow and formed a closed system, by which the brain used the products of degradation for resynthesis; thus, the need for transporting such compounds as preformed fatty acids was, for all practical purposes, unnecessary. Recent results reported by Spitzer and Wolf (1971) indicate that FFA supplied by CSF may serve as oxidizable substrates for the brain, we decided to examine the actual form in which fatty acids were transported into the brain (Dhopeshwarkar *et al.*, 1972).

Three main possibilities were examined. The fatty acids could be transported into the brain as free fatty acids, as components of triglycerides or as components of phospholipids. A group of rats was given an intravenous dose of palmitic acid-1[14]C–albumin complex and killed after 1 hour. In these rats, the triglycerides of the circulating plasma had 78% of the total lipid radioactivity, which is in agreement with the observations reported by Laurell (1959). Another group of animals was subjected to

Table XI

UPTAKE OF RADIOACTIVITY BY THE BRAIN AND LIVER AFTER INJECTION OF PALMITIC ACID-1-^{14}C AND DIPALMITOYL LECITHIN-1-^{14}C

Group	Period between dose and sacrifice	Blood plasma radioactivity (% of total radioactivity)			Brain lipids		Liver lipids	
		TG	FFA	PL	Specific activity (cpm/mg)	cpm/gm wet wt	Specific activity (cpm/mg)	cpm/gm wet wt
I. Control (IV injection)	1 hour	77.7	10.9	1.6	49	5242	6836	276,188
II. Hepatectomized (IV injection)	1 hour	10.6	77.4	11.9	314	36,688	243	9556
III. Intracarotid injection	15 seconds	0.7	90.1	2.3	878	93,331	1831	73,956
IV. IV injection of di-palmitoyl lecithin-1-^{14}C	1 hour	9.6	1.8	62.3	24	2019	8760	353,904

functional hepatectomy involving removal of the entire intestinal tract in addition to isolating the liver from the circulating blood. Palmitate-1-^{14}C was injected intravenously and the animals killed after 1 hour. In these rats the FFA of the circulating plasma had 78% of the total activity. In another group of animals palmitate-1-^{14}C was injected intracarotidly and the animals were killed within 15 seconds. We reasoned that since the time interval was very short, the circulating plasma lipids would have a very radioactive FFA fraction; experimentally this fraction turned out to contain 90% of the total radioactivity. Finally, the last group of animals was given an intravenous injection of dipalmitoyl-1-^{14}C lecithin (sonicated in physiological saline) and killed after 1 hour (G. A. Dhopeshwarkar and C. Subramanian, unpublished data). In these rats, phospholipids contained 62% of the total plasma lipid radioactivity.

When the radioactivity in the brain was examined, it was found that maximum activity appeared in the brain when the circulating plasma FFA were high in radioactivity and not when either the plasma triglyceride or phospholipid were the most radioactive components. This indicates that free fatty acids are the preferred form of transport into the brain (Table XI). This does not agree with the observations by Holzl and Franck (1969), who proposed lecithin as a vehicle for fatty acid transport. No comparison of uptake with free fatty acid was made in their study, which aimed to show that the BBB did not restrict the passage of intravenously administered lecithin into the brain.

VII. BBB and Malnutrition

A. EFA DEFICIENCY

Various workers have investigated the effects of EFA (essential fatty acid) deficiency on the structure of cell membranes giving evidence that the skin of rats deficient in EFA is more permeable to water than is that of normal rats (Basnayake and Sinclair, 1956). It has been reported that EFA deficiency resulted in fragility of erythrocytes and capillaries (Kramar and Levine, 1953). Applying these observations to the brain, DePury and Collins (1963) have noted that EFA deficiency caused alteration in the cytoplasmic membrane structure leading to increased uptake of ^{32}P into brain phosphatidic acid. Gerstl et al. (1965) have proposed that Pelizaeus-Merzbacher disease (familial centrolobar sclerosis) is caused by a genetically controlled deficiency of arachidonic acid. EFA deficiency had been implicated in multiple sclerosis (Sinclair, 1956; Baker et al., 1963; Thompson, 1966; Bernsohn and Stephanides, 1967). Whether changes in myelin metabolism are primary or secondary to metabolic lesions occurring elsewhere is unknown (Smith, 1967); thus, whether EFA deficiency is an etiological factor is still a speculation at best. Galli *et al.* (1970) stressed the importance of nutritional factors during the very early period before and immediately after birth and found that EFA deficiency initiated in rats prior to birth and continued for 1 year produced profound changes in brain weight and lipid composition. White *et al.* (1971) however, found that animals that were EFA deficient even during the brain's most actively growing period, were able to recover completely on restoration to the control diet.

From this discussion, it seems that EFA deficiency could have some effect on the permeability of brain capillaries affecting the BBB. No direct evidence has yet been presented.

B. OTHER DEFICIENCIES

Thiamine deficiency has been implicated in its effect on the proper functioning of the BBB by Warnock and Burkhalter (1968). When the labeling pattern of brain glutamic acid was studied after injecting pyruvate-2-^{14}C, it was found that in thiamine deficiency, pyruvate entered the brain because of malfunctioning of the BBB. In normal well fed animals, pyruvate did not permeate from the blood into the brain. This effect of thiamine deficiency may not be restricted to pyruvate. Whether this is the cause of the polyneuritis observed in thiamine deficiency in pigeons is also still speculative. More work along these lines will clarify some of the unknown parameters of BBB.

Damage to BBB by toxicants, such as mercury, has been studied by Steinwall (1969) and Steinwall and Snyder (1969).

VIII. Discussion of the Concept of the BBB as It Applies to Lipids

Considering all the evidence for direct uptake to fatty acids, lecithin, and cholesterol, one can generalize on several points. The restricted uptake of radioactivity from labeled lipids by the adult brain, as compared to the immature brain, may very well be explained on the basis of metabolic requirements and turnover rates (Dobbing, 1968). We have conclusively shown uptake of labeled fatty acids by the adult brain *in vivo* without appreciable degradation to acetate elsewhere, followed by resynthesis in the brain. The magnitude of uptake in the adult seems to depend on the route of entry and the form in which the test compound is presented to the brain. For example, when the tracer was administered via a carotid injection, very rapid uptake and incorporation into complex lipids was observed; in fact, the uptake by the brain was greater than by the liver. If the BBB had a profound influence on the uptake of lipids (fatty acids), the brain uptake would not be widely different when tracer was injected intravenously, intracarotidly or intraperitoneally. However, our data show that either when the liver is isolated from blood circulation or when the tracer is injected intracarotidly (thereby giving the brain the first chance to pick up the label), fatty acids were taken up readily by the brain. Our own studies, as well as those by Holzl and Franck (1969), have shown the uptake of the intact lecithin molecule. A small but definite uptake of cholesterol-^{14}C by adult animals has been shown by Kabara (1967). From all these findings, we return to the hypothesis proposed by Davson (1955) that, in general, lipid-soluble compounds are not restricted by the BBB and enter the brain much more freely than do water-soluble polar compounds. Thus, the term "blood–brain relationship" suggested by Dobbing (1968) is definitely more appropriate than the commonly used "blood–brain barrier" in describing lipid uptake by the brain.

IX. Summary

Long-chain fatty acids—palmitic, oleic, and the essential fatty acids (linoleic and linolenic)—were taken up by the adult brain and incorporated into complex lipids including the so-called "myelin lipids," i.e., cerebrosides and sphingomyelin. The labeling pattern of fatty acids isolated from the brain showed that the resynthesis of fatty acids from acetate, itself derived by oxidative degradation of the administered carboxy-labeled fatty acid, was only a minor metabolic reaction, thereby proving direct uptake of the intact molecule. There is some indication that linolenic acid is taken up in slightly higher rate than linoleic acid by the brain, when the ratios of radioactivity in the brain and liver are compared. This preferential uptake may result in higher concentration of the $\omega 3$ family fatty acids commonly found in the brain.

When labeled acetate or palmitate was injected into the carotid artery followed by decapitation within 15 seconds, there was greater uptake of radioactivity in the brain than in the liver. Brain palmitate, as well as cholesterol, was synthesized *de novo* from intracarotid injected acetate within 15 seconds, and the polar lipids were all labeled. This indicated a very rapid lipid metabolism *in vivo* in the adult brain contrary to earlier views.

Since the uptake of radioactivity in the brain was higher in animals whose plasma lipids contained a highly radioactive FFA component (hepatectomized and carotid-injected groups) as compared to animals whose plasma lipids contained either highly radioactive triglycerides (control group) or phospholipids (lecithin-^{14}C-injected group), it was concluded that FFA are the preferred form of transport into the brain.

The BBB did not influence the uptake of these lipid-soluble compounds and so the lower incorporation of radioactivity into adult, as compared to young brain, can be explained on the basis of metabolic requirement and turnover. Actually if the brain is presented with a tracer via carotid injection, this age-dependent difference can be overcome. In the absence of any barrier effect, we strongly support the use of the term "blood–brain relationship" in relation to lipid metabolism in the brain.

ACKNOWLEDGMENTS

Investigations discussed in this review and conducted in our laboratory were supported in part by Contract AT(04-1)GEN-12 between the Atomic Energy Commission and the University of California and by U. S. Public Health Service Research Career Award No. GM-K6-19, 177 from the Division of General Medical Sciences, National Institutes of Health.

The authors are very grateful for the excellent technical help from Mrs. Carole Subramanian in our investigations.

We extend our sincere thanks to Mrs. Dolores West and Frances Adams for their invaluable excellent assistance in the preparation of this manuscript.

We express our sincere thanks to the Elsevier Publishing Company for granting us permission to reproduce tabulated data, with minor changes, from our published work in the *Biochimica Biophysics Acta*.

References

Aeberhard, E., and Menkes, J. H. (1968). *J. Biol. Chem.* **243**, 3834.
Ansell, G. B., and Spanner, S. (1962). *Biochem. J.* **84**, 12P.
Ansell, G. B., and Spanner, S. (1968). *J. Neurochem.* **15**, 1371.
Baker, R. W. R., Thompson, R. H. S., and Zilkha, K. J. (1963). *Lancet* **1**, 26.
Bakay, L. (1953). *AMA Arch. Neurol. Psychiat.* **70**, 30.
Bakay, L. (1956). "The Blood Brain Barrier." Thomas, Springfield, Illinois.
Basnayake, V., and Sinclair, H. M. (1956). *In* "Biochemical Problems of Lipids" (G. Popjak and E. Le Breton, eds.), p. 476. Wiley (Interscience), New York.
Bernsohn, J., and Stephanides, L. M. (1967). *Nature* (*London*) **215**, 821.
Biran, L. A., and Bartley, W. (1961). *Biochem. J.* **79**, 159.
Bito, L. Z., Bradbury, M. W. B., and Davson, H. (1966). *J. Physiol.* (*London*) **185**, 323.
Bloch, K., Berg, B. N., and Rittenberg, D. (1943). *J. Biol. Chem.* **149**, 511.
Blomstrand, R., Dhopeshwarkar, G. A., and Gustafsson, B. E. (1963). *J. Atheroscler. Res.* **3**, 274.
Blotevogel, W. (1924). *Z. Zellen- Gewebelehre* **1**, 447.

Boone, S. C., and Wakil, S. J. (1970). *Biochemistry* **9**, 1470.
Borkenhagen, L. F., Kennedy, E. P., and Fielding, L. (1961). *J. Biol. Chem.* **236**, PC28.
Brady, R. O. (1960). *J. Biol. Chem.* **235**, 3099.
Brady, R. O., Bradley, R. M., and Trams, E. G. (1960). *J. Biol. Chem.* **235**, 3093.
Bragdon, J. H., and Gordon, R. S., Jr. (1958). *J. Clin. Invest.* **37**, 574.
Carroll, K. K. (1962). *Can. J. Biochem. Physiol.* **40**, 1229.
Davies, W. E., Hajra, A. K., Parmar, S. S., Radin, N. S., and Mead, J. F. (1966). *J. Lipid Res.* **7**, 270.
Davison, A. N., Dobbing, J., Morgan, R. S., and Payling Wright, G. (1958). *J. Neurochem.* **3**, 89.
Davson, H. (1955). *J. Physiol. (London)* **129**, 111.
Davson, H. (1967). "Physiology of the Cerebrospinal Fluid," p. 82. Churchill, London.
Davson, H., and Spaziani, E. (1959). *J. Physiol. (London)* **149**, 135.
Davson, H., Kleeman, C. R., and Levin, E. (1961). *J. Physiol. (London)* **159**, 67P.
DePury, G. G., and Collins, F. D. (1963). *Nature (London)* **198**, 788.
Dhopeshwarkar, G. A., and Bawa, S. R. (1971). *J. Sci. Ind. Res.* **30**, 22.
Dhopeshwarkar, G. A., and Mead, J. F. (1962). *J. Lipid Res.* **3**, 238.
Dhopeshwarkar, G. A., and Mead, J. F. (1969). *Biochim. Biophys. Acta* **187**, 461.
Dhopeshwarkar, G. A., and Mead, J. F. (1970). *Biochim. Biophys. Acta* **210**, 250.
Dhopeshwarkar, G. A., Maier, R., and Mead, J. F. (1969). *Biochim. Biophys. Acta* **187**, 6.
Dhopeshwarkar, G. A., Subramanian, C., and Mead, J. F. (1971a). *Biochim. Biophys. Acta* **231**, 8.
Dhopeshwarkar, G. A., Subramanian, C., and Mead, J. F. (1971b). *Biochim. Biophys. Acta* **239**, 162.
Dhopeshwarkar, G. A., Subramanian, C., and Mead, J. F. (1971c). *Biochim. Biophys. Acta* **248**, 41.
Dhopeshwarkar, G. A., Subramanian, C., McConnell, D. H., and Mead, J. F. (1972). *Biochim. Biophys. Acta* **255**, 572.
Dobbing, J. (1961). *Physiol. Rev.* **41**, 130.
Dobbing, J. (1968). *Prog. Brain Res.* **29**, 417.
Edstrom, R. (1964). *Int. Rev. Neurobiol.* **7**, 153.
Ehrlich, P. (1882). *Deut. Med. Wochenschr.* **8**, 21.
Folch-Pi, J. (1955). *In* "Biochemistry of the Developing Nervous System" (H. Waelsch, ed.), p. 200. Academic Press, New York.
Fredrickson, D. S., and Gordon, R. S., Jr. (1958). *Physiol. Rev.* **38**, 585.
Friedemann, U. (1942). *Physiol. Rev.* **22**, 125.
Fries, B. A., Changus, G. W., and Chaikoff, I. L. (1940). *J. Biol. Chem.* **132**, 23.
Fulco, A. J., and Mead, J. F. (1961). *J. Biol. Chem.* **236**, 2416.
Galli, C., White, H. B., Jr., and Paoletti, R. (1970). *J. Neurochem.* **17**, 347.
Gatt, S. (1963). *Biochim. Biophys. Acta* **70**, 370.
Gerstl, B., Tavaststjerna, M. G., Hayman, R. B., Eng, L. F., and Smith, J. K. (1965). *Ann. N. Y. Acad. Sci.* **122**, 405.
Goldmann, E. E. (1909). *Beitr. Klin. Chir.* **64**, 192.
Goldmann, E. E. (1913). *Abh. Preuss. Akad. Wiss., Phys-Math. Kl.* **1**, 1.
Goodman, D. S. (1958). *J. Amer. Chem. Soc.* **80**, 3892.

Gordon, R. S., Jr. (1957). *J. Clin. Invest.* **36**, 810.
Holzl, J., and Franck, H. P. (1969). *Proc. Int. Meet. Int. Soc. Neurochem. 2nd, 1969* p. 219.
Hooghwinkel, G. J. M., Borri, P., and Riemersma, J. C. (1964). *Rec. Trav. Chim. Pays-Bas* **83**, 576.
Johnston, P. V., Kopaczyk, K. C., and Kummerow, F. A. (1961). *J. Nutr.* **74**, 96.
Kabara, J. J. (1967). *Advan. Lipid Res.* **5**, 298.
Kishimoto, Y., and Radin, N. S. (1959). *J. Lipid Res.* **1**, 72.
Kishimoto, Y., and Radin, N. S, (1963). *J. Lipid Res.* **4**, 444.
Kishimoto, Y., and Radin, N. S. (1966). *Lipids* **1**, 47.
Kishimoto, Y., Davies, W. E., and Radin, N. S. (1965a). *J. Lipid Res.* **6**, 525.
Kishimoto, Y., Davies, W. E., and Radin, N. S. (1965b). *J. Lipid Res.* **6**, 532.
Klenk, E. (1928). *Hoppe-Seyler's Z. Physiol. Chem.* **174**, 214.
Klenk, E. (1955). *In* "Biochemistry of the Developing Nervous System" (H. Waelsch, ed.), p. 201. Academic Press, New York.
Klenk, E. (1961). *In* "Drugs Affecting Lipid Metabolism" (S. Garattini and R. Paoletti, eds.), p. 21. Elsevier, Amsterdam.
Kramar, J., and Levine, V. E. (1953). *J. Nutr.* **50**, 149.
Lajtha, A., and Ford, D. H. (1968). *Progr. Brain Res.* **29**, 1.
Lajtha, A., Furst, S., Gerstein, A., and Waelsch, H. (1957). *J. Neurochem.* **1**, 289.
Laurell, S. (1959). *Acta Physiol. Scand.* **46**, 97.
Levin, E., and Kleeman, C. R. (1970). *Proc. Soc. Exp. Biol. Med.* **135**, 685.
Levin, E., and Scicli, G. (1969). *Brain Res.* **13**, 1.
Levis, C. M., and Mead, J. F. (1964). *J. Biol. Chem.* **239**, 77.
McConnell, K. P., and Sinclair, R. G. (1937). *J. Biol. Chem.* **118**, 131.
McDonald, R. C., and Mead, J. F. (1968). *Lipids* **3**, 275.
Mead, J. F. (1961). *Fed. Proc., Fed. Amer. Soc. Exp. Biol.* **20**, 952.
Mead, J. F., and Hare, R. S. (1971). *Biochem. Biophys. Res. Commun.* **45**, 1451.
Mead, J. F., and Levis, C. M. (1962). *Biochem. Biophys. Res. Commun.* **0**, 231.
Mead, J. F., and Levis, C. M. (1963). *J. Biol. Chem.* **238**, 1634.
Mead, J. F., and Nevenzel, J. C. (1960). *J. Lipid Res.* **1**, 305.
Miyamoto, K., Stephanides, L. M., and Bernsohn, J. (1967). *J. Neurochem.* **14**, 227.
Mohrhauer, H., and Holman, R. T. (1963). *J. Neurochem.* **10**, 523.
O'Brien, J. S., Fillerup, D. L., and Mead, J. F. (1964). *J. Lipid Res.* **5**, 329.
Oldendorf, W. H. (1970). *Brain Res.* **24**, 372.
Oldendorf, W. H. (1971a). *Proc. Soc. Exp. Biol. Med.* **136**, 385.
Oldendorf, W. H. (1971b). *Amer. J. Physiol.* **221**, 1629.
Pakkala, S. G., Fillerup, D. L., and Mead, J. F. (1966). *Lipids* **1**, 449.
Rathbone, L. (1965). *Biochem. J.* **97**, 620.
Rothlin, M. D., and Bing, R. J. (1961). *J. Clin. Invest.* **40**, 1380.
Rouser, G., and Yamamoto, A. (1969). *In* "Handbook of Neurochemistry" (A. Lajtha, ed.), Vol. I, p. 121. Plenum, New York.
Schoenheimer, R., and Rittenberg, D. (1936). *J. Biol. Chem.* **114**, 381.
Sinclair, H. M. (1956). *Lancet* **1**, 381.
Smith, M. E. (1967). *Advan. Lipid Res.* **5**, 273.
Smith, M. E. (1968). *Biochim. Biophys. Acta* **164**, 285.
Sperry, W. M., Taylor, R. M., and Meltzer, H. L. (1953). *Fed. Proc., Fed. Amer. Soc. Exp. Biol.* **12**, 271.

Spitzer, J. J., and Wolf, E. H. (1971). *Amer. J. Physiol.* **221**, 1426.

Stein, R. A., and Slawson, V. (1968). *Anal. Chem.* **40**, 2017.

Steinberg, G., Slaton, W. H., Jr., Howton, D. R., and Mead, J. F. (1956). *J. Biol. Chem.* **220**, 257.

Steinwall, O. (1969). *Acta Neurol. Scand.* **45**, 362.

Steinwall, O., and Snyder, S. H. (1969). *Acta Neurol. Scand.* **45**, 369.

Sun, G. Y., and Horrocks, L. A. (1969). *J. Neurochem.* **16**, 181.

Sun, G. Y., and Horrocks, L. A. (1971). *J. Neurochem.* **18**, 1963.

Svennerholm, E., and Svennerholm, L. (1963). *Biochim. Biophys. Acta* **70**, 432.

Thompson, R. H. S. (1966). *Proc. Roy. Soc. Med.* **59**, 269.

Van Bruggen, J. T., Hutchens, T. T., Claycomb, C. K., and West, E. S. (1953). *J. Biol. Chem.* **200**, 31.

Waelsch, H. (1955). *In* "Biochemistry of the Developing Nervous System" (H. Waelsch, ed.), p. 191. Academic Press, New York.

Waelsch, H., Sperry, W. M., and Stoyanoff, V. A. (1940). *J. Biol. Chem.* **135**, 291.

Waelsch, H., Sperry, W. M., and Stoyanoff, V. A. (1941). *J. Biol. Chem.* **140**, 885.

Warnock, L. G., and Burkhalter, V. J. (1968). *J. Nutr.* **94**, 256.

Wells, M. A., and Dittmer, J. C. (1967). *Biochemistry* **6**, 3169.

White, H. B., Jr., Galli, C., and Paoletti, R. (1971). *J. Neurochem.* **18**, 869.

Wilson, J. D., Gibson, K. D., and Udenfriend, S. (1960). *J. Biol. Chem.* **235**, 3539.

Wright, J. D., and Green, C. (1971). *Biochem. J.* **123**, 837.

Microbiological Transformation of Bile Acids

SHOHEI HAYAKAWA

Shionogi Research Laboratory, Shionogi & Co., Ltd., Fukushima-ku, Osaka, Japan

I. Introduction

Since Murray and Peterson succeeded in 1952 in accomplishing the effective hydroxylation of steroids by fungi, the microbiological transformation of steroids has received special attention in connection with the practical problem of economical synthesis of steroid hormones. The method offered a valuable tool for preparing adrenal, androgenic, and estrogenic steroids as well as new steroidal compounds. An excellent comprehensive survey of this subject has been provided by the book, "Microbial Transformations of Steroids: A Handbook," by Charney and Herzog (1967). As can be seen from this book, however, bile acids have not so far been intensively studied in this field.

During the course of studies on the biosynthesis and metabolism of bile acids, Bergström and collaborators found that there is an intimate relationship between bile acid metabolism *in vivo* and intestinal micro-

143

organisms, and they subsequently established a new concept of "primary" and "secondary" bile acids (cf. Bergström *et al.*, 1960). Indeed, the concept is very important for an understanding of the formation and metabolism of bile acids. Ever since this appeared, interest in the microbiological transformation of bile acids has been focused on elucidation of the nature of the intestinal organisms concerned in the formation of secondary bile acids.

Since before the tetracyclic carbon skeleton of cyclopentenophenanthrene was presented for the structure of bile acids, several studies on the microbiological degradation of bile acids *in vitro* have been conducted as a practical working model for the prediction of possible intermediates in the bile acid metabolism *in vivo*. Microorganisms used in these studies are roughly classified as intestinal and nonintestinal organisms according to their habitat. *In vitro* studies with the latter organisms are still being made in attempts to define the intermediates and the reaction sequence involved in the bile acid degradation by microorganisms, even though it was established that no splitting of the carbon-carbon bond in bile acids usually occurs in animals, including man.

The present review will attempt to trace the development of these studies during the last decade.

II. Microbiological Transformation of Bile Acids in the Intestinal Tract

An important role of intestinal microorganisms in the transformation of bile acids in the intestine was conclusively demonstrated by Gustafsson and Norman (1962) through their comparative studies on bile acids in the intestinal contents of conventional and germ-free rats. At present it is generally believed that the conjugated primary bile acids are attacked by intestinal microorganisms in the lower small intestine and cecum and transformed into various metabolites which are absorbed and further transformed by liver enzymes prior to reexcretion into the bile. The liver enzymes mainly catalyze the following reactions: conjugation of free bile acids with taurine or glycine, reduction of keto groups to alcohols, and hydroxylation of the cholane nucleus. Thus, the final composition of the bile acids in normal bile is the result of an intimate interaction between the liver and intestinal microorganisms.

The bile acid transformations in the intestine can be classified as follows: hydrolysis of the conjugated bile acids; elimination of hydroxyl groups, mainly at the C-7 position of the cholane nucleus; oxidation of the hydroxyl groups at C-3, C-7, and C-12 to oxo groups; reduction of oxo groups to both α- and β-hydroxyl groups; other miscellaneous reactions. Although the last may not be quantitatively important, it contains several interesting types of reactions known as microbiological transformations. In the following sections, some aspects of each of these transformations will be discussed with emphasis on the isolation and identification of the organisms responsible for various reactions. In this connection it must be kept in mind that the bile acid-transforming abilities of certain bacterial species vary from strain to strain and that strains of a particular bacterial species are able to catalyze more than one transformation. No attempt will be made to discuss the bile acid transformation by intestinal microorganisms in gastrointestinal disorders, since this has already been discussed in some detail by Finegold (1969), Gorbach (1971), and Garbutt *et al.* (1971). Before discussing the transformations, the nature of intestinal microorganisms will be briefly mentioned.

A. Intestinal Microorganisms

More than sixty different species have been isolated from the intestinal tracts or feces of healthy animals, including man. The species most often present in significant numbers are as follows (Donaldson, 1964): *Aerobacter aerogenes, A. cloacae, Alcaligenes faecalis, Bacillus subtilis, Bacteroides fragilis, B. funduliformis, B. nigrescens, B. pneumosintes, B. putidus, B. serpens, Clostridium bifermentans, C. botulinum, C. perfringens, C. sporogenes, C. tetani, Escherichia coli, E. freundii, Klebsiella oxytoca, K. rhinoscleromatis, Lactobacillus acidophilus, L. bifidus, L. brevis, L. casei, L. exilis, Proteus mirabilis, P. morganii, P. rettgeri, P. vulgaris,* Providence group, *Pseudomonas aeruginosa, P. fluorescens, P. ovalis, Streptococcus durans, S. faecalis, S. faecium,* and *S. lactis.*

Although it appears that only 10 to 25% of the normal intestinal bacterial flora has so far been elucidated, it is known that anaerobes are predominant in the normal human fecal flora of adults, aerobes accounting for less than 1% of the cultivable organisms (Finegold, 1969). The commonest anaerobic microorganism is *B. fragilis* and its mean count is 10^{10} to 10^{11} per gram of wet feces. The second most prevalent anaerobe is a *Bifidobacterium* sp. which is known by such names as *Lactobacillus bifidus* and *Actinomyces bifidus.* Anaerobic members of the tribe Lactobacilleae belong to the genera *Eubacterium* and *Ramibacterium.* Although the genus *Lactobacillus* belongs to this tribe, it is microaerophilic. The major elements of the aerobic organisms are *E. coli* and *S. faecalis.* The nature of intestinal microorganisms of laboratory animals is similar to that of the human intestinal flora, and their types and members are altered by factors such as the kind of diet, age of the host, and administration of drugs (Scheline, 1968). For further information on intestinal microorganisms, see the review articles mentioned above and also additional literature cited in the review by Gorbach (1971).

B. Hydrolysis of Conjugated Bile Acids

Unlike peptide bonds in proteins and peptides, the carbon-nitrogen bond in conjugated bile acids is resistant to hydrolysis by most of the known proteolytic enzymes (Nair *et al.*, 1967) and to chemical hydrolysis with alkali (cf. Eneroth and Sjövall, 1971) (cf. Fig. 1). Recently, however, many strains of intestinal organisms capable of splitting these peptide bonds have been isolated and identified. In addition, it has been found that many strains in international type culture collections possess such an ability. Information available in many reports concerning the identification of the organisms responsible for deconjugation is generally in agreement, and it seems likely that deconjugation is a common feature among a wide variety of intestinal microorganisms.

With the aid of ^{14}C-labeled cholic acid it was established that conjugated bile acids are hydrolyzed during their passage through the intestinal tract (cf. Bergström *et al.*, 1960). The *in vivo* results have subsequently been studied in *in vitro* systems, and Norman and Grubb (1955) were the first to demonstrate the *in vitro* hydrolysis of conjugated acids by several species of intestinal organisms such as *Clostridium* and *Enterococcus*. The subsequent work of Norman and associate showed that *in vitro* ability to hydrolyze either glycocholic acid or taurocholic acid could be found in members of the families of Bacteroidaceae and Lactobacillaceae isolated from the cecum and the feces of rats and also in many type cultures: i.e., *Alcaligenes faecalis, Bacteroides fragilis, B. necrophorus, Bifidobacterium appendicitis, B. bifidum, Catenabacterium helminthoides, Clostridium butyricum, C. difficile, C. perfringens, Eubacterium cadaveris, E. minutum, E. niosii, E. quintum, E. rettgeri, E. ventriosum, Lactobacillus arabinosus, L. brevis, Proteus mirabilis, Ramibacterium alactolyticum, R. dentium, R. ramosum,* and *Streptococcus*

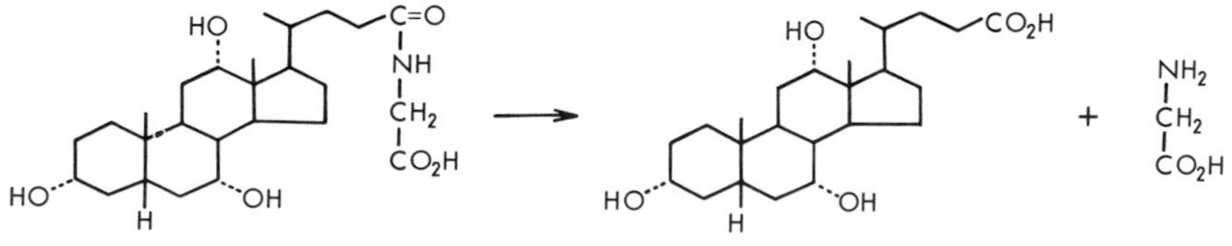

(I)   (II)   (III)

Fig. 1. Scheme for the hydrolytic cleavage of glycocholic acid (I) to cholic acid (II) and glycine (III).

faecalis (Midtvedt and Norman, 1967, 1968b). Gustafsson *et al.* (1968) have demonstrated the *in vivo* hydrolysis of conjugated bile acids with the use of rats monocontaminated with a strain of S. *faecalis* ATCC 8043 which shows the corresponding *in vitro* activity. Similar work with mice has also been reported by Suzuki (1970), who found both *in vitro* and *in vivo* activities in cultures of *Bacteroides* sp., *C. perfringens*, *Enterococcus* sp., and *Lactobacillus* sp. isolated from the intestine of the mouse. In addition, Dickinson *et al.* (1971) recently reported a detailed study on the transformation of bile acids by intestinal microorganisms. More than 100 facultative and strictly anaerobic strains from 22 genera isolated from the digestive tract of the rat were examined for the *in vitro* ability to split glycodeoxycholic acid and taurodeoxycholic acid. Deconjugating ability was found in many strains belonging to 14 of these genera: namely, *Acuformis*, *Bifidobacterium*, *Butyribacterium*, *Catenabacterium*, *Clostridium*, *Corynebacterium* (strictly anaerobic species), *Endosporus*, *Eubacterium*, *Inflabilis*, *Lactobacillus*, *Pasteurella* (strictly anaerobic species), *Ramibacterium*, *Sphaerophorus*, and *Streptococcus* (facultative and strictly anaerobic species). Some of these strains were established as monocontaminants in ex-germ-free rats and the strains of the genera *Clostridium*, *Eubacterium*, and *Streptococcus* gave approximately 80% splitting of the cecal bile acids. It is of interest that certain strains capable of splitting conjugated bile acids *in vitro* were either inactive or low in the *in vivo* activity.

The above-mentioned deconjugating microorganisms mainly originate from experimental small animals, although the author does not know the historical origin of all of the type cultures. On the other hand, Drasar *et al.* (1966) and Hill and Drasar (1968) demonstrated the *in vitro* hydrolysis of conjugated bile acids by many strains of *Bacteroides* spp., *Bifidobacterium* spp., *Clostridium* spp., *Staphylococcus aureus*, S. *faecalis*, and *Veillonella* spp. isolated from human saliva, jejunal juice, and feces. The same authors (1968) also found that some strains originally unable to deconjugate developed the ability after repeated subculture on a medium containing bile. Therefore, it is possible that some oral bacteria, when swallowed, may develop deconjugating activity. Shimada *et al.* (1969) investigated the *in vitro* deconjugating activity of a large number of well-characterized strains recovered from human feces, and found activity in cultures of the following anaerobic bacterial species: *Bacteroides fragilis*, *B. melaninogenicus*, *Bifidobacterium adolescentis*, *B. bifidum*, *B. breve*, *B. liberorum*, *B. longum* B. *parvulorum*, *Catenabacterium catenaforme*, *Clostridium paraputrificum*, *C. perfringens*, and *Sphaerophorus necrophorus*. Aerobic species such as *Lactobacillus buchneri*, *L. lactis*, and S. *faecalis* also showed activity. Their paper contains a comprehensive tabulation of the experimental conditions and results of studies on the same subject carried out by other investigators in the period 1955–1968. Aries *et al.* (1969) have also found activity in many strains from the genera *Bacillus, Bacteroides, Bifidobacterium, Clostridium, Enterococcus,* anaerobic *Sarcina,* and *Veillonella* isolated from feces of normal human beings.

In addition to these *in vitro* studies using growing cultures or washed cell suspensions, some studies on the enzymes which catalyze the hydrolysis of conjugated bile acids have been carried out. Nair *et al.* (1965) were the first to show that cell-free extracts from *C. perfringens* ATCC 19574, isolated from human pathological specimens and anaerobically grown in a medium containing no bile acid conjugates, contain an active peptide bond hydrolase which is specific for a group of naturally occurring bile acid conjugates. Through subsequent work by Nair *et al.* (1967) the clostridial enzyme, cholylglycine hydrolase (EC 3.5), was partially purified and several enzymatic properties were elucidated. The Km values for glycochenodeoxycholic acid, glycodeoxycholic acid, glycocholic acid, taurochenodeoxycholic acid, taurodeoxycholic acid, and taurocholic acid in $0.01\,M$ acetate buffer (pH 5.6) were 1.4×10^{-2}, 1.2×10^{-3}, 3.6×10^{-3}, 3.0×10^{-3}, 3.5×10^{-3}, and $3.7 \times 10^{-2}\,M$, respectively. Glycodehydrocholic acid (3,7,12-trioxo-5β-cholan-24-oylglycine), the trioxo analog of glycocholic acid which was used as substrate, and 3,7,12-trioxo-5β-cholan-24-oic acid inhibited the cleavage of glycocholic acid, and cholic acid exhibited competitive product inhibition. The enzyme showed a requirement for the presence of both a terminal carboxyl group in the side chain and free hydroxyl groups in the cholane nucleus. The activity was inhibited by sulfhydryl group inhibitors such as *p*-chloromercuribenzoate and iodoacetate. The purified enzyme retained full activity after storage for 8 weeks at $-20°$ and quantitatively recovered cholic acid from its conjugate without any oxidative attack of the hydroxyl groups in the resulting cholic acid molecule. These properties were applied to bile acid analysis by Nair and Garcia (1969) who developed a rapid method for the micro-determination of bile acids in biological fluids. Although the ordinary alkaline hydrolysis of conjugated bile acids usually resulted in some degradative losses, the enzymatic hydrolysis showed a quantitative recovery from the reaction mixture. The enzymatic method was applied to studies of the analysis of bile acids of rat liver and human liver by Okishio *et al.* (1967) and Nair *et al.* (1970), respectively. Similar enzymatic works have also been reported by Hill and associates (Hill and Drasar, 1968; Aries and Hill, 1970a). They found that the properties of hydrolases from the strains of *B. fragilis,* unidentified *Bacteroides* sp., unidentified *Bifidobacterium* sp., *Clostridium welchii,* and

S. *faecalis* were relatively similar to those of cholylglycine hydrolase isolated from C. *perfringens* by Nair *et al.* (1967) with respect to pH optimum, product inhibition, and the effect of inhibitors. The hydrolase preparations from the above organisms varied in the degree of substrate specificity: those from the strains of *Bifidobacterium* sp. and one of two strains tested of S. *faecalis* had no activity on taurine conjugates, while those from the strains of B. *fragilis* and *Bacteroides* sp. and one of two strains tested of C. *welchii* were equally active on both taurine and glycine conjugates. Although Norman and Widström (1964) previously reported the presence of a deconjugating enzyme(s) in cell-free rat cecal fluids, Hill and Drasar (1968) have considered that this extracellular activity probably originated from extracellular enzyme(s) from *Bifidobacterium* sp., since other strains tested produced only intracellular enzymes. However, the preparations of Norman and Widström (1964) could split taurine conjugates while those from *Bifidobacterium* sp. by Aries and Hill (1970a) showed no such activity.

As is apparent from the foregoing discussion, deconjugating microorganisms in the intestine are chiefly anaerobic. It is also known, however, that aerobically growing cultures of A. *aerogenes* (Ogura and Ozaki, 1964) and of some isolates from feces of man, rat, and chicken, and from soil (Yesair and Himmelfarb, 1970) are capable of splitting conjugated bile acids, although the identification of microorganisms was not conducted in the latter work.

C. DEHYDROXYLATION

The removal of hydroxyl groups from organic molecules by intestinal microorganisms was first demonstrated to occur with bile acids. The reaction is unique in the metabolism of steroids by animals and microorganisms. 7α-Dehydroxylation is the most important; it is involved in the formation of the typical secondary bile acids, deoxycholic acid and lithocholic acid, from the primary bile acids, cholic acid and chenodeoxycholic acid, respectively. The occurrence of *in vivo* 7α-dehydroxylation has been demonstrated in studies of the bile acid metabolism in the rabbit (Lindstedt and Sjövall, 1957), man (Lindstedt, 1957), and rat (Norman and Sjövall, 1958; Portman, 1958). Since deoxycholic acid is widespread in mammalian normal bile (Hayakawa, 1958; Haslewood, 1967), it is likely that the reaction occurs in many species. The mechanism for the 7α-dehydroxylation of cholic acid is schematically given in Fig. 2. The initial reaction is a diaxial *trans* elimination of the 7α-hydroxyl group and the 6β-hydrogen atom in the cholic acid (II) molecule, yielding $3\alpha,12\alpha$-dihydroxy-5β-chol-6-en-24-oic acid (IV). The Δ^6-acid is then

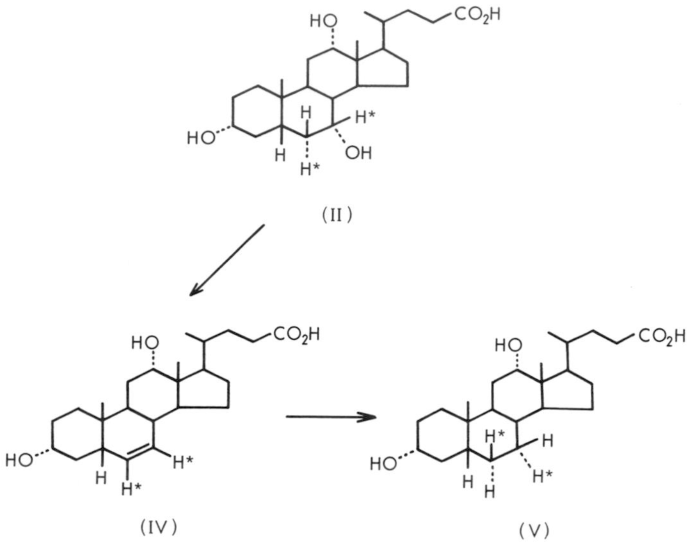

FIG. 2. Scheme for the mechanism of 7α-dehydroxylation of cholic acid (II) to yield deoxycholic acid (V).

reduced by *trans* hydrogenation at the 6α- and 7β-positions to give deoxycholic acid (V) (Samuelsson, 1960a). The same reaction mechanism appears to operate in the formation of hyodeoxycholic acid from hyocholic acid in pig intestine (Samuelsson, 1960b) and probably also in the microbiological 7α-dehydroxylation of chenodeoxycholic acid in various animals. Recently, however, Haslewood (1971) has found that the bile of germ-free pigs contains glycine and taurine conjugates of chenodeoxycholic acid, hyodeoxycholic acid, hyocholic acid, and probably cholic acid. The evidence indicates that hyodeoxycholic acid belongs to both primary and secondary bile acids in the pig, although the direct conversion of cholesterol into this acid in the conventional pig was not established (Samuelsson, 1959b).

The above-mentioned mechanistic studies were carried out with *in vivo* systems using bile acids specifically labeled with tritium because of the difficulty of isolation of the single bacterial strains responsible for 7α-dehydroxylation. The *in vivo* results were at first reproduced in *in vitro* systems with mixed cultures of anaerobic intestinal organisms from rat (Norman and Bergman, 1960; Cocucci and Ferrari, 1963a) and man (Norman and Shorb, 1962; Cocucci and Ferrari, 1963b). Portman *et al.* (1962) were the first to isolate a pure culture of the organisms responsible for the 7α-dehydroxylation of cholic acid from rat cecum. However, the strain showed activity on the first two transfers only. Shortly after, single strains of *C. bifermentans, E. coli,* and *P. aeruginosa* were isolated from human feces as bacteria capable of 7α-dehydroxylating cholic acid (Cocucci and Ferrari, 1964, 1965), but these strains lost the activity after serial transfers as did those of Portman *et al.* (1962). In spite of considerable effort, Carini *et al.* (1967) were unsuccessful in their search for biochemical factors involved in the loss of the activity by transfer. Consequently, they considered that the ready 7α-dehydroxylation *in vivo* by intestinal flora is controlled by complicated unknown factors and that the reaction can be reproduced *in vitro* only with mixed cultures. On the basis of this notion, Ferrari and colleague selected a mixed subculture from human feces through serial dilutions and obtained a highly selected mixed culture (Ferrari, 1967, 1969; Ferrari and Pacini, 1968). The selected culture effected the complete *in vitro* conversion of cholic acid into only deoxycholic acid and consisted of only six bacterial species: two species of *Clostridium,* three of *Streptococcus,* and one of *Micrococcus.*

Gustafsson *et al.* (1966) isolated eight single strains of strictly anaerobic microorganisms capable of 7α-dehydroxylating chenodeoxycholic acid from rat and human feces. These strains were tentatively classified as members of the tribe Lactobacilleae by Midtvedt (1967). The strains could also remove the 7α-hydroxyl group of cholic acid, but the resulting deoxycholic acid was further metabolized to a complex mixture of products (Gustafsson *et al.,* 1966; Midtvedt and Norman, 1968a). In contrast to free bile acids, taurine and glycine conjugates of cholic acid could not be transformed to the corresponding conjugated deoxycholic acid by one of these strains in either *in vitro* systems or *in vivo* tests with monocontaminated rats, while taurocholic acid was converted into deoxycholic acid in rats di- and polycontaminated with both deconjugating bacteria and 7α-dehydroxylating organisms (Midtvedt and Norman, 1968a; Gustafsson *et al.,* 1968). Therefore, the conjugated primary bile acids excreted into the intestine appear to be deconjugated prior to dehydroxylation. Midtvedt and Norman (1968b) have found that 7α-dehydroxylating organisms are not present in the contents of the small intestine but occur in the cecum and feces. The same authors (1967) collected a large number of strains known as intestinal inhabitants from international culture collections and examined their activity; they could not find any strain having the *in vitro* ability to remove the 7α-hydroxyl group from either cholic acid or chenodeoxycholic acid. In addition, it has been recently reported that many strains isolated from the digestive tracts of the mouse (Suzuki, 1970) and the rat (Dickinson *et al.,* 1971) possess no such activity.

Through the work of Scandinavian workers (Midtvedt and Norman, 1967; Dickinson *et al.,* 1971), it can be surmised that 7α-dehydroxylation is a rare property in intestinal organisms and hence there is no widespread occurrence of 7α-dehydroxylating microorganisms among pure cultures isolated from intestinal contents or in the type cultures of intestinal microflora. However, Hill and colleagues have recently found the *in vitro* activity in many pure cultures of the human intestinal flora, including international type cultures (Hill and Drasar, 1968; Aries and Hill, 1970b). They demonstrated that strains of the genera *Bacteroides, Bifidobacterium, Clostridium, Enterococcus,* and *Veillonella* were capable of 7α-dehydroxylating cholic acid or chenodeoxycholic acid (or both). The subsequent work of Aries and Hill (1970b) has led to the first isolation of cell-free extracts with the activity from *Bacteroides fragilis* NCTC 9343, *C. welchii,* unidentified *Clostridium* sp. (possibly *C. sporogenes*), nonlactose-fermenting *E. coli,* and *S. faecalis.* The enzyme(s) was produced only by bacteria grown in a bile acid-containing medium with a pH above 6.5. The evidence indicates that the 7α-dehydroxylating enzyme(s) in these strains is inducible. Anaerobic conditions were required for the appearance of activity and the enzyme(s) could dehydroxylate cholic acid and chenodeoxycholic acid to a similar extent, while glycocholic acid and methyl cholate were not utilized as substrates. The activity was inhibited by Cu^{2+}, periodate, and iodoacetate. Midtvedt and Norman (1967) have reported that *B. fragilis* NCTC 9343 has no *in vitro* 7α-dehydroxylating activity, though Aries and Hill (1970b) have demonstrated the presence of the activity in this culture through the isolation of the enzyme(s) responsible for 7α-dehydroxylation. It is not clear to the author, however, what is responsible for this discrepancy.

Hattori and Hayakawa (1969) also isolated an anaerobic bacterium capable of 7α-dehydroxylating cholic acid from human feces and classified it as a member of the genus *Bacteroides.* In their subsequent work, they found that type cultures *Clostridium bifermentans* ATCC 9714 and *Clostridium sordelli* NCIB 6929 are responsible for the same transformation (Hayakawa and Hattori, 1970). More recently, the author obtained, through the courtesy of Novotný, seven strains of nonpathogenic *C. sordellii* and sixteen strains of *C. bifermentans* used in his taxonomic study (Novotný, 1969). These strains were examined for their *in vitro* 7α-dehydroxylating activity, and it was found that all of the strains of *C. sordellii,* except for a urease-negative strain S_{21}, had the expected activity but no strains of *C. bifermentans* showed such activity (Hattori and Hayakawa, 1972). The result was in good agreement with their early view that the 7α-dehydroxylating activity might be one of the taxonomic characters defining differences between *C. sordellii* and *C. bifermentans* (Hayakawa and Hattori, 1970).

It has been demonstrated that the 7β-isomer of cholic acid is transformed *in vivo* to the same extent as cholic acid to yield deoxycholic acid (Samuelsson, 1960c) and the same transformation also occurs with a mixed culture of human fecal organisms (Ferrari, 1967). However, the mechanism of the 7β-dehydroxylation and its relation to the elimination of the 7α-hydroxyl group are not known.

Allocholic acid is the major acidic biliary metabolite of cholestanol (Karavolas *et al.*, 1965; Noll and Elliott, 1967). Hofmann and Mosbach (1964) have identified glycoallodeoxycholic acid as an important component of gallstones from rabbits fed a diet of 1% cholestanol. Mosbach and collaborators extended this work and found that the stone formation is preventable by oral administration of the antibiotic neomycin (Hofmann *et al.*, 1968) and also that allocholic acid is transformed to allodeoxycholic acid by the intestinal flora of rabbits (Hofmann *et al.*, 1969). These results clearly suggest that intestinal organisms play an important role in the formation of gallstones in this species. Subsequently, Bokkenheuser *et al.* (1969) isolated an anaerobic organism capable of 7α-dehydroxylating both cholic acid and allocholic acid from rabbit feces and identified it as *Bacteroides* sp. The organism was very similar to one of the strains of the Scandinavian workers (Midtvedt, 1967; Midtvedt and Norman, 1968a), although it differed in a few characteristics.

Although Ali *et al.* (1966) have provided evidence for the presence of 5ξ-cholan-24-oic acid in human feces, no information regarding its precursor is available at the present time. In this connection it is of interest to note that Hill and colleagues have identified deoxycholic acid, lithocholic acid, 3α,12α-dihydroxy-7-oxo-5β-cholan-24-oic acid, and possibly 5ξ-cholan-24-oic acid as metabolites of cholic acid produced by pure cultures of *Bacteroides* sp. and *Clostridium* sp. isolated from human feces (Hill and Drasar, 1967; Aries *et al.*, 1969). The results suggest that microbiological 12α-dehydroxylation and possibly 3α-dehydroxylation of bile acids can occur *in vitro* and possibly *in vivo*. Therefore, it is presumed that 5ξ-cholan-24-oic acid in human feces mentioned above is a bacterial artifact of the primary bile acids, cholic acid and chenodeoxycholic acid. In addition, evidence for the occurrence of 12α-dehydroxylation in the intestine would place chenodeoxycholic acid, which was generally believed to be a major primary bile acid, in the position of both a primary and a secondary bile acid. However, it appears that further work is needed for a definite proof of the occurrence of the microbiological 3α- or 12α-dehydroxylation (or both) of bile acids in the intestine.

As will be mentioned in Section III,A,1, aerobically growing cultures of the soil microorganism *Arthrobacter* (*Corynebacterium*) *simplex* are able to transform cholic to deoxycholic acid derivatives (Hayakawa and Kurokawa, 1963; Hayakawa and Samuelsson, 1964). One of these is

12α-hydroxy-3-oxo-4-cholen-24-oic acid (X), which has been proposed by Kallner (1967a,b,c) as an intermediate in the reversible conversion of deoxycholic acid (V) into allodeoxycholic acid (XII) in rat intestine (cf. Fig. 4). Hence it is conceivable that limited amounts of cholic acid can be 7α-dehydroxylated to deoxycholic acid by the rat intestinal flora via 12α-hydroxyl-3-oxo-4-cholen-24-oic acid (X), although the conversion of cholic acid into compound (X) is not established in the rat. The possibility is supported by the work of Aries et al. (1971) who demonstrated the in vitro formation of Δ⁴-3-oxo bile acids from 3-oxo bile acids by Clostridium paraputrificum isolated from human feces. The 3-oxo bile acids could be transformed from deconjugated primary bile acids by intestinal flora as will be mentioned in the following subsection.

D. Oxidation of Alcohols to Ketones and the Reverse Reaction

In vitro oxidation-reduction by intestinal microorganisms was the earliest of studies made on the microbiological transformation of bile acids, and some publications on the subject appeared before 1940. An example of such a transformation is given in Fig. 3. Early work has been previously mentioned in reviews by Hayakawa (1958), Bergström et al. (1960), and Okuda (1961), and it may be summarized as follows: stepwise oxidation of the three hydroxyl groups of cholic acid by A. faecalis

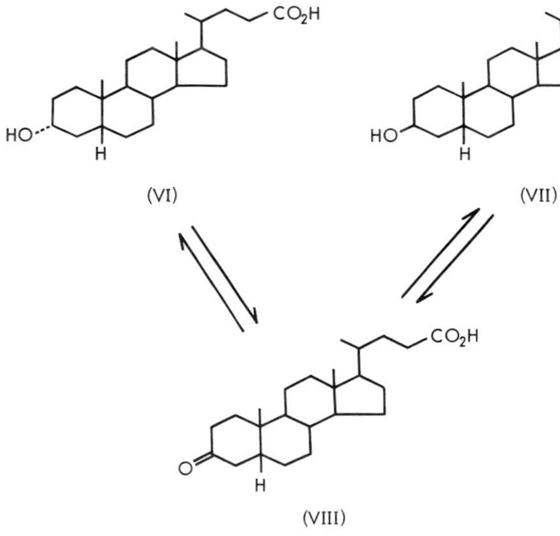

FIG. 3. Scheme for the reversible transformation of lithocholic acid (VI) and its 3β-isomer (VII) to 3-oxo-5β-cholan-24-oic acid (VIII).

and .E. coli, yielding 3α,12α-dihydroxy-7-oxo-5β-cholan-24-oic acid, 3α-hydroxy-7,12-dioxo-5β-cholan-24-oic acid, and 3,7,12-trioxo-5β-cholan-24-oic acid; reduction of the oxo group at the C-3, C-6, or C-7 position in some 5β-cholan-24-oic acid derivatives to the corresponding α-hydroxyl group by *E. coli* and *P. vulgaris*.

Although the hydroxyl groups of conjugated bile acids can be oxidized *in vitro* by intestinal microorganisms catalyzing the oxidation of free bile acids, the extent of such reaction is comparatively small (Midtvedt and Norman, 1968a; Gustafsson *et al.*, 1968; Aries and Hill, 1970b). It is generally accepted that the free bile acids resulting from deconjugation of the conjugated primary and secondary bile acids are exposed to microbiological oxidation-reduction in the intestine.

In vitro oxidation of cholic acid to 3α,12α-dihydroxy-7-oxo-5β-cholan-24-oic acid by *E. coli* mentioned above was recently reconfirmed by several workers (Norman and Bergman, 1960; Portman *et al.*, 1962; Aries *et al.*, 1969; Suzuki, 1970; Aries and Hill, 1970b). The activity was also found in members of the family Bacteroidaceae isolated from rat cecum and the feces (Midtvedt and Norman, 1968b). The same authors (1967) have reported that the ability to oxidize the hydroxyl group at the C-3, C-7, or C-12 in lithocholic acid, chenodeoxycholic acid, and cholic acid is found in many type cultures belonging to the genera which are normally present in the intestinal tract of man and rat: namely, *Bacillus cereus*, *Bacteroides fragilis*, *B. necrophorus*, *Clostridium difficile*, *C. perfringens*, *Escherichia coli*, *Eubacterium cadaveris*, *E. lentum*, *E. minutum*, *E. parvum*, *E. quintum*, and .E. ventriosum. All these strains tested, capable of oxidizing the hydroxyl groups at the C-3 of lithocholic acid and chenodeoxycholic acid, could reduce the 3-oxo groups to 3β-hydroxyl groups. Aries and Hill (1970b) have recently reported in preliminary form that several strains of human intestinal flora are responsible for the reduction of a 3- or 12-oxo group to the corresponding β-hydroxyl group. More recently, Dickinson *et al.* (1971) have reported that many facultative or strictly anaerobic strains isolated from the digestive tract of rats possess the *in vitro* or *in vivo* ability to perform oxidation-reduction of the hydroxyl groups of lithocholic acid, chenodeoxycholic acid, and cholic acid. They found the *in vitro* ability to oxidize either hydroxyl group of cholic acid in cultures of several genera: *Clostridium*, *Endosporus*, *Eubacterium*, *Escherichia*, *Lactobacillus* (homofermentative species), *Ramibacterium*, *Sphaerophorus*, and *Streptococcus* (strictly anaerobic species), although no definite structure of the transformation products was established. Some of the strains also produced mainly 3α-hydroxy-7-oxo-5β-cholan-24-oic acid and 3β,7α-dihydroxy-5β-cholan-24-oic acid from chenodeoxycholic acid and 3-oxo-5β-cholan-24-oic acid and 3β-hydroxy-5β-cholan-24-oic acid from lithocholic acid, respectively. It might be of interest to note that in this study the obvious transformation of cholic acid was observed in rats monocontaminated with a strain of *Bifidobacterium* sp. unable to oxidize this acid *in vitro*, while two strains of *Clostridium* sp. capable of *in vitro* oxidation of the same acid showed no *in vivo* transformation ability.

Although bile acids containing 7β-hydroxyl groups have been isolated from human and dog feces (cf. Section II,F), no intestinal microorganisms responsible for the reduction of 7-oxo groups to the corresponding 7β-hydroxyl groups are known, though liver enzymes can catalyze the reaction (Samuelsson, 1959a; Gustafsson *et al.*, 1960). Therefore, it appears that reabsorbed 7-oxo bile acids are reduced to 7β-hydroxy bile acids in the liver and then reexcreted into the intestine to constitute the components of fecal bile acids.

Dehydroxylating microorganisms discussed in a preceding subsection also catalyze the oxidation-reduction of free bile acids, including dehydroxylated bile acids. The strains of Gustafsson *et al.* (1966) produced 3α-hydroxy-7-oxo-5β-cholan-24-oic acid, 7α-hydroxy-3-oxo-5β-cholan-24-oic acid, lithocholic acid, and 3-oxo-5β-cholan-24-oic acid from chenodeoxycholic acid. The same strains could oxidize cholic acid to 3α,12α-dihydroxy-7-oxo-5β-cholan-24-oic acid and also reduce the oxo groups in both 3-oxo-5β-cholan-24-oic acid and 3α-hydroxy-7-oxo-5β-cholan-24-oic acid to the corresponding α-hydroxyl groups (Midtvedt and Norman, 1968a). Hill and colleagues have reported that many dehydroxylating bacteria belonging to the genera *Bacteroides, Bifidobacterium, Clostridium, Enterobacterium,* and *Enterococcus* are responsible for the oxidation-reduction of bile acids (Aries *et al.*, 1969; Aries and Hill, 1970b). They also observed the reduction of 12-oxo groups to the corresponding 12α-hydroxyl groups by some human intestinal organisms. A strain of Bokkenheuser *et al.* (1969) could convert cholic acid into 3α,12α-dihydroxy-7-oxo-5β-cholan-24-oic acid, deoxycholic acid, 3α-hydroxy-12-oxo-5β-cholan-24-oic acid, and 12α-hydroxy-3-oxo-5β-cholan-24-oic acid. Hayakawa and colleague observed the formation of deoxycholic acid and 3α,12α-dihydroxy-7-oxo-5β-cholan-24-oic acid from cholic acid by several strains of their 7α-dehydroxylating bacteria, *Bacteroides* sp. and *Clostridium sordellii* (Hattori and Hayakawa, 1969, 1972; Hayakawa and Hattori, 1970).

The oxidation-reduction of bile acids is also effected by microorganisms with the ability to split conjugated bile acids. The following type cultures possess the ability: *Bacteroides fragilis, B. necrophorus, Clostridium difficile, C. perfringens, Eubacterium cadaveris, E. minutum, E. quintum, E. ventriosum,* and *Streptococcus faecalis* (Midtvedt and Norman, 1967;

Aries and Hill, 1970a,b). In addition, *Bifidobacterium* sp., *C. welchii,* *Endosporus* sp., and homofermentative *Lactobacillus* sp. also have the same ability (Aries and Hill, 1970a,b; Dickinson *et al.,* 1971).

As was discussed above, it appears that, like deconjugating microorganisms, organisms capable of effecting oxidation-reduction of bile acids are widespread in intestinal flora. It is of particular interest that the most prevalent organism in human feces, *B. fragilis,* is responsible for all of the main transformations of bile acids in the intestine, although 7α-dehydroxylating ability was not observed by Norman and colleague (cf. Section II,C).

Enzymes catalyzing the oxidation-reduction of bile acids have been isolated from several bacteria, although they have not been completely purified because of their instability. Hayaishi *et al.* (1955) were the first to isolate a crude NAD+-dependent 3α-hydroxycholanoyl dehydrogenase from *Escherichia freundii* which catalyzes a reversible dehydrogenation of the 3α-hydroxyl group (cf. Fig. 3). The partially purified enzyme showed an absolute specificity for 3-hydroxyl groups and a requirement for the presence of a terminal carboxyl group in the side chain (Hayaishi *et al.,* 1960). Portman *et al.* (1962) obtained cell-free extracts from *E. coli* which can oxidize the 7α-hydroxyl group of cholic acid. Recently, Aries and Hill (1970b) isolated three kinds of dehydrogenase, specific for the 7α-hydroxyl group, the 3α- and 7α-hydroxyl groups, and the 3α- and 12α-hydroxyl groups, from *B. fragilis, Bifidobacterium* sp., *C. welchii,* and *E. coli.* Enzymes produced by the Gram-negative bacteria, *E. coli* and *B. fragilis,* were NAD+-dependent, while those from Gram-positive bacteria, *C. welchii* and *Bifidobacterium* sp.,required NADP+.

Iwata and Yamasaki (1964) found that a bacterial dehydrogenase was useful for the determination of bile acids in blood. The finding was further developed by several workers and hence 3α-hydroxysteroid dehydrogenase (EC 1.1.1.50) from *Pseudomonas testosteroni* has been used for the determination of various C_{19}, C_{21}, and C_{24} steroids with 3α-hydroxyl group in biological fluids (cf. Palmer, 1969).

E. MISCELLANEOUS REACTIONS

The efficient conversion of 3α,12α-dihydroxy-7-oxo-5β-cholan-24-oic acid into deoxycholic acid in the intestine of both rats and rabbits has been reported by Norman and Sjövall (1958) and Bergström *et al.* (1959), respectively. The same *in vitro* transformation has been demonstrated with a mixed culture of the human intestinal microflora (Ferrari, 1967). However, the 7-oxo acid cannot be an important intermediate in the *in vivo* transformation of cholic acid into deoxycholic acid, since the

7β-hydrogen of cholic acid is retained in deoxycholic acid (cf. Fig. 2). In addition, there are as yet no grounds for believing that a mechanism exists for the direct *in vitro* reduction of the 7-oxo group to the corresponding methylene group by microorganisms. Therefore, it is possible that the 7-oxo acid is reduced to cholic acid and then subjected to the microbiological 7α-dehydroxylation, yielding deoxycholic acid.

The formation of allodeoxycholic acid from deoxycholic acid by intestinal microorganisms has been reported by Danielsson *et al.* (1963b) and Kallner (1967a,b). The transformation is reversible and a possible pathway has been proposed by Kallner (1967a,b,c) (cf. Fig. 4): i.e., deoxycholic acid (V) → 12α-hydroxy-3-oxo-5β-cholan-24-oic acid (IX) → 12α-hydroxy-3-oxo-4-cholen-24-oic acid (X) → 12α-hydroxy-3-oxo-5α-cholan-24-oic acid (XI) → allodeoxycholic acid (XII). In this connection Aries *et al.* (1971) have recently reported that microorganisms capable of dehydrogenating 3-oxo-5β-cholan-24-oic acids to the corresponding Δ^4- and $\Delta^{1,4}$-derivatives are present in human feces. Growing cultures and washed

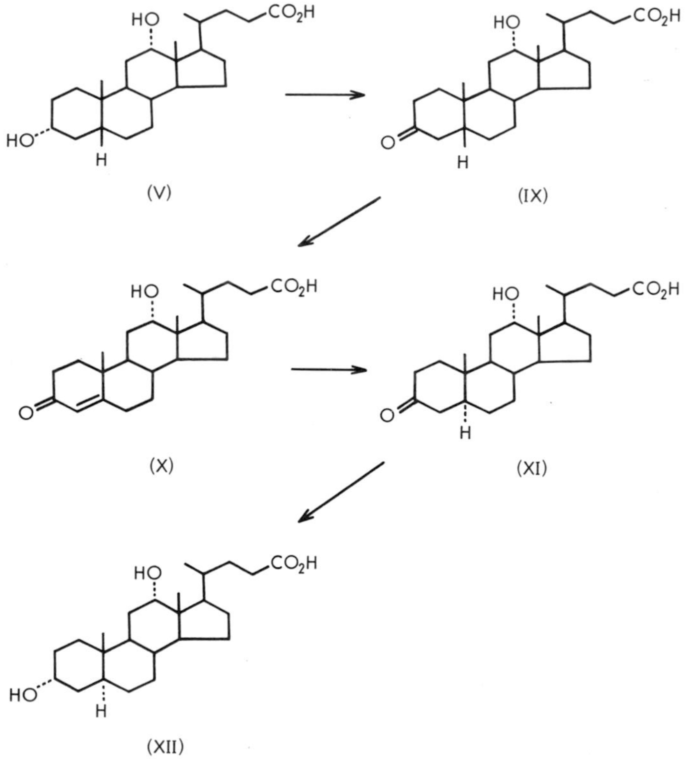

FIG. 4. Proposed scheme for the conversion of deoxycholic acid (V) into allodeoxycholic acid (XII) by intestinal microorganisms.

cell suspensions of one of the isolates, *C. paraputrificum,* converted 3-oxo-5β-cholan-24-oic acid and 3,12-dioxo-5β-cholan-24-oic acid into 3-oxo-4-cholen-24-oic acid and 3,12-dioxo-4-cholen-24-oic acid respectively, while cell-free extracts of the same strain produced the corresponding $\Delta^{1,4}$-derivatives from the same substrates. Although not conclusively shown, they have presumed the presence of two kinds of enzymes in this strain, 3-oxo-5β-steroid Δ^1-dehydrogenase (EC 1.3.99.4) and 3-oxo-5β-steroid Δ^4-dehydrogenase (EC 1.3.99.5). The latter resembled a Δ^4-dehydrogenase from *P. testosteroni,* reported by Davidson and Talalay (1966), in some properties but differed in pH optimum. In a preliminary form the same authors have reported that the clostridial Δ^4-dehydrogenase produces only 3-oxo-5β-cholan-24-oic acids from the corresponding 3-oxo-4-cholen-24-oic acids, while many strains of other genera can reduce the same substrates to the corresponding 3-oxo-5α-cholan-24-oic acids. The finding affords a bacteriological basis for a proposed pathway for the allodeoxycholic acid formation and also indicates that the microbiological epimerization at C-5 of bile acids with 5β-configuration proceeds by way of Δ^4-3-oxo bile acids (cf. Fig. 4).

Most of the microbiological reactions so far mentioned such as deconjugation, dehydroxylation, and dehydrogenation generally have a common character in that they involve reduction in molecular size. The number of reports dealing with synthetic reactions by intestinal micro organisms is limited. Norman (1964) found that the 3β-isomer of 3,12-dihydroxy-5β-cholan-24-oic acids in human feces occurred as esters, probably with long-chain fatty acids. Norman and Palmer (1964) also found that almost all of 3β-hydroxy-5β-cholan-24-oic acid transformed in human intestine from lithocholic acid was esterified through the action of intestinal flora. Although the substrates are not bile acids, a similar microbiological transformation of steroids has been reported by Rosenfeld *et al.* (1967) who showed the esterification of coprostanol and cholesterol by fecal microorganisms.

In addition to these, there are other reports dealing with the action of intestinal organisms on bile acids. These will be briefly discussed below. When some strains isolated from human feces were incubated with cholic acid under aerobic conditions, they were able to degrade cholic acid to nonsteroidal compounds (Ferrari, 1967). However, a search for the degradation products was not made. Norman and Palmer (1964) found that lithocholic acid was transformed in human intestine into an unsaturated derivative of 5ξ-cholan-24-oic acid, possibly 5β-chol-2(or 3)-en-24-oic acid. More recently, Palmer (1971) has reported that lithocholic acid is metabolized to the sulfate esters of its glycine and taurine conjugates in the rat, and that the ester bond is hydrolytically cleaved by intestinal

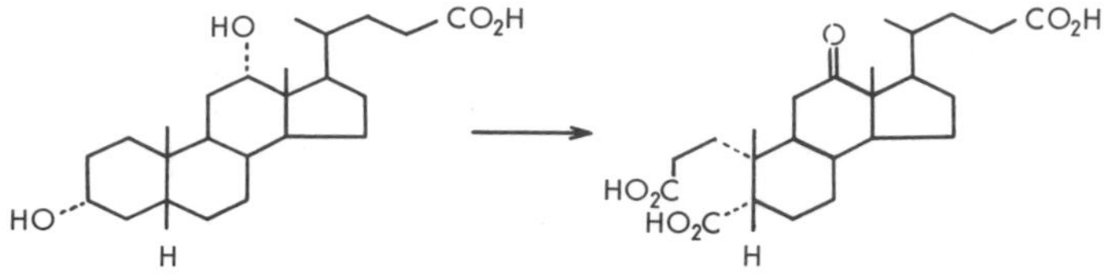

FIG. 5. Proposed scheme for the oxidative degradation of deoxycholic acid (V) to deoxybilianic acid (XIII) in human liver.

flora as in hydrolysis of the peptide bond in conjugated bile acids; whereas drastic alkaline hydrolysis of the ester bond results in the formation of several modified products, presumed to be 3β-hydroxy-5β-cholan-24-oic acid, a cholen-24-oic acid, and others (Palmer and Bolt, 1971). Consequently there is a possibility that the origin of the unsaturated acid, previously detected as the lithocholic acid metabolite by Norman and Palmer (1964), is the above sulfate ester.

Howe and Bosshardt (1962) found that hyodeoxycholic acid and lithocholic acid could prevent the hypercholesterolemia in mice caused by feeding both cholesterol and cholic acid. The effect of lithocholic acid was decreased by an administration of antibacterial agents, while that of hyodeoxycholic acid was not influenced by such agents. Thus, they considered that the antihypercholesterolemic effect of lithocholic acid might be due to its metabolites formed through the action of intestinal microorganisms. However, nothing is known about the nature of the metabolites.

Dirscherl and Pelzer (1970) have recently reported the very interesting finding that deoxybilianic acid (12-oxo-3,4-seco-5β-cholan-3,4,24-trioic acid, XIII) is one of the components of normal human urine (cf. Fig. 5). They have isolated 12.4 mg of this acid from 500 liters of the hydrolyzed urine as crystals and considered that the compound is probably formed through the hepatic oxidative degradation of deoxycholic acid (V). However, it appears that one cannot neglect the role of intestinal microorganisms in the biogenetic pathway, including oxidation of the hydroxyl groups of deoxycholic acid.

F. NATURE OF EXCRETORY PRODUCTS OF BILE ACIDS

According to the current concepts, bile acids are excreted under normal conditions mainly with the feces. After administration of 24-^{14}C-labeled bile acids insignificant amounts of isotope are recovered in expired carbon dioxide. The excretion of bile acids with urine constitutes approximately 1%, 4%, and 10% of the total amount excreted in the rat, man, and rabbit, respectively (Danielsson and Tchen, 1968). The composition of fecal bile acids which occur as a wide range of molecular forms is really complicated, as would be expected from the foregoing discussion. A variety of bile acids have been isolated from or detected in the feces of animals, including man.

In connection with studies on the influence of diet and drugs on the metabolism and turnover of cholesterol, the human fecal bile acids have been most extensively studied. The main bile acids have been identified as: deoxycholic acid; lithocholic acid; $3\beta,12\alpha$-dihydroxy-5β-cholan-24-oic acid; 3α-hydroxy-12-oxo-5β-cholan-24-oic acid; 3β-hydroxy-12-oxo-5β-cholan-24-oic acid; and 3β-hydroxy-5β-cholan-24-oic acid (Danielsson *et al.*, 1963a; Eneroth *et al.*, 1968). In addition to these, a large number of other components, although individually present in small amounts, have been identified: namely, cholic acid; allocholic acid; chenodeoxycholic acid; $3\alpha,7\beta,12\alpha$-trihydroxy-5β-cholan-24-oic acid; $3\beta,7\alpha,12\alpha$-trihydroxy-5β-cholan-24-oic acid; $3\beta,7\beta,12\alpha$-trihydroxy-5β-cholan-24-oic acid; $3\alpha,12\alpha$-dihydroxy-7-oxo-5β-cholan-24-oic acid; $3\alpha,7\alpha$-dihydroxy-12-oxo-5β-cholan-24-oic acid; $3\alpha,7\beta$-dihydroxy-5β-cholan-24-oic acid; $3\alpha,12\beta$-dihydroxy-5β-cholan-24-oic acid; $3\beta,7\alpha$-dihydroxy-5β-cholan-24-oic acid; $3\beta,12\beta$-dihydroxy-5β-cholan-24-oic acid; 3α-hydroxy-7-oxo-5β-cholan-24-oic acid; 7α-hydroxy-3-oxo-5β-cholan-24-oic acid; 12α-hydroxy-3-oxo-5β-cholan-24-oic acid; 3,12-dioxo-5β-cholan-24-oic acid; and 3-oxo-5β-cholan-24-oic acid (Eneroth *et al.*, 1966a,b). Ali *et al.* (1966) have also provided evidence for the presence of 7β-hydroxy-5β-cholan-24-oic acid and 5ξ-cholan-24-oic acid in human feces.

Through the work of several investigators, it is evident that the quantitatively most significant bile acids in human feces are deoxycholic acid and lithocholic acid (Danielsson *et al.*, 1963a; Eneroth *et al.*, 1966a; Ali *et al.*, 1966; Connor *et al.*, 1969). However, the individual quantitation of mixed bile acids in feces has not been established because of the complexity of the mixture. In other words, an entirely satisfactory method for the quantitative determination of individual fecal bile acids is still lacking in spite of considerable efforts by several investigators (cf. Eneroth and Sjövall, 1971). Consequently, the amount of bile acids in feces is usually measured as the total daily excretion. The values reported by a number of workers vary within a very wide range, 50 to over 2000 mg per day. The differences between the reported values appear to be ascribed to differences in methodology. For further discussion of the problem, the reader should consult an article by Grundy *et al.* (1965) which contains a comprehensive tabulation of the various procedures and results obtained by other workers. However, the values recently reported by several groups of investigators agree relatively well; these are from 50 to 650 mg per day (Grundy *et al.*, 1965; Ali *et al.*, 1966; Eneroth *et al.*, 1968; Evrard and Janssen, 1968; Connor *et al.*, 1969).

Although animal feces have not been as intensively studied as human feces, there are a few papers dealing with the fecal bile acids of experimental animals. Norman and Sjövall (1958) found the presence of 3α-hydroxy-12-oxo-5β-cholan-24-oic acid, deoxycholic acid, and 3α,12α-dihydroxy-7-oxo-5β-cholan-24-oic acid in rat feces. 3β-Hydroxy-5β-cholan-24-oic acid, 3β-hydroxy-12-oxo-5β-cholan-24-oic acid, 3α-hydroxy-12-oxo-5β-cholan-24-oic acid, 3β,12α-dihydroxy-5β-cholan-24-oic acid, deoxycholic acid, and 3α,12α-dihydroxy-5α-cholan-24-oic acid (β-lagodeoxycholic acid) were isolated from rabbit feces and the presence of lithocholic acid was also detected (Danielsson *et al.*, 1962, 1963b). Hirofuji (1965) demonstrated the presence of chenodeoxycholic acid, deoxycholic acid, cholic acid, 3α,7β,12α-trihydroxy-5β-cholan-24-oic acid, 3β,7α,12α-trihydroxy-5β-cholan-24-oic acid, and 3α,12α-dihydroxy-7-oxo-5β-cholan-24-oic acid in dog feces, in most cases through their isolation. Two kinds of bile acid containing a 7β-hydroxyl group occur in feces as mentioned above; the metabolic origin has been already discussed in Section II,D.

No transformation products which suggest the occurrence of cleavage of carbon-carbon bonds in the bile acid molecule by intestinal microorganisms have been isolated from feces so far.

III. Microbiological Degradation of Bile Acids *in Vitro*

Many investigators have studied the *in vitro* metabolism of bile acids using various microorganisms which are not intestinal inhabitants. Early works in the field dealt mainly with the oxidation-reduction of hydroxyl groups (cf. Section II,D), and the results have been previously summarized in reviews by Hayakawa (1958) and Okuda (1961). The period from 1961 to 1967 was rather quiet with respect to further evolution of the subject. On the other hand, there was considerable activity in the study of both the biosynthesis of bile acids and the microbiological degradation of other steroids during this period and excellent results were obtained (cf. Charney and Herzog, 1967; Danielsson and Tchen, 1968).

Current studies in the field have led to the conclusion that some steroidal compounds are probably degraded to carbon dioxide and water by microorganisms via a common intermediate. This section will discuss how cholic acid is degraded to compounds still containing C and D rings intact, including the common intermediate, which are then further degraded to lower molecular weight products, although the nature of these

has not been conclusively established. Also, the possibility that microbiological degradation of the ring structure of bile acids occurs in animals will be briefly considered. During the last decade, however, there
have been only a limited number of reports dealing with the degradative
reaction of bile acids *in vitro*. Consequently this section will contain some
unpublished data by the author and colleagues which will be published
in the near future.

A. CHARACTERIZATION OF DEGRADATION PRODUCTS

Although a wide variety of the metabolites of bile acids have been isolated and identified so far, the aim of this subsection is to show the
precursor-product relationship among the metabolites through a schematic description of their structures and not to give a detailed discussion
on the structure determination. Nevertheless, the structure of unpublished
compounds will be briefly discussed.

1. *Cholic Acid Degradation with Arthrobacter simplex*

Incubation of cholic acid (II) with *Arthrobacter simplex* in a medium
containing the acid at a concentration of 0.2% produced several metabolites (cf. Fig. 6): namely, 7α,12α-dihydroxy-3-oxo-5β-cholan-24-oic acid
(XIV); 7α,12α-dihydroxy-3-oxo-4-cholen-24-oic acid (XV); 12α-hydroxy
3-oxo-4,6-choladien-24-oic acid (XVI); 12α-hydroxy-3-oxo-4-cholen-24-
oic acid (X); and 12α-hydroxy-3-oxo-1,4-choladien-24-oic acid (XVII)
(Hayakawa and Kurokawa, 1963; Hayakawa and Samuelsson, 1964). However, Hayakawa *et al.* (1967, 1969b) found that when the concentration of
cholic acid was 0.1%, the above products formed in an early stage of the
incubation were further metabolized by this organism and (4R)-4-[4α-
(2-carboxyethyl)-3aα-perhydro-7aβ-methyl-5-oxoindan-1β-yl]valeric acid
(XVIII) accumulated as the major degradation product. In addition,
(+)-(5R)-5-methyl-4-oxo-octane-1,8-dioic acid (XIX) has also been isolated as its racemate in the latter case (Hayakawa and Fujiwara, 1969).

2. *Degradation of Other Bile Acids by Arthrobacter simplex*

Lithocholic acid was degraded to (4R)-4-[4α-(2-carboxyethyl)-3aα-
perhydro-7aβ-methyl-5-oxoindan-1β-yl]valeric acid (XVIII) by *A. simplex* in the same manner as cholic acid (Hayakawa *et al.*, 1969b). In contrast, disubstituted 5β-cholan-24-oic acids such as chenodeoxycholic acid,
deoxycholic acid, and hyodeoxycholic acid could not be utilized by the
same organism. However, Hayakawa and Fujiwara (1972) have found
that when mixtures of each of these acids and cholic acid are incubated

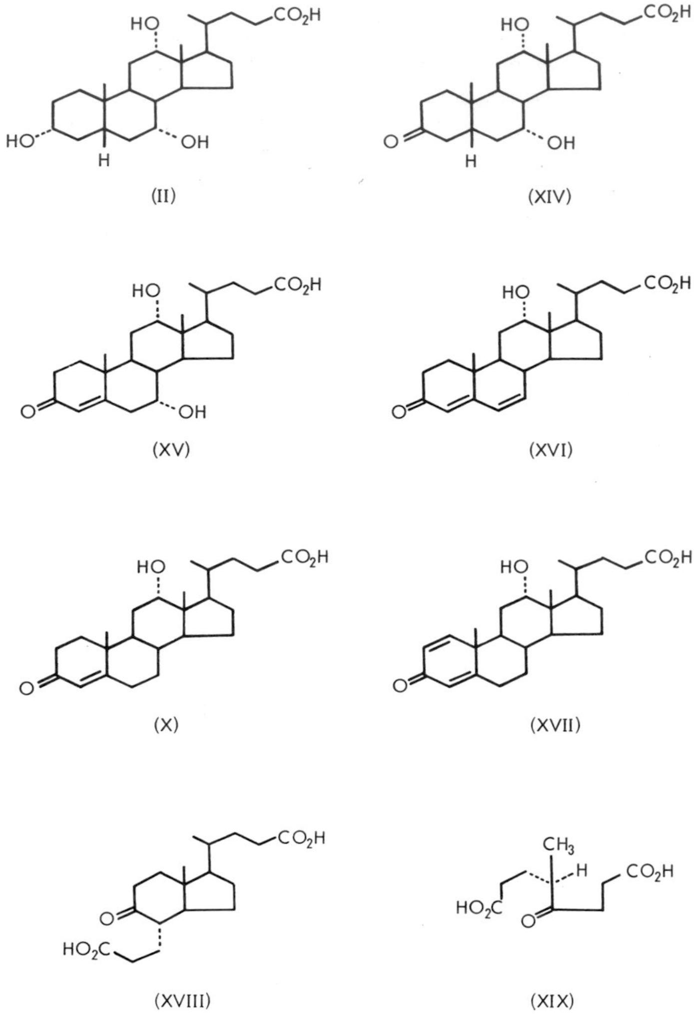

FIG. 6. Structures of the products of degradation of cholic acid (II) by *Arthrobacter simplex*.

with the organism, both bile acids are utilized as carbon sources and compound (XVIII) accumulates as the major degradation product. The finding shows that the above disubstituted 5β-cholan-24-oic acids can be utilized by *A. simplex* only in the presence of cholic acid, and it does not indicate the conversion of these acids into compound (XVIII) by this organism. The function of cholic acid in the utilization of other bile acids is unknown, and further investigation should be made from the viewpoint of the evolution of bacterial enzyme systems that attack bile acids.

3. *Further Degradation of (4R)-4-[4α-(2-Carboxyethyl)-3aα-perhydro-7aβ-methyl-5-oxoindan-1β-yl]valeric Acid (XVIII) by Corynebacterium equi*

Although Hayakawa *et al.* (1968) expected that incubation of (4R)-4-[4α-(2-carboxyethyl)-3aα-perhydro-7aβ-methyl-5-oxoindan-1β-yl]valeric acid (XVIII) with *A. simplex* would result in the formation of its further degradative products, they could detect no apparent degradative intermediates and recovered only starting materials. However, the same authors have found that *C. equi* is able to utilize this compound as its only source of carbon and to produce a variety of metabolites (cf. Fig. 7): namely, *N*-{(4R)-4-[4α-(2-carboxyethyl)-3aα-perhydro-7aβ-methyl-5-oxoindan-1β-yl]valeryl}alanine (XX*a*); *N*-{(4R)-4-[4α-(2-carboxyethyl)-3aα-perhydro-7aβ-methyl-5-oxoindan-1β-yl]valeryl}glutamic acid (XX*b*); N^{α}-{(4R)-4-[4α-(2-carboxyethyl)-3aα-perhydro-7aβ-methyl-5-oxoindan-1β-yl]valeryl}glutamine (XX*c*); and *N*-{(4R)-4-[4α-(2-carboxyethyl)-3aα-perhydro-7aβ-methyl-5-oxoindan-1β-yl]-valeryl}-*O*-acetylhomoserine (XX*d*). Subsequent work of Hayakawa and Fujiwara (1972) had led to

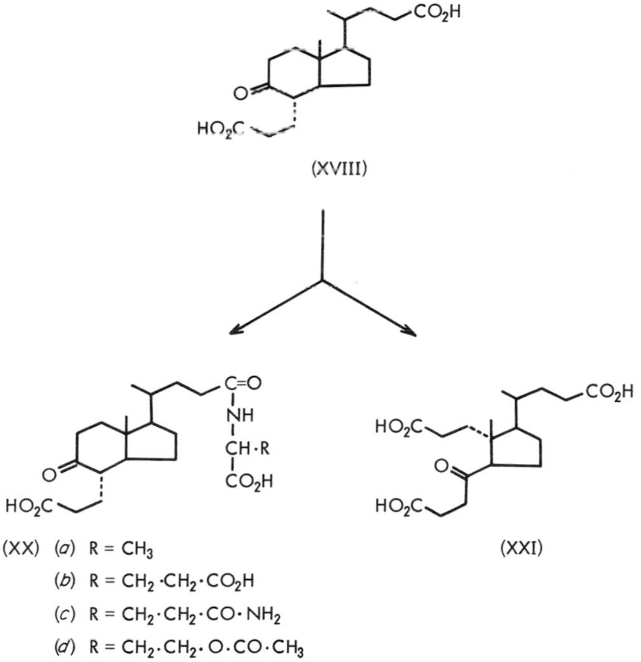
CO₂H
O
HO₂C
(XVIII)
C=O
NH
CH·R
CO₂H
O
HO₂C
HO₂C
CO₂H
O
HO₂C
(XX) (a) R = CH₃
(b) R = CH₂·CH₂·CO₂H
(c) R = CH₂·CH₂·CO·NH₂
(d) R = CH₂·CH₂·O·CO·CH₃
(XXI)

FIG. 7. Scheme for the metabolism of (4R)-4-[4α-(2-carboxyethyl)-3aα-perhydro-7aβ-methyl-5-oxoindan-1β-yl]valeric acid (XVIII) by *Corynebacterium equi*, yielding its amino acid conjugates (XX*a*–XX*d*) and compound (XXI).

the isolation of (4R)-4-[2α-(2-carboxyethyl)-3β-(3-carboxypropionyl)-2β-methylcyclopent-1β-yl]valeric acid (XXI) as one of the degradation products of compound (XVIII) by *C. equi*. The structure was chemically established as follows: the dimethyl ester of compound (XVIII) was oxidized with *m*-chloroperbenzoic acid to yield methyl (4R)-4-[2α-(2-carboxyethyl)-3β-(1(S)-hydroxy-3-methoxycarbonylpropyl)-2β-methyl-cyclopent-1β-yl]valerate ε-lactone. After alkaline hydrolysis of the lactone, the resulting trisodium salt of the hydroxytricarboxylic acid was oxidized with ruthenium tetroxide to afford the trisodium salt of an oxotricarboxylic acid. The free acid, recovered in the usual manner, was completely identical with the product (XXI) obtained from growing cultures (cf. Fig. 15).

4. *Cholic Acid Degradation with Streptomyces rubescens*

Previous works of Hayakawa *et al.* (1958b,c) showed that *S. rubescens* was able to convert cholic acid into 7α,12α-dihydroxy-3-oxo-4-cholen-24-oic acid (XV); 7α-hydroxy-3,12-dioxo-4-cholen-24-oic acid (XXII); 12α-hydroxy-3-oxo-4,6-choladien-24-oic acid (XVI); 3,12-dioxo-4,6-choladien-24-oic acid (XXIII); and some unknown metabolites (cf. Fig. 8). Recently, Hayakawa *et al.* (1969a) have found that as in the cholic acid degradation with *A. simplex* (cf. Section III,A,1), additional incubation of *S. rubescens* with cholic acid results in further degradation of these products with the subsequent formation of (4R)-4-[4α-(2-carboxyethyl)-3aα-perhydro-7aβ-methyl-5-oxoindan-1β-yl]valeric acid (XVIII) and a variety of nitrogen-containing products: namely, (4R)-4-[4α-(2-carboxyethyl)-3aα-perhydro-7aβ-methyl-5-oxoindan-1β-yl]-valeramide (XXIV); (4R)-4-(2,3,4,6,6aβ,7,8,9,9aα,9bβ-decahydro-6aβ-methyl-3-oxo-1*H*-cyclopenta[*f*]quinolin-7β-yl)valeric acid (XXVa); (4R)-4-(2,3,4,6,6aβ,7,8,9,9aα,9bβ-decahydro-6aβ-methyl-3-oxo-1*H*-cyclopenta[*f*]quinolin-7β-yl)valeramide (XXVb); (3S)-3-(2,3,4,6,6aβ,7,8,9,9aα,9bβ-decahydro-6aβ-methyl-3-oxo-1*H*-cyclopenta[*f*]-quinolin-7β-yl)butan-2-one (XXVc); (2S)-2-(2,3,4,6,6aβ,7,8,9,9aα,9bβ-decahydro-6aβ-methyl-3-oxo-1*H*-cyclo-penta[*f*]quinolin-7β-yl)propionic acid (XXVd); and 2,3,4,6,6aβ,7,8,9,9aα,9bβ-decahydro-6aβ-methyl-1*H*-cyclopenta[*f*]quinoline-3,7-dione (XXVI).

5. *Cholic Acid Degradation with Corynebacterium equi, Mycobacterium mucosum, and Streptomyces gelaticus*

Severina *et al.* (1968, 1969a) have reported that *M. mucosum* is capable of transforming cholic acid to various products (cf. Fig. 9): namely, 7α,12α-dihydroxy-3-oxo-4-cholen-24-oic acid (XV); 7α-hydroxy-3,12-dioxo-4-cholen-24-oic acid (XXII); (20S)-7α,12α-dihydroxy-3-oxo-4-preg-nene-20-carboxylic acid (XXVII); (20S)-7α-hydroxy-3,12-dioxo-4-preg-

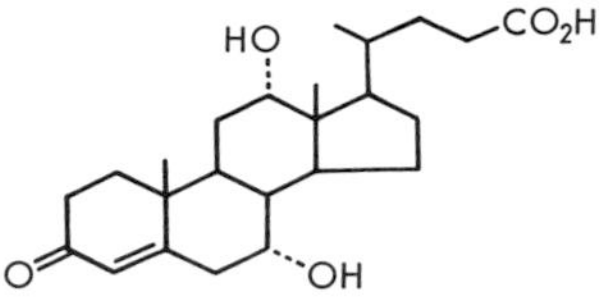

(XV)

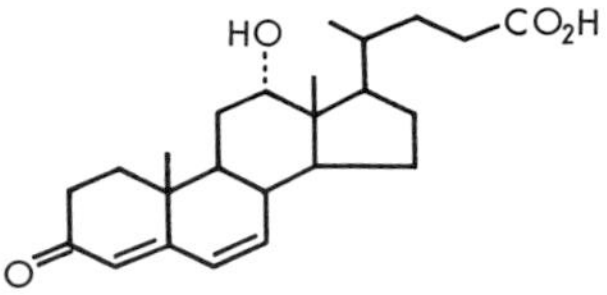

(XVI)

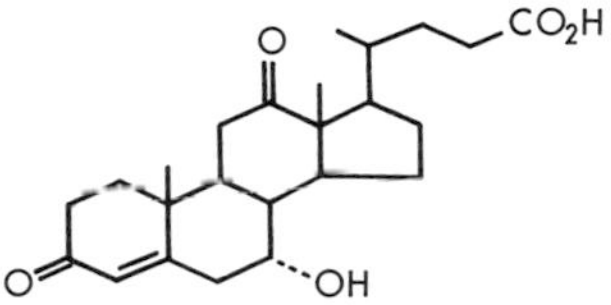

(XXII)

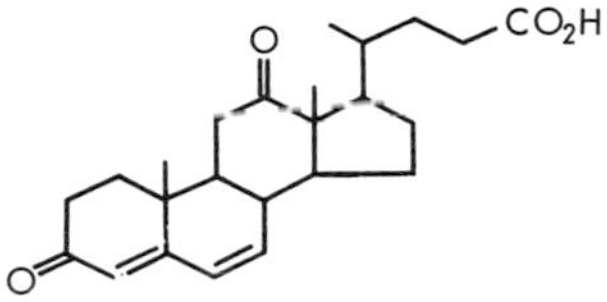

(XXIII)

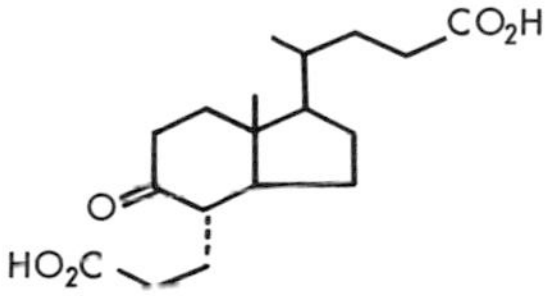

(XVIII)

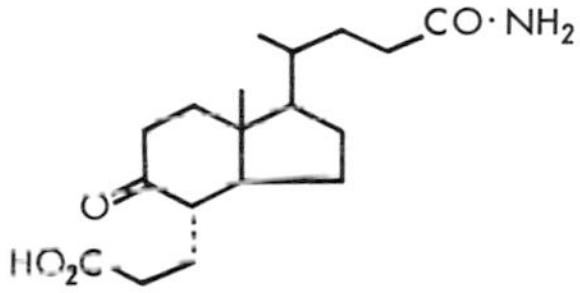

(XXIV)

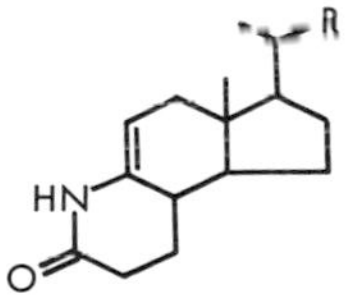

(XXV) (*a*) $R = CH_2\cdot CH_2\cdot CO_2H$

(*b*) $R = CH_2\cdot CH_2\cdot CO\cdot NH_2$

(*c*) $R = CO\cdot CH_3$

(*d*) $R = CO_2H$

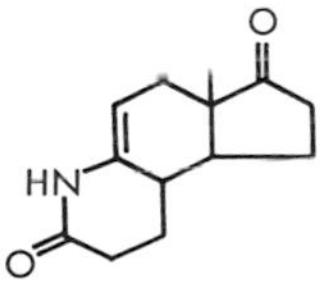

(XXVI)

FIG. 8. Structures of the products of degradation of cholic acid by *Streptomyces rubescens.*

nene-20-carboxylic acid (XXVIII); (20S)-7α-hydroxy-3,12-dioxo-4,8-pregnadiene-20-carboxylic acid (XXIX); and (20S)-7-hydroxy-3,12-dioxo-4,6-pregnadiene-20-carboxylic acid (XXX). In addition to these metabolites, evidence for the presence of 3,12-dioxo-24-nor-4,6-choladien-23-oic acid (XXXI) as one of the degradation products has also been provided

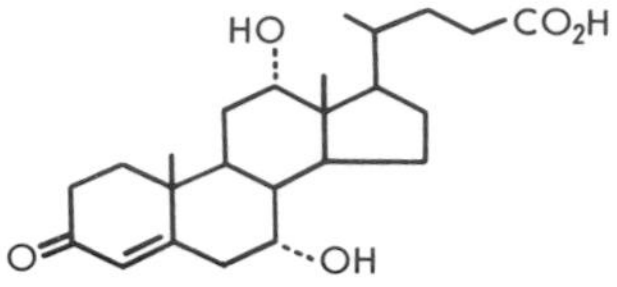

(XV)

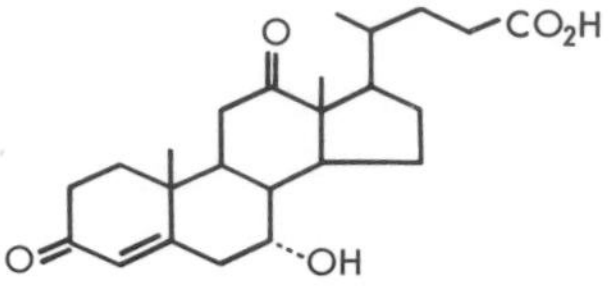

(XXII)

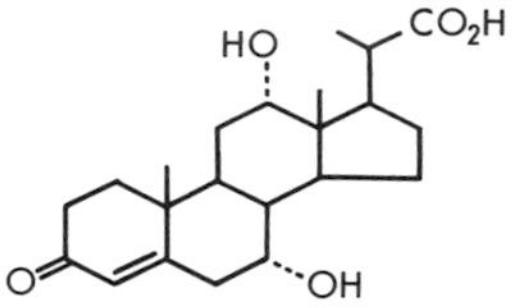

(XXVII)

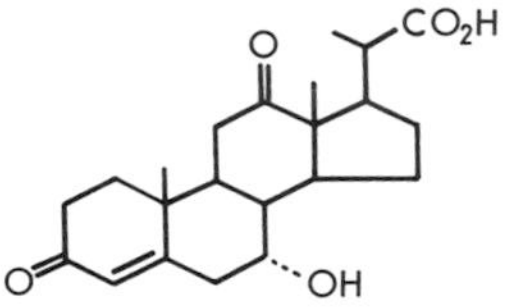

(XXVIII)

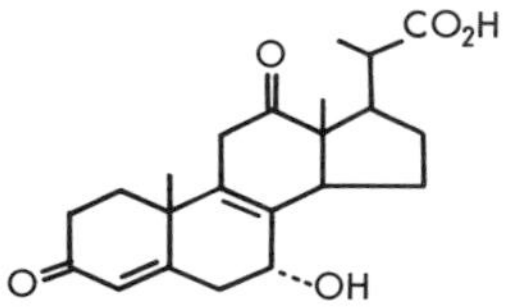

(XXIX)

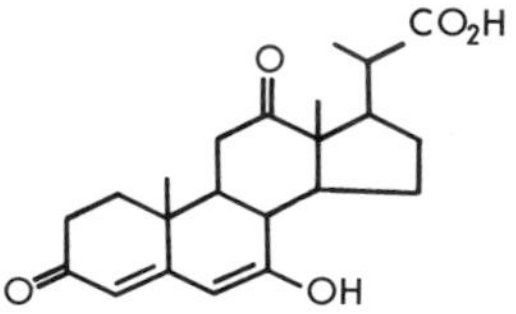

(XXX)

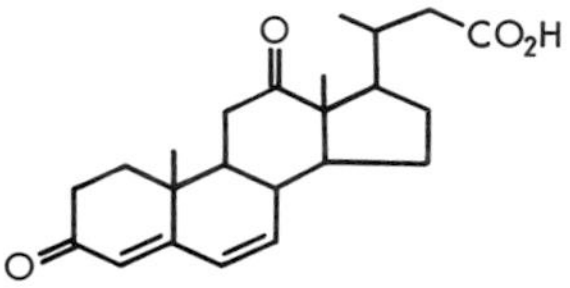

(XXXI)

FIG. 9. Structures of the products of degradation of cholic acid by *Corynebacterium equi, Mycobacterium mucosum,* and *Streptomyces gelaticus.*

through mass spectral studies on the metabolites. Although (20S)-12α-hydroxy-3-oxo-4,6-pregnadiene-20-carboxylic acid, 3,12-dioxo-4,6-choladien-24-oic acid, and 12α-hydroxy-3-oxo-4,6-choladien-24-oic acid were isolated and identified, the same authors (1969a) postulated that these dienoic acids containing a $\Delta^{4,6}$-3-oxo group, including compound (XXXI), are artifacts formed through dehydration of the 7α-hydroxyl groups in the corresponding compounds containing a Δ^{4}-7α-hydroxy-3-oxo structure.

Hayakawa *et al.* (1957) previously isolated and identified (20S)-7α-hydroxy-3,12-dioxo-4-pregnene-20-carboxylic acid (XXVIII) as one of the products of degradation of cholic acid by S. *gelaticus*. Recently, Hayakawa and Fujiwara (1972) have studied the action of *C. equi* on cholic acid to learn whether or not the organism is able to degrade cholic acid to (4R)-4-[4α-(2-carboxy-ethyl)-3aα-perhydro-7aβ-methyl-5-oxo-indan-1β-yl]valeric acid (XVIII). They found that *C. equi*, when cultured in a medium containing 0.5% cholic acid as the sole source of carbon, produced 7α-hydroxy-3,12-dioxo-4-cholen-24-oic acid (XXII); (20S)-7α, 12α-dihydroxy-3-oxo-4-pregnene-20-carboxylic acid (XXVII); and (20S)-7α-hydroxy-3,12-dioxo-4-pregnene-20-carboxylic acid (XXVIII) as the main metabolites, while cholic acid was rapidly metabolized without the apparent accumulation of compound (XVIII) or any other degradation products when its concentration was 0.1%.

6. Deoxycholic Acid Degradation with Mycobacterium mucosum

Bacterium sp. (Schatz *et al.*, 1949), *Streptomyces* spp. (Saburi *et al.*, 1956), and *A. simplex* (cf. Section III,A,2) were able to utilize cholic acid but they could not utilize deoxycholic acid as the sole source of carbon. As far as the author is aware, there is no record up to the present dealing with the microbiological cleavage of the carbon-carbon bond in deoxycholic acid. However, Severina *et al.* (1969b) have reported that deoxycholic acid (V) is degraded to (20S)-3,12-dioxo-4-pregnene-20-carboxylic acid (XXXIIa) and (20S)-9α-hydroxy-3,12-dioxo-4-pregnene-20-carboxylic acid (XXXIIb) by *M. mucosum* (cf. Fig. 10).

7. Further Degradation of 3-(3aα Perhydro-7aβ methyl-1,5-dioxoindan-4α-yl)propionic Acid (XXXIII) by Streptomyces rubescens

Streptomyces rubescens can metabolize cholic acid to various degradation products (cf. Section III,A,4). Of these, however, the metabolite with the lowest molecular weight, 2,3,4,6,6aβ,7,8,9,9aα,9bβ-decahydro-6aβ-methyl-1*H*-cyclopenta[*f*]quinoline-3,7-dione (XXVI), was not utilized by this organism. To explain this problem, Hayakawa and Hashi-

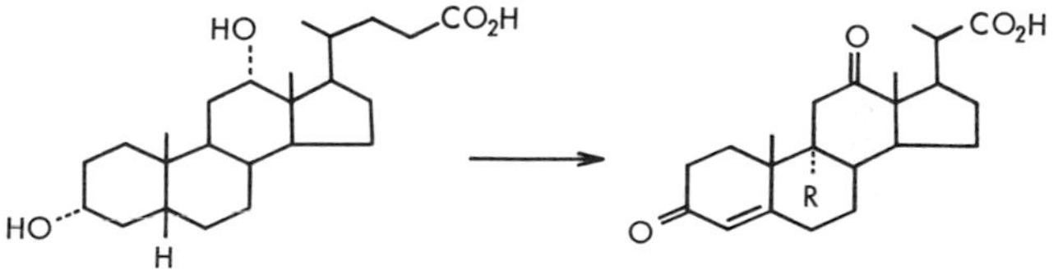

(V)   (XXXII) (*a*) R = H

(*b*) R = OH

FIG. 10. Scheme for the degradation of deoxycholic acid (V) to compounds (XXXIIa) and (XXXIIb) by *Mycobacterium mucosum*.

moto (1969) suggested that compound (XXVI) might not necessarily be a reaction intermediate in the degradative pathway of cholic acid but a metabolite in a side pathway, and that the precursor of compound (XXVI) might be 3-(3aα-perhydro-7aβ-methyl-1,5-dioxoindan-4α-yl)-propionic acid (XXXIII), which can be easily utilized by this organism. This view is strongly supported by the evidence that (4R)-4-(2,3,4,6, 6aβ,7,8,9,9aα,9bβ-decahydro-6aβ-methyl-3-oxo-1H-cyclopenta[f]quinolin-7β-yl)valeric acid (XXVa) and its possible precursor, (4R)-4-[4α-(2-carboxyethyl)-3aα-perhydro-7aβ-methyl-5-oxoindan-4α-yl]valeric acid (XVIII), which correspond to compounds (XXVI) and (XXXIII) respectively, were isolated simultaneously in the cholic acid degradation with S. *rubescens* (cf. Section III,A,4). Also, that exposure of compound (XXXIII) to the same organism resulted in the formation of compound (XXVI) in very low yield supports this (Hayakawa *et al.*, 1969a). On the basis of this consideration, Hayakawa and Hashimoto (1969) have studied in some detail the degradation of compound (XXXIII) by S. *rubescens* and isolated and identified (+)-(5R)-5-methyl-4-oxo-octane-1,8-dioic acid (XIX) as one of the degradation products (cf. Fig. 11). Subsequently, Hayakawa and colleagues have isolated and identified 3-(3aα-perhydro-1β-hydroxy-7aβ-methyl-5-oxoindan-4α-yl)propionic acid (XXXIV), 3-(3aα-perhydro-5α-hydroxy-7aβ-methyl-1-oxoindan-4α-yl)-propionic acid δ-lactone (XXXV), and 3-(3aα-perhydro-5α-hydroxy-7aβ-methyl-1-oxoindan-4α-yl)-*trans*-acrylic acid (XXXVI) as degradation products (Hashimoto *et al.*, 1969). The first two compounds (XXXIV) and (XXXV) were already identified as the metabolites of compound (XXXIII) produced by *Nocardia corallina* (Lee and Sih, 1967).

In addition to these metabolites, (3R)-3-(3aα-perhydro-5α-hydroxy-7aβ-methyl-1-oxoindan-4α-yl)-3-hydroxypropionic acid δ-lactone (XXXVII) and 3-(4-hydroxy-3-methyl-6-oxo-6H-pyran-2-yl)propionic acid (XXXVIII) have been recently isolated and identified as degradation products of compound (XXXIII), although the latter was isolated as methyl 3-(4-methoxy-3-methyl-6-oxo-6H-pyran-2-yl)propionate (XLIII) (Hayakawa and Hashimoto, 1972). These structures were chemically established as shown in Fig. 12. Dehydrogenation of compound (XXXV) with 2,3-dichloro-5,6-dicyano-1,4-benzoquinone (DDQ) gave an α,β-unsaturated lactone, 3-(3aα-perhydro-5α-hydroxy-7aβ-methyl-1-oxoindan-4α-yl)-*cis*-acrylic acid δ-lactone (XXXIX). Treatment of the lactone with alkali introduced stereospecifically a hydroxyl group into the C-3 of the acrylic acid side chain, yielding compound (XL) which corresponds to an epimer of the metabolite (XXXVII) isolated from growing cultures. This stereochemical relation was established through oxidation of both compounds by Jones reagent to the same β-oxolactone, 3-(3aα-perhydro-5α-hydroxy-7aβ-methyl-1-oxoindan-4α-yl)-3-oxopropionic acid δ-lactone

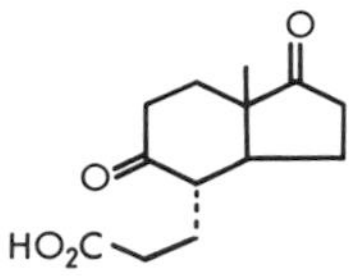

(XXXIII)

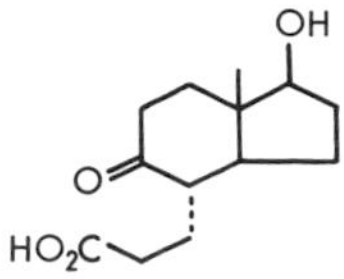

(XXXIV)

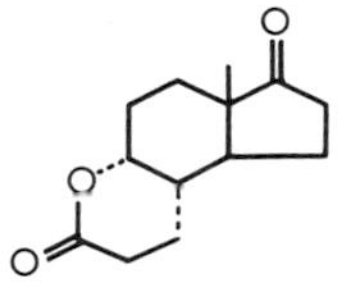

(XXXV)

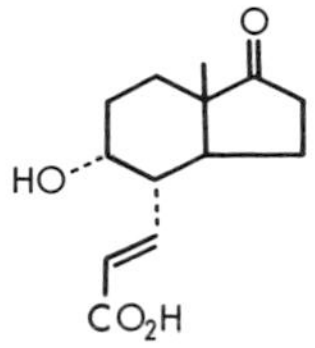

(XXXVI)

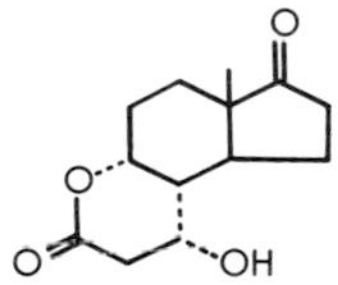

(XXXVII)

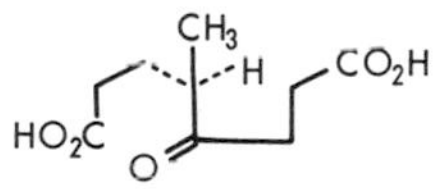

(XIX)

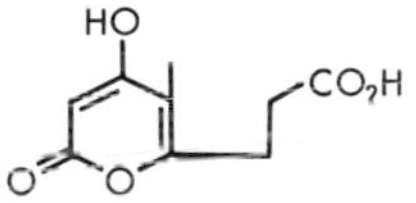

(XXXVIII)

FIG. 11. Structures of the products of degradation of 3-(3aα-perhydro-7aβ-methyl-1,5-dioxoindan-4α-yl)propionic acid (XXXIII) by *Streptomyces rubescens*.

(XLI). The stereochemistry of the hydroxyl group in compound (XXXVII) has been tentatively assigned as an R-configuration. The 3-methyl analog (XLII) of 4-methoxy-6-oxo-6*H*-pyran-2-ylacetic acid known in the literature (Douglas and Money, 1968) was synthesized in a similar manner. The Arndt-Eistert reaction of the α-pyrone derivative (XLII) gave the desired compound (XLIII), completely identical with the metabolite isolated from growing cultures.

B. POSSIBLE PATHWAYS FOR BILE ACID DEGRADATION

There is presently no information regarding the manner in which bile acids are completely degraded to carbon dioxide and water by micro-organisms. As was mentioned in a preceding subsection, however, a wide

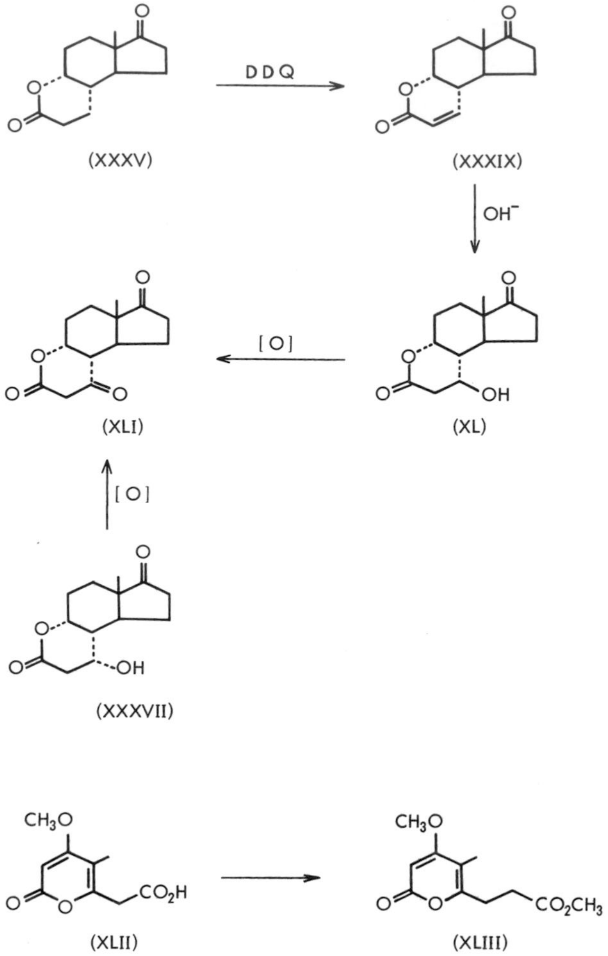

Fig. 12. Scheme for the structure determination of compounds (XXXVII) and (XLIII).

variety of metabolites of bile acids by microorganisms have been isolated and identified, and some of their structures appear to have a precursor-product relationship. In addition, through the works of Dodson, Sih, Schubert, Talalay, and their collaborators much knowledge on the micro-biological degradation of C_{19} and C_{21} steroidal compounds has been accumulated (cf. Charney and Herzog, 1967). Consequently, one can predict possible pathways for bile acid degradation. Although the pre-diction is mainly based on chemical logic, the representation of hypo-thetical pathways may be important for the further evolution of general problems in the microbiological degradation of various steroids including bile acids. Thus some aspects of these pathways will be discussed below with emphasis on the problems characteristic of bile acids.

1. Degradation of the Side Chain of Bile Acids

Since the first demonstration of the degradation of cholic acid to a derivative of pregnene-20-carboxylic acid by *S. gelaticus* (Hayakawa, 1954), a few additional examples of such type of the bile acid degradation, which probably proceeds in a manner analogous to the conventional fatty acid β-oxidation, have been found with the use of several species of fungi at Kazuno's laboratory (cf. Okuda, 1961). Recently, in the course of studies on the mechanism of degradation of the cholesterol side chain by microorganisms, Sih *et al.* (1968) found that acetic acid-1-^{14}C could be isolated as its S-benzylisothiuronium salt after exposure of lithocholic acid-24-^{14}C to *Nocardia restrictus*. In this experiment, they also found that 6,19-oxido-3-oxo-4-cholen-24-oic acid could be converted into (20S)-9α-hydroxy-6,19-oxido-3-oxo-4-pregnene-20-carboxylic acid by the same organism. The same authors also showed conversion of 6,19-oxido-3-oxo-4-cholen-24-oic acid into 6,19-oxido-4-androstene-3,17-dione by another *Nocardia* sp., although the substrate was not a naturally occurring bile acid. Shortening of the side chain of bile acids to that of pregnene-20-carboxylic acids has also been observed in the degradation of cholic acid and deoxycholic acid by *M. mucosum* (cf. Sections III,A,5 and III,A,6) and in that of cholic acid by *C. equi* (cf. Section III,A,5). In addition, Severina *et al.* (1969a) have detected 3,12-dioxo-24-nor 4,6-choladien-23-oic acid (XXXI) (probably in the culture broth as 7α-hydroxy-3,12-dioxo-24-nor-4-cholen-23-oic acid) as one of the products of degradation of cholic acid by *M. mucosum*. Considering the structure, they concluded that the α-oxidation of the side chain could occur in the cholic acid degradation. However, whether the mechanism for the loss of one or two carbon atoms from the side chain of bile acids by microorganisms is the same as that for conventional fatty acid α- or β-oxidation has not been established.

Hayakawa *et al.* (1957) indicated in their early work that cholic acid might be degraded, via C_{22} or C_{24} intermediates containing a Δ^4-7α-hydroxy-3-oxo structure, by several species of *Streptomyces*. In this connection it is of interest that all of the pregnene-20-carboxylic acids isolated so far as degradation products of bile acids contain a Δ^4-3-oxo group in their molecules. Thus it appears that a Δ^4-3-oxo group is introduced into the cholane nucleus prior to shortening of the side chain. In addition, as will be discussed in the following subsection, the introduction of a Δ^4-3-oxo group into the cholic acid molecule by *A. simplex* and *S. rubescens* is an early step in the microbiological ring A cleavage. Consequently, it is likely that this group may be an essential structure for shortening of the side chain and cleavage of the ring A of bile acids by microorganisms. However, it is not clear whether the actions of the enzymes responsible for these degradative reactions follow an obligatory order. It is possible that both reactions occur simultaneously and independently and that differences in the reaction rate and other unknown factors cause the accumulation of pregnene-20-carboxylic acids in metabolism by *C. equi, M. mucosum,* and *S. gelaticus* and that of perhydroindan derivatives in metabolism by *A. simplex* and *S. rubescens,* respectively.

2. Conversion of Cholic Acid into (4R)-4-[4α-(2-Carboxyethyl)-3aα-perhydro-7aβ-methyl-5-oxoindan-1β-yl]valeric Acid (XVIII)

Structures of the metabolites of cholic acid produced by *A. simplex* show the possibility that cholic acid (II) is degraded stepwise and that the first step leads to the formation of 7α,12α-dihydroxy-3-oxo-5β-cholan-24-oic acid (XIV). Although the metabolic relationship among the other metabolites, 7α,12α-dihydroxy-3-oxo-4-cholen-24-oic acid (XV); 12α-hydroxy-3-oxo-4,6-choladien-24-oic acid (XVI); 12α-hydroxy-3-oxo-4-cholen-24-oic acid (X); and 12α-hydroxy-3-oxo-1,4-choladien-24-oic acid (XVII), is not as yet elucidated, Hayakawa *et al.* (1967, 1969b) have tentatively proposed the following degradative sequence of cholic acid: cholic acid (II) → compound (XIV) → compound (XV) → compound (XVI) → compound (X) → compound (XVII). In the proposed pathway, the sequence (II) → (XIV) → (XV) → (XVI) has previously been proposed by Hayakawa *et al.* (1958a) for the degradation of cholic acid by *S. rubescens.* Reduction of compound (XVI) to compound (X) probably proceeds analogously to microbiological hydrogenation of the Δ^6 bond in 17β-hydroxy-4,6-androstadien-3-one reported by Tsong *et al.* (1964), and the last dehydrogenation step is a well-known reaction in many organisms, including *A. simplex* (cf. Charney and Herzog, 1967). Thus the proposed pathway may be the correct assignment but other routes to the same product are not excluded. Also whether the elimination of the 7α-hydroxyl group in compound (XV) by *A. simplex* and *S. rubescens* is enzyme-catalyzed or merely a purely chemical reaction has not been established. However, it may be catalyzed by enzymes as discussed in a previous work with *S. rubescens* (Hayakawa *et al.,* 1958a).

Since cholic acid was degraded by *A. simplex* and *S. rubescens* to the common metabolites, 7α,12α-dihydroxy-3-oxo-4-cholen-24-oic acid (XV); 12α-hydroxy-3-oxo-4,6-choladien-24-oic acid (XVI); and (4R)-4-[4α-(2-carboxyethyl)-3aα-perhydro-7aβ-methyl-5-oxoindan-1β-yl]valeric acid (XVIII), both organisms are probably able to degrade cholic acid to compound (XVIII) via a relatively similar route. In this connection 3,12-dioxo-4,6-choladien-24-oic acid (XXIII) was previously assigned as an intermediate in the sequence of degradation of cholic acid by S. *rubescens* (Hayakawa *et al.*, 1958a), but the assignment might be not correct, because in the degradation of cholic acid by A. *simplex*, the oxygen function at the C-12 may be eliminated as a hydroxyl group and not an oxo group as will be discussed later. On this question, Hashimoto *et al.* (1969) have interpreted that in S. *rubescens*, 7α,12α-dihydroxy-3-oxo-4-cholen-24-oic acid (XV) and 12α-hydroxy-3-oxo-4,6-choladien-24-oic acid (XVI) are probably in equilibrium with 7α-hydroxy-3,12-dioxo-4-cholen-24-oic acid (XXII) and 3,12-dioxo-4,6-choladien-24-oic acid (XXIII), respectively, and that compound (XVI) is probably further metabolized to compound (XVIII). Evidence supporting the interpretation has been reported by Severina *et al.* (1969a) who demonstrated a reversible conversion between 7α,12α-dihydroxy-3-oxo-4-cholen-24-oic acid (XV) and 7α-hydroxy-3,12-dioxo-4-cholen-24-oic acid (XXII) in M. *mucosum*.

Mainly through the works of Dodson, Sih, Talalay, and their associates the mechanism for the microbiological degradation of 4-androstene-3,17-dione (XLIV) to 3-(3aα-perhydro-7aβ-methyl-1,5-dioxoindan-4α-yl)-propionic acid (XXXIII) has been fully elucidated (Dodson and Muir, 1961a,b; cf. Sih and Whitlock, 1968). The degradative sequence is as follows (cf. Fig. 13): 4-androstene-3,17-dione (XLIV) → 1,4-androstadiene-3,17-dione (XLV) or 9α-hydroxy-4-androstene-3,17-dione (XLVI) → 9α-hydroxy-1,4-androstadiene-3,17-dione (XLVII, postulated intermediate) → 3-hydroxy-9,10-seco-1,3,5(10)-androstatriene-9,17-dione (XLVIII) → 3,4-dihydroxy 9,10-seco 1,3,5(10)-androstatriene-9,17-dione (XLIX) → 3-hydroxy-5,9,17-trioxo 4(5),9(10)-diseco 1(10),2-androstadien-4-oic acid (L, not isolated as this form) → 3-(3aα-perhydro-7aβ-methyl-1,5-dioxoindan-4α-yl)-propionic acid (XXXIII) and 2-oxo-*cis*-4-hexenoic acid (LI). The last C₆ compound is further metabolized to propionaldehyde and pyruvic acid via 4-hydroxy-2-oxo-hexanoic acid. Hayakawa *et al.* (1967, 1969b) have proposed that 12α-hydroxy-3-oxo-4-cholen-24-oic acid (X) and 12α-hydroxy-3-oxo-1,4-choladien-24-oic acid (XVII) are further metabolized to (4R)-4-[4α-(2-carboxyethyl)-3aα-perhydro-7aβ-methyl-5-oxoindan-1β-yl]valeric acid (XVIII) by A. *simplex* in analogy with the degradation of 4-androstene-3,17-dione mentioned above. However, if the proposed pathway is the actual one and no additional modification other than the ring A cleavage occurs, then the expected intermediate, which corresponds to 3-(3aα-perhydro-7aβ-methyl-1,5-dioxoindan-4α-yl)propionic acid (XXXIII) in the degradation of 4-androsten-3,17-dione, should be (4R)-4-[4α-(2-carboxyethyl)-3aα-perhydro-7α-hydroxy-7aβ-methyl-5-oxoindan-1β-yl]valeric acid (LIV) and not compound (XVIII). In connection with this question, Hayakawa *et al.* (1972) synthesized compound (LIV) and (4R)-4-[4α-(2-carboxyethyl)-3a,4,5,7a-tetrahydro-7aβ-methyl-5-oxoindan-1β-yl]valeric acid (LII) and

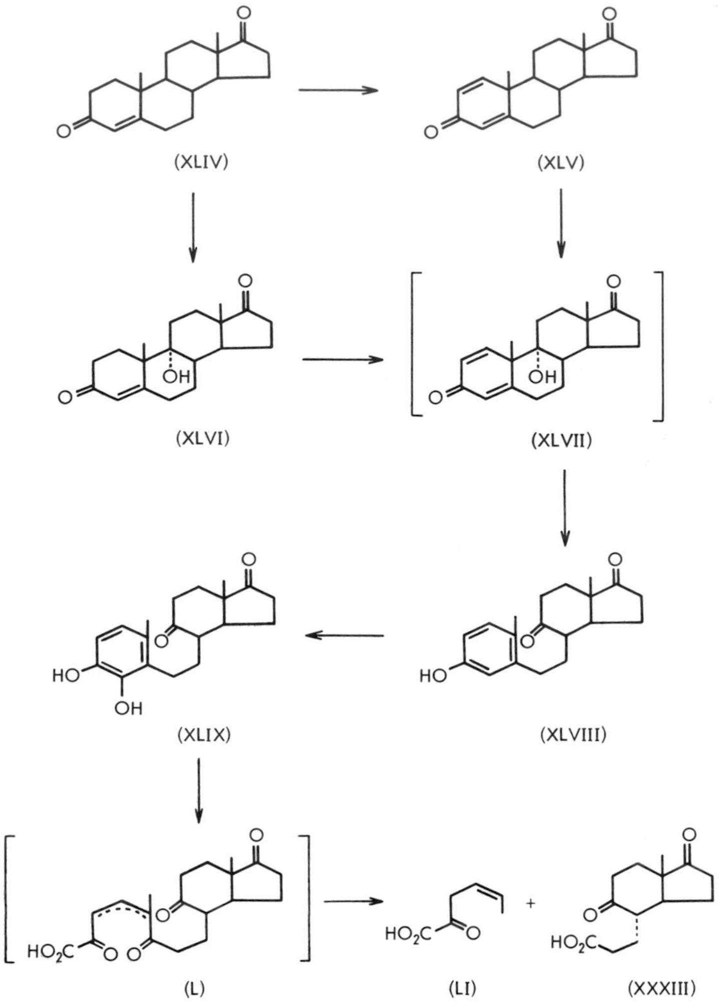

FIG. 13. Metabolic pathway for the microbiological degradation of 4-androstene-3,17-dione (XLIV).

showed that washed cell suspensions of A. *simplex* could transform compound (LIV) to compound (XVIII) via compound (LII) (cf. Fig. 14). They also observed that the transformation of compound (LIV) to compound (LII) appears to proceed faster in the presence of the cells than in their absence, indicating that the dehydration might be enzyme-catalyzed. Pan *et al.* (1969) have reported a similar enzymatic dehydration observed in the transformation of 9α-hydroxy-19-nor-4-androstene-3,17-dione by A. *simplex*. Thus, it is likely that one mechanism for the 12α-dehydroxylation observed in the degradation of cholic acid by A. *sim-*

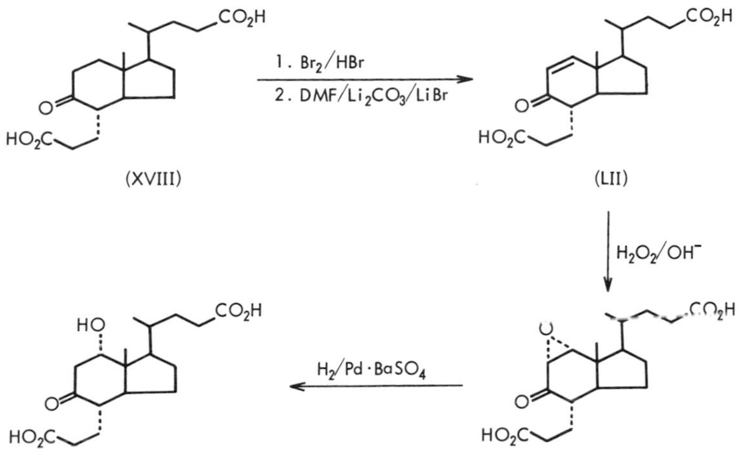

Fig. 14. Scheme for syntheses of compounds (LII) and (LIV).

plex and *S. rubescens* involves dehydration yielding a Δ^{11}-9-oxo (in the steroid skeleton: Δ^6-5-oxo in the perhydroindan skeleton) intermediate followed by hydrogenation. However, whether the substrate for dehydration is compound (LIV) itself or the 9,10-secosteroid intermediate(s) (or both) has not been established.

Chemical syntheses of compounds (LII) and (LIV) were carried out as follows (cf. Fig. 14): the dimethyl ester of compound (XVIII) was treated with bromine in acetic acid to yield its 6ξ-bromosubstituted derivative. The α-bromoketone was converted into the dimethyl ester of a carboxylic acid (LII) having an α,β-unsaturated oxo group by refluxing with lithium carbonate and lithium bromide in dimethylformamide (DMF) followed by hydrolysis with alkali to yield the desired compound (LII). Reaction of compound (LII) with alkaline hydrogen peroxide afforded (4R)-4-[4α-(2-carboxyethyl)-3aα-perhydro-7aβ-methyl-6α,7α-oxido-5-oxoindan-1β-yl]valeric acid (LIII), which was submitted to catalytic reduction with the use of palladium-barium sulfate to afford the desired compound (LIV). The stereochemistry of a newly introduced hydroxyl group at the C-7 was deduced from the nuclear magnetic resonance spectrum.

3. *Conversion of Cholic Acid into (20S)-7α-Hydroxy-3,12-dioxo-4,8-pregnadiene-20-carboxylic Acid (XXIX)*

Severina *et al.* (1969a) isolated 7α,12α-dihydroxy-3-oxo-4-cholen-24-oic acid (XV) as one of the metabolites of cholic acid (II) produced by *Mycobacterium mucosum,* and showed that it is converted into 7α-hydroxy-3,12-dioxo-4-cholen-24-oic acid (XXII), (20S)-7α-hydroxy-3,12-dioxo-4-pregnene-20-carboxylic acid (XXVIII), and (20S)-7α-hydroxy-3,12-dioxo-4,8-pregnadiene-20-carboxylic acid (XXIX) by the same organism. On the basis of the result, they have proposed the following degradative pathway of cholic acid by *M. mucosum* (cf. Fig. 9): cholic acid (II) → compound (XV) → compound (XXII) → compound (XXVIII) → compound (XXIX). A degradative sequence, (II) → (XV) → (XXII) → (XXVIII), is similar to that previously postulated for the cholic acid degradation with *Streptomyces gelaticus* (Hayakawa *et al.*, 1957) and several species of fungi (cf. Okuda, 1961), and it is also possible that 7α,12α-dihydroxy-3-oxo-5β-cholan-24-oic acid may be placed between compounds (II) and (XV) in the sequence as in the cholic acid degradation with *Arthrobacter simplex* (cf. Section III,B,2). The conversion of compound (XV) into compound (XXIX) is the first example of the microbiological introduction of a Δ^8 bond into the cholane nucleus, although the mechanism is unknown. The fate of the Δ^8 bond in the further degradation of compound (XXIX) is a very interesting problem.

4. Further Degradation of (4R)-4-[4α-(2-Carboxyethyl)-3aα-perhydro-7aβ-methyl-5-oxoindan-1β-yl]valeric Acid (XVIII)

a. With Corynebacterium equi. It is evident that incubation of cholic acid with *Arthrobacter simplex* results in the formation of (4R)-4-[4α-(2-carboxyethyl)-3aα-perhydro-7aβ-methyl-5-oxoindan-1β-yl]valeric acid (XVIII) and that on further incubation the metabolite is gradually degraded without the apparent accumulation of detectable amounts of further degradation products (Hayakawa *et al.*, 1969b). In addition, since the first report on the microbiological degradation of progesterone to 3-(1β-acetyl-3aα-perhydro-7aβ-methyl-5-oxoindan-4α-yl)propionic acid by Schubert *et al.* (1961), a wide variety of perhydroindan derivatives have been isolated and identified as the microbiological degradation products of various kinds of steroidal compounds (cf. Sih *et al.*, 1968; Schubert *et al.*, 1970). There seems no doubt therefore that a perhydroindan derivative, compound (XVIII), is an intermediate of degradative rather than synthetic origin. Nevertheless, Hayakawa *et al.* (1968) were unsuccessful in causing the degradation of compound (XVIII) by its producing organism, *A. simplex,* in spite of considerable effort. Although no explanation was given for the nonutilization, Hayakawa and colleagues found that compound (XVIII) could be metabolized to its amino acid conjugates (XXa–XXd) and (4R)-4-[2α-(2-carboxyethyl)-3β-(3-carboxypropionyl)-2β-methylcyclopent-1β-yl]valeric acid (XXI) by *C. equi* (cf. Section III,A,3). From structures of these metabolites, Hayakawa and Fujiwara (1972) have considered that the conjugates are probably not degradative intermediates but only by-products, and that compound (XXI) may be an actual intermediate. They have also presumed that its precursor is a hydroxycarboxylic acid (LVI), corresponding to an opened form of the lactone ring in a seven-membered lactone intermediate, (4R)-4-[2α-(2-carboxyethyl)-3β-(3-carboxy-1(S)-hydroxypropyl)-2β-methylcyclopent-1β-yl]valeric acid ε-lactone (LV) (cf. Fig. 15). Although compound (LV) has not yet been isolated as a metabolite, they have postulated that oxygenation of the Baeyer-Villiger type of compound (XVIII)

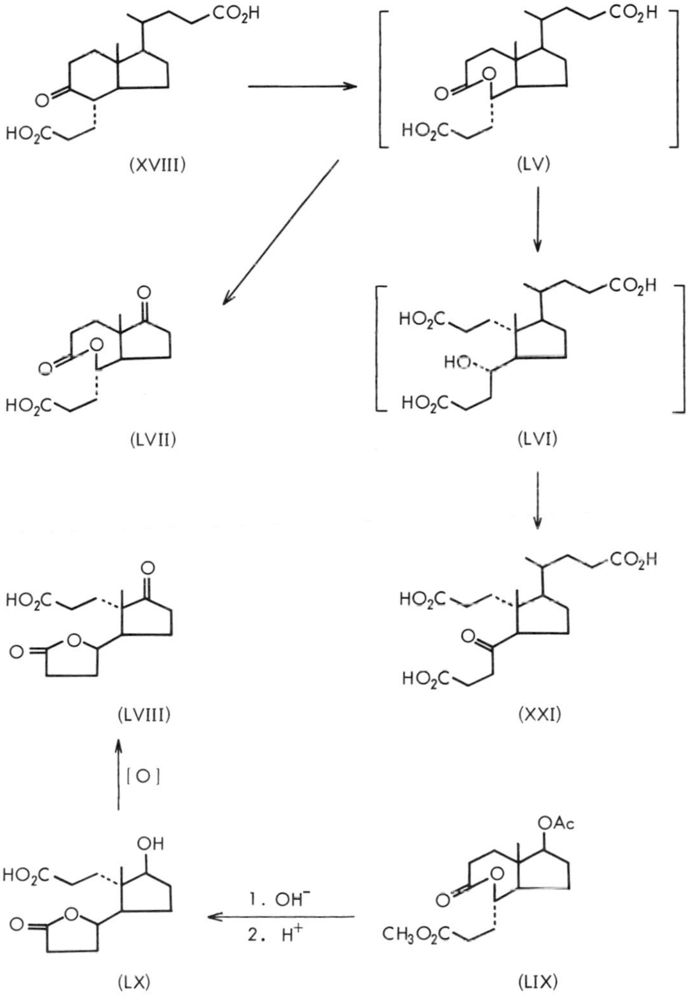

FIG. 15. Proposed pathway for the degradation of compound (XVIII) to compounds (XXI) and (LVII) by *Corynebacterium equi,* and scheme for the chemical synthesis of compound (LVIII).

would produce the seven-membered lactone (LV), since such a micro-biological oxygenation is known in nature (Laskin *et al.,* 1964). However, *C. equi* could not utilize the oxotricarboxylic acid (XXI) as expected, thus resembling the nonutilization of compound (XVIII) by *A. simplex* mentioned earlier. While the organism was able to utilize compound (LV) as its only source of carbon and yielded (4S)-4-[2α-(2-carboxy-ethyl)-2β-methyl-3-oxocyclopent-1β-yl]-4-hydroxybutyric acid ε-lactone (LVII), which was isolated as the methyl ester of its isomer, a five-membered lactone (LVIII). In this connection it should be noted that when (4R)-4-[2α-(2-carboxyethyl)-3β-(3-carboxy-1(S)-hydroxypropyl)-2β-methylcyclopent-1β-yl]valeric acid ε-lactone (LV) was treated by alkali followed by acid, it was readily converted into the corresponding five-membered lactone which was not utilized by this organism. The evidence strongly supports the suggestion that the isolated five-membered lactone (LVIII) is present mainly as its ε-lactone (LVII) in the culture broth. It also suggests that an initial bacterial attack in the breakdown of com-pound (XVIII) by *C. equi* is oxygenation of the Baeyer-Villiger type yielding the seven-membered (LV), and that this seven-membered lac-tone structure is required for shortening of the side chain yielding the lactone (LVII). Thus it appears that the previously isolated oxotricar-boxylic acid (XXI) is a side metabolite, which may be produced through the action of less specific dehydrogenase systems of *C. equi* on the hy-droxytricarboxylic acid (LVI).

The structure of compound (LVIII) was established through its chem-ical synthesis (cf. Fig. 15): oxidation of the methyl ester acetate of 3-(3aα-perhydro-1β-hydroxy-7aβ-methyl-5-oxoindan-4α-yl)propionic acid (XXXIV, see Fig. 11) with *m*-chloroperbenzoic acid gave methyl (4S)-4-[3β-acetyloxy-2α-(2-carboxyethyl)-2β-methylcyclopent-1β-yl]-4-hydroxy-butyrate ε-lactone (LIX) which was treated by alkali followed by mineral acid to yield a carboxylic acid containing a γ-lactone ring. The γ-lactone (LX) was oxidized with Jones reagent to afford the desired compound (LVIII).

b. With Streptomyces rubescens. Cholic acid is degraded to (4R)-4-[4α-(2-carboxyethyl)-3aα-perhydro-7aβ-methyl-5-oxoindan-1β-yl]valeric acid (XVIII) and several nitrogen-containing products by *S. rubescens* (cf. Section III,A,4). Although no information on the mechanism of the formation of such nitrogenous products is available, Hayakawa *et al.* (1969a) have presented some possible pathways for their formation (cf. Fig. 16). Each of two carboxyl groups of compound (XVIII) is inde-pendently activated by a reaction of acyl-CoA synthetase type and then transformed to the corresponding two kinds of amides, the indanbutyra-mide (XXIV) and (4R)-4-[4α-(2-carbamoylethyl)-3aα-perhydro-7aβ-methyl-5-oxoindan-1β-yl]valeric acid (LXI), respectively. The latter

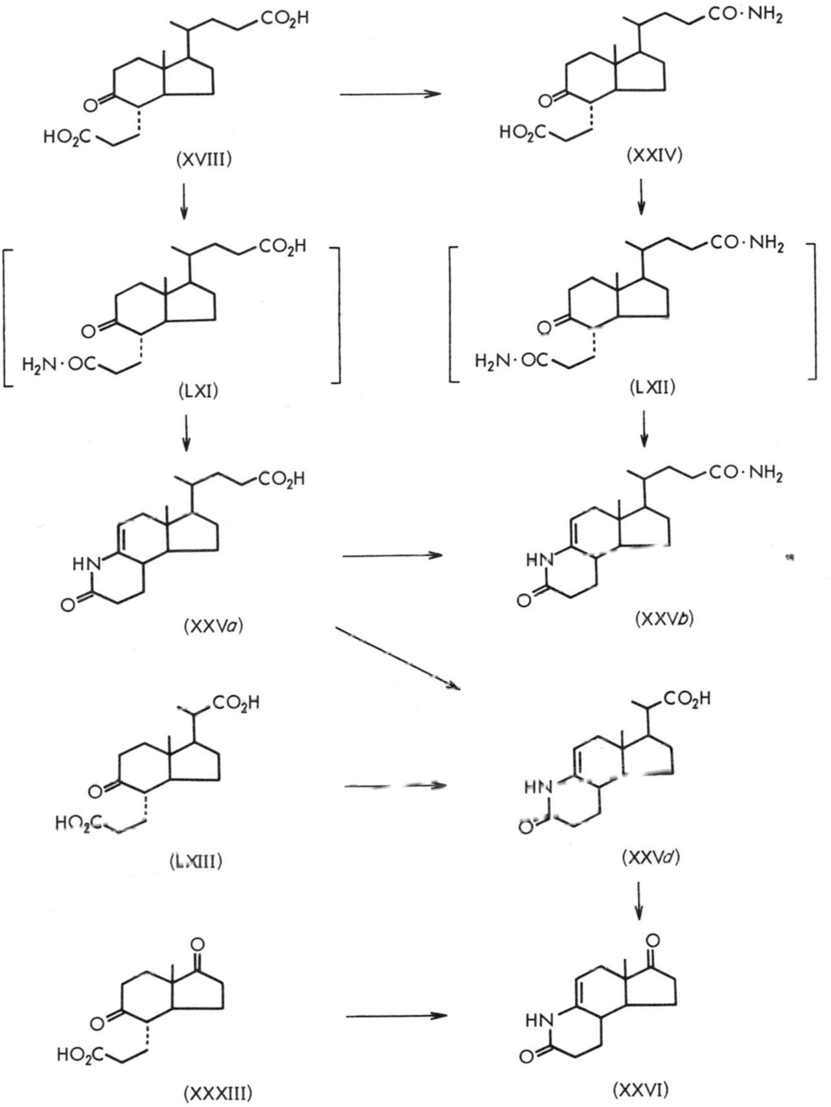

FIG. 16. Possible pathways for the formation of nitrogen-containing metabolites by *Streptomyces rubescens*.

compound may be further transformed to yield the enamine lactam (XXV*a*) through either enzymatic or spontaneous reaction, since such compounds are known to be easily cyclized to yield enamine lactams in a weakly acidic medium. In a similar manner the indanbutyramide (XXIV) may be metabolized via a postulated intermediate (LXII) to the ena-minolactam amide (XXV*b*) which is also formed from the enaminolactam carboxylic acid (XXVa) as in the amidation of compound (XVIII) to compound (XXIV). As was mentioned in Section III,A,4, a compound has been isolated which is probably formed through an artificial decarboxylation of (4S)-4-(2,3,4,6,6aβ,7,8,9,9aα,9bβ-decahydro-6aβ-methyl-3-oxo-1H-cyclopenta[f]quinolin-7β-yl)-3-oxovaleric acid corresponding to an intermediate in the reaction of the β-oxidation type of the side chain of compound (XXVa), (3S)-3-(2,3,4,6,6aβ,7,8,9,9aα9bβ-decahydro-6aβ-methyl-3-oxo-1H-cyclopenta[f]quinolin-7β-yl)butan-2-one (XXVc). Therefore, it has been presumed that compound (XVIII) is first converted into the enamine lactam (XXVa) and subsequently degraded to the enamine lactams (XXVd) and (XXVI) in a manner analogous to the fatty acid β-oxidation mechanism. However, a pathway by which compound (XVIII) is first oxidized to the δ-oxocarboxylic acids (LXIII) and (XXXIII), which are then enaminolactamized to yield the enamine lactams (XXVd) and (XXVI) respectively, is not excluded. Thus, the same authors have tentatively proposed the following degradative pathway: (XVIII $\rightleftharpoons$ XXIV $\rightleftharpoons$ XXVb) and/or (XVIII $\rightleftharpoons$ XXVa $\rightleftharpoons$ XXVb) $\rightarrow$ (XXVd $\rightleftharpoons$ LXIII) $\rightarrow$ (XXXIII $\rightleftharpoons$ XXVI). Although much of this representation is largely hypothetical, it is the author's opinion that there is little doubt as to the formation of compound (XXXIII) from compound (XVIII) or cholic acid by *S. rubescens*.

c. *With Arthrobacter simplex.* The most highly degraded product in the degradation of cholic acid by *A. simplex* is (+)-(5R)-5-methyl-4-oxooctane-1,8-dioic acid (XIX) and the next most degraded one is (4R)-4-[4α-(2-carboxyethyl)-3aα-perhydro-7aβ-methyl-5-oxoindan-1β-yl]valeric acid (XVIII) (cf. Fig. 6). On the other hand, *S. rubescens* is able to degrade cholic acid to compound (XVIII) and 3-(3aα-perhydro-7aβ-methyl-1,5-dioxoindan-4α-yl)propionic acid (XXXIII) as discussed above, and the latter is further metabolized to compound (XIX) as mentioned in Section III,A,7. It is therefore conceivable that the precursor of compound (XIX) in the sequence of degradation of cholic acid by *A. simplex* is compound (XVIII). However, no intermediates indicating a precursor-product relationship between these compounds have been isolated because the organism could not utilize compound (XVIII), and there were many difficulties in isolating the desired intermediates from a mixture of the degradation products of cholic acid.

5. *Further Degradation of 3-(3aα-Perhydro-7aβ-methyl-1,5-dioxoindan-4α-yl)propionic Acid (XXXIII)*

In 1963 Sih and Wang isolated the title compound as a product of degradation of 4-androstene-3,17-dione by *Nocardia restrictus*. Subsequently Sih and colleagues have expended considerable effort directed at the isolation of the intermediates in the further microbiological degradation of this compound, though relatively little progress has been made (cf. Kondo *et al.*, 1969; Schubert *et al.*, 1970).

As an extension of studies on the microbiological degradation of cholic acid by *Streptomyces rubescens*, Hayakawa and colleagues investigated the metabolism of compound (XXXIII) by the same organism and isolated some metabolites that could give an insight into the mechanism of the further microbiological degradation of this compound (cf. Section III,A,7). Structures of the metabolites (XXXIV) and (XXXV), which were the only reduction products of the parent compound, afforded no information on the further degradation of compound (XXXIII). In contrast, the side chains of 3-(3aα-perhydro-5α-hydroxy-7aβ-methyl-1-oxoindan-4-yl)-*trans*-acrylic acid (XXXVI) and (3R)-3-(3aα-perhydro-5α-hydroxy-7aβ-methyl-1-oxoindan-4α-yl)-3-hydroxypropionic acid δ-lactone (XXXVII) have *trans*-acrylic acid and optically active β-hydroxycarboxylic acid structures, corresponding respectively to the first two intermediates in the degradative sequence of fatty acids by the conventional β-oxidation mechanism. This strongly suggests that the propionic acid side chain of compound (XXXIII) is degraded to the corresponding dinorcarboxylic acid in a manner analogous to the β-oxidation mechanism. Thus, Hashimoto *et al.* (1969) tentatively proposed the following sequence for the degradation of compound (XXXIII) by S. *rubescens* (cf. Fig. 17): compound (XXXIII) → compound (LXIV) → compound (XXXVI) → compound (LXV) → compound (LXVI) → compound (LXVII) → compound (XIX).

The structures of compounds (LXIV) and (LXV) in Fig. 17 refer to the opened forms of the lactone rings in the isolated δ-lactones (XXXV) and (XXXVII), respectively, and these lactones are probably present as such opened forms in the culture broth (cf. Fig. 11). Intermediates 3-(3aα-perhydro-5α-hydroxy-7aβ-methyl-1-oxoindan-4α-yl)-3-oxopropionic acid (LXVI) and 3aα-perhydro-5α-hydroxy-7aβ-methyl-1-oxoindan-4α-carboxylic acid (LXVII) in the proposed pathway have not yet been isolated. In addition, an initial step in the degradative pathway is represented as a reductive process which converted compound (XXXIII) into compound (LXIV) but it must be energetically an oxidative one, since compound (XXXIII) is used as carbon and energy sources for the growth of S. *rubescens*. On this question, the same authors proposed the possibility that in the culture broth, compounds (LXIV), (XXXVI), (LXV), and possibly compounds (LXVI) and (LXVII) are in equilibrium with the corresponding 1,5-dioxoperhydroindancarboxylic acids, though because of differences in their degradation rates only 5α-hydroxy-1-oxoperhydroindan derivatives could be isolated. They also suggested another

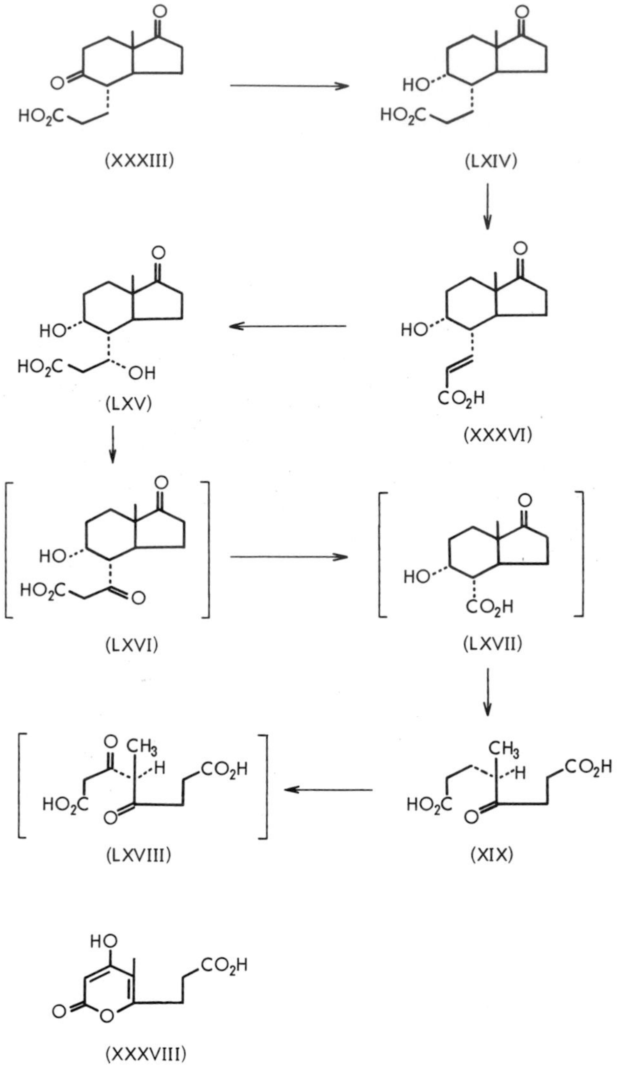

Fig. 17. Proposed pathway for the degradation of 3-(3aα-perhydro-7aβ-methyl-1,5-dioxoindan-4α-yl)propionic acid (XXXIII) by *Streptomyces rubescens*.

possibility that the first step in the microbiological attack of compound (XXXIII) could be initiated by the organism inoculum itself. The former possibility is relatively consistent with the view of Lee and Sih (1967) who reported the idea that compound (XXXIII) may be metabolized by microorganisms to its dinorcarboxylic acid, 3aα-perhydro-7aβ-methyl-1,5-dioxoindan-4α-carboxylic acid. The structures of the isolated products, however, support the latter suggestion. Although the actual pathway is unknown, the results by Hashimoto *et al.* (1969) and Hayakawa and Hashimoto (1972) give some information regarding shortening of the propionic acid side chain of compound (XXXIII) in its microbiological degradation.

No information is available on the intermediates and reaction sequence in the formation of (+)-(5R)-5-methyl-4-oxo-octane-1,8-dioic acid (XIX) from the postulated intermediate (LXVII). From the structure of compound (XIX), however, Hayakawa and Hashimoto (1972) considered that if the stereochemistry of compound (LXVII) remains the same at C-5 in its metabolite (XIX), fission of ring D must occur between C-1 and C-7a. They also considered that the precursor of the recently isolated α-pyrone derivative (XXXVIII) may be a compound having the opened form of the α-pyrone ring, 4-methyl-3,5-dioxo-octane-1,8-dioic acid (LXVIII), which is probably metabolized further to smaller fragments. In this connection several attempts were made to transform compound (XIX) to compounds (XXXVIII) or (LXVIII) with S. *rubescens.* However, the oxodicarboxylic acid (XIX) could not be utilized by the organism, similarly as in the degradation of compounds (XVIII), (XXI), and (XXVI) with *A. simplex* (cf. Section III,A,3), *C. equi* (cf. Section III,B,4,a), and *S. rubescens* (cf. Section III,A,7), respectively.

C. COMMON INTERMEDIATE IN DEGRADATIVE PATHWAYS OF BILE ACIDS AND OTHER STEROIDS

Current research on the microbiological degradation of steroids *in vitro* has demonstrated that several species of microorganisms are able to degrade some steroidal compounds to a common intermediate, 3-(3aα-perhydro-7aβ-methyl-1,5-dioxoindan-4α-yl)propionic acid (XXXIII). An outline of the results is given in Fig. 18. The microbiological degradation of 4-androstene-3,17-dione (XLIV) to compound (XXXIII) has been already discussed in Section III,B,2 (cf. Fig. 13). Formation of the same compound from progesterone (LXIX) and deoxycorticosterone (LXX) has also been reported by Schubert *et al.* (1968, 1970). Whitmarsh (1964) first demonstrated conversion of cholesterol (LXXI) into 4-androstene-3,17-dione (XLIV) and its 1-dehydrogenated derivative by *Nocardia* spp. Later, this type of the sterol degradation by microorganisms was extensively investigated by several workers because of commercial prospects (Wix *et al.*, 1968; Van der Waard *et al.*, 1969; Nagasawa *et al.*, 1969; Marsheck *et al.*, 1972). Sih *et al.* (1968) have reported the enzymatic mechanism for the side-chain degradation of cholesterol. These studies on the sterol degradation indicate that some of the naturally occurring sterols

F<small>IG</small>. 18. Scheme for the microbiological degradation of cholic acid (II), 4-androstene-3,17-dione (XLIV), progesterone (LXIX), deoxycorticosterone (LXX), and cholesterol (LXXI) to 3-(3aα-perhydro-7aβ-methyl-1,5-dioxoindan-4α-yl)propionic acid (XXXIII).

may be degraded to compound (XXXIII) by way of compound (XLIV) by microorganisms. As was mentioned in Section III,B,4,b, conversion of cholic acid (II) into this compound has also been indirectly demonstrated. From the viewpoint of comparative biochemistry, it is of particular interest that several naturally occurring and structurally different steroids are metabolized to the same intermediate by different species of microorganisms. Since microorganisms do not live by a rigid system of particular rules, however, it is not surprising to find exceptions to these degradations.

D. C<small>AN</small> D<small>EGRADATION</small> OF THE B<small>ILE</small> A<small>CID</small> S<small>KELETON</small> O<small>CCUR</small> IN A<small>NIMALS</small>?

It is generally believed that the cleavage of the carbon-carbon bond in steroids does not occur in animals, although cholesterol is metabolized to bile acids and steroid hormones in the mammalian tissues (cf. Talalay, 1957). Ahrens and associates, however, have reported in their series of publications that sizable losses of neutral sterols containing a Δ^5-3β-hydroxy group can occur during their intestinal transit in man (Grundy and Ahrens, 1966, 1969; Grundy *et al.*, 1968). They have also presumed that the losses are due to degradation of the ring structure of neutral sterols by intestinal microorganisms. The losses reported are as great as 60% of fed sterols, but in some patients no losses were found. The observation has been reconfirmed by several workers (Connor *et al.*, 1969; Borgström, 1969; Denbesten *et al.*, 1970) although their values for the losses are different from those of Grundy *et al.* (1968). A problem of great interest is what kinds of degradation products are produced from neutral sterols in the human intestine, but no information about this is available at the present time.

In contrast to neutral sterols, administered bile acids are completely recovered in feces and urine as mentioned in Section II,E. In addition, Grundy *et al.* (1968) have reported that administered bile acids are completely recovered even in patients in whom neutral sterol losses are large during the same study periods. Thus no evidence to indicate ring-opening or side-chain-shortening of bile acids *in vivo* has been reported so far, except for works by Ferrari (1967) and Dirscherl and Pelzer (1970). The former author showed *in vitro* cleavage of cholic acid to nonsteroidal compounds by the action of human intestinal microflora incubated under aerobic conditions. The latter authors suggested the oxidative degradation of deoxycholic acid to deoxybilianic acid in human liver (cf. Fig. 5). However, these studies are only indicative of the possibility of *in vivo* degradation of the bile acid skeleton, and do not constitute very strong evidence.

Although there are a few reports indicating the *in vivo* formation of some Δ^4-3-oxo bile acids from the primary bile acids through the action of intestinal microorganisms (cf. Section II,E), it is not yet established whether the Δ^4-3-oxo bile acids are further metabolized *in vivo* to nonsteroidal compounds such as (4R)-4-[4α-(2-carboxyethyl)-3aα-perhydro-7aβ-methyl-5-oxoindan-4α-yl]valeric acid (XVIII) and (+)-(5R)-5-methyl-4-oxo-octane-1,8-dioic acid (XIX) as in the microbiological degradation of cholic acid *in vitro*. Further development of this subject will be awaited with interest.

IV. Conclusions

The nature of intestinal microorganisms involved in the transformation of bile acids in the intestine has been extensively investigated in both *in vitro* and *in vivo* systems during the last decade. Much information on the bacteriological character of these organisms and on various enzymatic reactions effected by them has been accumulated, and should provide a basis for further studies of medically important problems on bile acid metabolism *in vivo*.

Little progress relative to the microbiological degradation of the bile acid skeleton was made until 1967, only certain degradation products of bile acids by soil microorganisms having been isolated and identified by that time. However, the demonstration of microbiological degradation of bile acids and some other naturally occurring steroids to a common degradative intermediate sparked biochemical interest on the subject and some information on the degradation of the common metabolite and of the bile acid skeleton was obtained. Since elucidation of the degradative mechanism of steroids in nature is equally as important as that of the biogenetic mechanism, investigations in this area will continue until the complete degradative sequence of steroids including bile acids is established.

References

Ali, S. S., Kuksis, A., and Beveridge, J. M. R. (1966). *Can. J. Biochem.* **44**, 957.

Aries, V. C., and Hill, M. J. (1970a). *Biochim. Biophys. Acta* **202**, 526.

Aries, V. C., and Hill, M. J. (1970b). *Biochim. Biophys. Acta* **202**, 535.

Aries, V. C., Crowther, J. S., Drasar, B. S., and Hill, M. J. (1969). *Gut* **10**, 575.

Aries, V. C., Goddard, P., and Hill, M. J. (1971). *Biochim. Biophys. Acta* **248**, 482.

Bergström, S., Lindstedt, S., and Samuelsson, B. (1959). *J. Biol. Chem.* **234**, 2022.

Bergström, S., Danielsson, H., and Samuelsson, B. (1960). *In* "Lipide Metabolism" (K. Bloch, ed.), pp. 291–336. Wiley, New York.

Bokkenheuser, V., Hoshita, T., and Mosbach, E. H. (1969). *J. Lipid Res.* **10**, 421.

Borgström, B. (1969). *J. Lipid Res.* **10**, 331.

Carini, S., Cocucci, M. C., and Ferrari, A. (1967). *Progr. Biochem. Pharmacol.* **2**, 62.

Charney, W., and Herzog, H. L. (1967). "Microbial Transformations of Steroids: A Handbook." Academic Press, New York.

Cocucci, M. C., and Ferrari, A. (1963a). *Rend. Ist. Lomb. Sci. Lett.* B **97**, 255.

Cocucci, M. C., and Ferrari, A. (1963b). *Rend. Ist. Lomb. Sci. Lett.* B **97**, 398.

Cocucci, M. C., and Ferrari, A. (1964). *Atti Accad. Naz. Lincei, Cl. Sci. Fis., Mat. Natur., Rend.* [8] **36**, 851.

Cocucci, M. C., and Ferrari, A. (1965). *Ann. Microbiol. Enzimol.* **15**, 157.

Connor, W. E., Witiak, D. T., Stone, D. B., and Armstrong, M. L. (1969). *J. Clin. Invest.* **48**, 1363.

Danielsson, H., and Tchen, T. (1968). *In* "Metabolic Pathways" (D. M. Greenberg, ed.), Vol. 2, pp. 117–168. Academic Press, New York.

Danielsson, H., Eneroth, P., Hellström, K., and Sjövall, J. (1962). *J. Biol. Chem.* **237**, 3657.

Danielsson, H., Eneroth, P., Hellström, K., Lindstedt, S., and Sjövall, J. (1963a). *J. Biol. Chem.* **238**, 2299.

Danielsson, H., Kallner, A., and Sjövall, J. (1963b). *J. Biol. Chem.* **238**, 3846.

Davidson, S. J., and Talalay, P. (1966). *J. Biol. Chem.* **241**, 906.

Denbesten, L., Connor, W. E., Kent, T. H., and Lin, D. (1970). *J. Lipid Res.* **11**, 341.

Dickinson, A. B., Gustafsson, B. E., and Norman, A. (1971). *Acta Pathol. Microbiol. Scand., Sect. B* **79**, 691.

Dirscherl, W., and Pelzer, U. (1970). *Hoppe-Seyler's Z. Physiol. Chem.* **351**, 1151.

Dodson, R. M., and Muir, R. D. (1961a). *J. Amer. Chem. Soc.* **83**, 4627.

Dodson, R. M., and Muir, R. D. (1961b). *J. Amer. Chem. Soc.* **83**, 4631.

Donaldson, R. M., Jr. (1964). *N. Engl. J. Med.* **270**, 938.

Douglas, J. L., and Money, T. (1968). *Can. J. Chem.* **46**, 695.

Drasar, B. S., Hill, M. J., and Shiner, M. (1966). *Lancet* **1**, 1237.

Eneroth, P., and Sjövall, J. (1971). *In* "The Bile Acids. Chemistry, Physiology, and Metabolism" (P. P. Nair and D. Krichevsky, eds.), Vol. 1, pp. 121–171. Plenum, New York.

Eneroth, P., Gordon, B., Ryhage, R., and Sjövall, J. (1966a). *J. Lipid Res.* **7**, 511.

Eneroth, P., Gordon, B., and Sjövall, J. (1966b). *J. Lipid Res.* **7**, 524.

Eneroth, P., Hellström, K., and Sjövall, J. (1968). *Acta Chem. Scand.* **22**, 1729.

Evrard, E., and Janssen, G. (1968). *J. Lipid Res.* **9**, 226.

Ferrari, A. (1967). *Ann. Microbiol. Enzimol.* **17**, 165.

Ferrari, A. (1969). *Atti Accad. Naz. Lincei, Cl. Sci. Fis., Mat. Natur., Rend.* **46**, 576.

Ferrari, A., and Pacini, N. (1968). *Ann. Microbiol. Enzimol.* **18**, 147.

Finegold, S. M. (1969). *Calif. Med.* **110**, 455.

Garbutt, J. T., Lack, L., and Tyor, M. P. (1971). *Amer. J. Med.* **51**, 627.

Gorbach, S. L. (1971). *Gastroenterology* **60**, 1110.

Grundy, S. M., and Ahrens, E. H., Jr. (1966). *J. Clin. Invest.* **45**, 1503.

Grundy, S. M., and Ahrens, E. H., Jr. (1969). *J. Lipid Res.* **10**, 91.

Grundy, S. M., Ahrens, E. H., Jr., and Miettinen, T. A. (1965). *J. Lipid Res.* **6**, 397.

Grundy, S. M., Ahrens, E. H., Jr., and Salen, G. (1968). *J. Lipid Res.* **9**, 374.

Gustafsson, B. E., and Norman, A. (1962). *Proc. Soc. Exp. Biol. Med.* **110**, 387.

Gustafsson, B. E., Norman, A., and Sjövall, J. (1960). *Arch. Biochem. Biophys.* **91**, 93.

Gustafsson, B. E., Midtvedt, T., and Norman, A. (1966). *J. Exp. Med.* **123**, 413.

Gustafsson, B. E., Midtvedt, T., and Norman, A. (1968). *Acta Pathol. Microbiol. Scand.* **72**, 433.

Hashimoto, S., Fujiwara, T., and Hayakawa, S. (1969). *Seikagaku* **41**, 394.

Haslewood, G. A. D. (1967). "Bile Salts." Methuen, London.

Haslewood, G. A. D. (1971). *Biochem. J.* **123**, 15.

Hattori, T., and Hayakawa, S. (1969). *Microbios* **1**, 287.

Hattori, T., and Hayakawa, S. (1972). To be published.

Hayaishi, O., Sato, Y., Jokoby, W. B., and Stohlman, E. F. (1955). *Arch. Biochem. Biophys.* **56**, 554.

Hayaishi, O., Slaughter, C., and Jokoby, W. B. (1960). *J. Bacteriol.* **79**, 145.

Hayakawa, S. (1954). *Proc. Jap. Acad.* **30**, 128.

Hayakawa, S. (1958). *In* "Chemistry of Lipids" (S. Funahashi *et al.*, eds.), Vol. 1, pp. 143–197. Kyoritsu Shuppan, Tokyo.

Hayakawa, S., and Fujiwara, T. (1969). *FEBS Lett.* **4,** 288.

Hayakawa, S., and Fujiwara, T. (1972). To be published.

Hayakawa, S., and Hashimoto, S. (1969). *Biochem. J.* **112,** 127.

Hayakawa, S., and Hashimoto, S. (1972). To be published.

Hayakawa, S., and Hattori, T. (1970). *FEBS Lett.* **6,** 131.

Hayakawa, S., and Kurokawa, K. (1963). *Nature (London)* **199,** 490.

Hayakawa, S., and Samuelsson, B. (1964). *J. Biol. Chem.* **239,** 94.

Hayakawa, S., Fujii, T., Saburi, Y., and Eguchi, T. (1957). *Nature (London)* **179,** 537.

Hayakawa, S., Saburi, Y., Tamaki, K., and Hoshijima, H. (1958a). *Nature (London)* **181,** 906.

Hayakawa, S., Saburi, Y., and Tamaki, K. (1958b). *J. Biochem. (Tokyo)* **45,** 419.

Hayakawa, S., Saburi, Y., and Hoshijima, H. (1958c). *J. Biochem. (Tokyo)* **45,** 465.

Hayakawa, S., Kanematsu, Y., and Fujiwara, T. (1967). *Nature (London)* **214,** 520.

Hayakawa, S., Fujiwara, T., and Tsuchikawa, H. (1968). *Nature (London)* **219,** 1160.

Hayakawa, S., Hashimoto, S., and Onaka, T. (1969a). *Lipids* **4,** 224.

Hayakawa, S., Kanematsu, Y., and Fujiwara, T. (1969b). *Biochem. J.* **115,** 249.

Hayakawa, S., Ichiba, T., and Fujiwara, T. (1972). To be published.

Hill, M. J., and Drasar, B. S. (1967). *Biochem. J.* **104,** 55P.

Hill, M. J., and Drasar, B. S. (1968). *Gut* **9,** 22.

Hirofuji, S. (1965). *J. Biochem. (Tokyo)* **58,** 27.

Hofmann, A. F., and Mosbach, E. H. (1964). *J. Biol. Chem.* **239,** 2813.

Hofmann, A. F., Bokkenheuser, V., Hirsch, R. L., and Mosbach, E. H. (1968). *J. Lipid Res.* **9,** 244.

Hofmann, A. F., Mosbach, E. H., and Sweeley, C. C. (1969). *Biochim. Biophys. Acta* **176,** 204.

Howe, E. E., and Bosshardt, D. K. (1962). *J. Nutr.* **77,** 171.

Iwata, T., and Yamasaki, K. (1964). *J. Biochem. (Tokyo)* **56,** 424.

Kallner, A. (1967a). *Acta Chem. Scand.* **21,** 87.

Kallner, A. (1967b). *Acta Chem. Scand.* **21,** 315.

Kallner, A. (1967c). *Ark. Kemi* **26,** 567.

Karavolas, H. J., Elliott, W. H., Hsia, S. L., Doisy, E. A., Jr., Matschiner, J. T., Thayer, S. A., and Doisy, E. A. (1965). *J. Biol. Chem.* **240,** 1568.

Kondo, E., Stein, B., and Sih, C. J. (1969). *Biochim. Biophys. Acta* **176,** 135.

Laskin, A. I., Grabowich, P., Meyers, C. deL., and Fried, J. (1964). *J. Med. Chem.* **7,** 406.

Lee, S. S., and Sih, C. J. (1967). *Biochemistry* **6,** 1395.

Lindstedt, S. (1957). *Ark. Kemi* **11,** 145.

Lindstedt, S., and Sjövall, J. (1957). *Acta Chem. Scand.* **11,** 421.

Marsheck, W. J., Kraychy, S., and Muir, R. D. (1972). *Appl. Microbiol.* **23,** 72.

Midtvedt, T. (1967). *Acta Pathol. Microbiol. Scand.* **71,** 147.

Midtvedt, T., and Norman, A. (1967). *Acta Pathol. Microbiol. Scand.* **71,** 629.

Midtvedt, T., and Norman, A. (1968a). *Acta Pathol. Microbiol. Scand.* **72,** 313.

Midtvedt, T., and Norman, A. (1968b). *Acta Pathol. Microbiol. Scand.* **72,** 337.

Murray, H. C., and Peterson, D. H. (1952). U. S. Patent 2,602,769.

Nagasawa, M., Bae, M., Tamura, G., and Arima, K. (1969). *Agr. Biol. Chem.* **33,** 1644.

Nair, P. P., and Garcia, C. (1969). *Anal. Biochem.* **29,** 164.

Nair, P. P., Gordon, M., Gordon, S., Reback, J., and Mendeloff, A. I. (1965). *Life Sci.* 4, 1887.

Nair, P. P., Gordon, M., and Reback, J. (1967). *J. Biol. Chem.* 242, 7.

Nair, P. P., Banwell, J. G., Gorbach, S. L., Lilis, C., and Alcaraz, A. (1970). *Amer. J. Clin. Nutr.* 23, 1569.

Noll, B. W., and Elliott, W. H. (1967). *Fed. Proc., Fed. Amer. Soc. Exp. Biol.* 26, 851.

Norman, A. (1964). *Brit. J. Nutr.* 18, 173.

Norman, A., and Bergman, S. (1960). *Acta Chem. Scand.* 14, 1781.

Norman, A., and Grubb, R. (1955). *Acta Pathol. Microbiol. Scand.* 36, 537.

Norman, A., and Palmer, R. H. (1964). *J. Lab. Clin. Med.* 63, 986.

Norman, A., and Shorb, M. S. (1962). *Proc. Soc. Exp. Biol. Med.* 110, 552.

Norman, A., and Sjövall, J. (1958). *J. Biol. Chem.* 233, 872.

Norman, A., and Widström, O. A. (1964). *Proc. Soc. Exp. Biol. Med.* 117, 442.

Novotný, P. (1969). *J. Med. Microbiol.* 2, 81.

Ogura, M., and Ozaki, K. (1964). *Yonago Acta Med.* 8, 41.

Okishio, T., Nair, P. P., and Gordon, M. (1967). *Biochem. J.* 102, 654.

Okuda, K. (1961). *Seikagaku* 33, 193.

Palmer, R. H. (1969). *In* "Methods in Enzymology" (R. B. Clayton, ed.), Vol. 15, pp. 280–288. Academic Press, New York.

Palmer, R. H. (1971). *J. Lipid Res.* 12, 680.

Palmer, R. H., and Bolt, M. G. (1971). *J. Lipid Res.* 12, 671.

Pan, S. C., Semar, J., Junta, B., and Principe, P. A. (1969). *Biotech. Bioeng.* 11, 1183.

Portman, O. W. (1958). *Arch. Biochem. Biophys.* 78, 125.

Portman, O. W., Shah, S., Antonis, A., and Jorgensen, B. (1962). *Proc. Soc. Exp. Biol. Med.* 109, 959.

Rosenfeld, R. S., Paul, I., and Yamauchi, T. (1967). *Arch. Biochem. Biophys.* 122, 653.

Saburi, Y., Hayakawa, S., Fujii, T., and Akaeda, I. (1956). *J. Biochem. (Tokyo)* 39, 711.

Samuelsson, B. (1959a). *Acta Chem. Scand.* 13, 236.

Samuelsson, B. (1959b). *J. Biol. Chem.* 234, 2852.

Samuelsson, B. (1960a). *J. Biol. Chem.* 235, 361.

Samuelsson, B. (1960b). *Ark. Kemi* 15, 425.

Samuelsson, B. (1960c). *Acta Chem. Scand.* 14, 21.

Schatz, A., Savard, K., and Pintner, I. J. (1949). *J. Bacteriol.* 58, 117.

Scheline, R. R. (1968). *J. Pharm. Sci.* 57, 2021.

Schubert, K., Böhme, K.-H., and Hörhold, C. (1961). *Hoppe-Seyler's Z. Physiol. Chem.* 325, 260.

Schubert, K., Böhme, K.-H., Ritter, F., and Hörhold, C. (1968). *Biochim. Biophys. Acta* 152, 401.

Schubert, K., Hörhold, C., Böhme, K.-H., Groh, H., Ritter, F., and Schumann, W. (1970). *Steroidologia* 1, 201.

Severina, L. O., Torgov, I. V., Skrjabin, G. K., Wulfson, N. S., Zaretskii, V. I., and Papernaja, I. B. (1968). *Tetrahedron* 24, 2145.

Severina, L. O., Torgov, I. V., Skrjabin, G. K., Wulfson, N. S., Zaretskii, V. I., and Papernaja, I. B. (1969a). *Tetrahedron* 25, 485.

Severina, L. O., Torgov, I. V., Skrjabin, G. K., Zaretskii, V. I., Wulfson, N. S., and Papernaja, I. B. (1969b). *Tetrahedron* 25, 5617.

Shimada, K., Bricknell, K. S., and Finegold, S. M. (1969). *J. Infec. Dis.* **119**, 273.

Sih, C. J., and Wang, K. C. (1963). *J. Amer. Chem. Soc.* **85**, 2135.

Sih, C. J., and Whitlock, H. W., Jr. (1968). *Annu. Rev. Biochem.* **37**, 661.

Sih, C. J., Tai, H. H., Tsong, Y. Y., Lee, S. S., and Coombe, R. G. (1968). *Biochemistry* **7**, 808.

Suzuki, R. (1970). *Keio J. Med.* **19**, 73.

Talalay, P. (1957). *Physiol. Rev.* **37**, 362.

Tsong, Y. Y., Wang, K. C., and Sih, C. J. (1964). *Biochim. Biophys. Acta* **93**, 398.

Van der Waard, W. F., Doodeward, J., De Flines, J., and Van der Weele, S. (1969). *Abh. Deut. Akad. Wiss. Berlin, Kl. Med.* No. 2, p. 101.

Whitmarsh, J. M. (1964). *Biochem. J.* **90**, 23P.

Wix, G., Büki, K. G., Tömörkény, E., and Ambrus, G. (1968). *Steroids* **11**, 401.

Yesair, D. W., and Himmelfarb, P. (1970). *Appl. Microbiol.* **19**, 295.

Phytosterols

GEORGE A. BEAN

Department of Botany, University of Maryland, College Park, Maryland

I. Introduction

This review is concerned with the extraction and identification of phytosterols, their possible role(s) in plant metabolism, and changes in sterols during plant growth, and includes a listing of sterols that have been reported in plants and their locations within the plants. The subject of phytosterol biosynthesis has been reviewed by Heftmann (1963, 1968), Goad and Goodwin (1966), and Goad (1967), and will not be discussed.

The current and increasing interest in phytosterols probably began with the report that gas-liquid chromatography (GLC) could be used to identify sterols (Beerthius and Recourt, 1960). The advances that have been made since then in the extraction and identification of sterols have greatly expanded our knowledge of the sterols that are present in plants, their function(s), and probable biosynthetic pathways. It does appear, however, that phytosterol research is entering into a new era with the emphasis being placed on application of the knowledge that has been accumulating on phytosterols toward more efficient crop production. For example, Heftmann (1971) suggests that since many of the products of sterol metabolism in plants may have "regulatory as well as ecological function" they may be involved in helping plants survive against fungi, insects, and higher animals, and Elliott and Knights (1969) proposed that the manipulation of the sterol content of the host by plant breeding

193

could lead to more resistant crops. The demands of world population for increased food productivity will undoubtedly force a more "applied approach" to research on phytosterols than in the past.

II. Extraction and Identification

A method used in our laboratory for the extraction and identification of phytosterols is as follows: freeze-dried material is extracted with $CHCl_3$ − MeOH (2:1 v/v) in a Soxhlet apparatus and the lipid saponified for 1 hour with 20% KOH in 80% EtOH (ethyl alcohol); ether extraction gives the nonsaponifiable fraction which is chromatographed on aluminum oxide. The sterol fraction is precipitated with 1% digitonin in 60% EtOH according to Windaus and Vibrig (1914). Following centrifugation and decantation, the digitonide is split using pyridine or dimethyl sulfoxide and the sterols are extracted with *n*-hexane. Free sterol mixtures are identified by gas-liquid chromatography (GLC) by comparison of relative retention times of unknown sterols with known sterols according to Patterson (1971a). The free sterols are then chromatographed on Woelm Grade II alumina column and eluted with increasing concentrations of ether in *n*-hexane which will separate C-4-methylated sterols from nonmethylated sterols (Goad and Goodwin, 1966). The sterol fractions are then acetylated with acetic anhydride and separated on silver nitrate–silica gel columns by the method of Vroman and Cohen (1967). The individual sterol acetates are identified by GLC by comparison of retention times relative to cholesterol acetate (Patterson, 1971a). Additional information concerning the identity of phytosterols can be obtained by determining the melting points of sterols and their derivatives, and by means of mass spectrometry (Enroth *et al.*, 1964), nuclear magnetic resonance (NMR) spectrometry (Thompson *et al.*, 1972), infrared (IR) and ultraviolet (UV) spectrometry, molecular rotation and rotary dispersion (Fieser and Fieser, 1959), and a combination of the gas chromatograph and mass spectrometer (Knights, 1967).

Recent variations in the extraction and identification of phytosterols have been reported. Adams and Parks (1967, 1968) found in yeast, (*Saccharomyces cerevisiae*), the usual lipid-soluble ergosterol plus a water-soluble form of ergosterol which was released only after treatment with dimethyl sulfoxide or acid-alkaline pyrogallol. Water-soluble sterols have also been found in the green algae (*Euglena gracilis*) (Brandt *et al.*, 1969, 1970), and in the higher plants (*Kalanchoe blossfeldiana*) (Pryce, 1971) and corn (*Zea mays*) (Anding *et al.*, 1972). Although this suggests a normal occurrence throughout the plant kingdom we were unable to detect water-soluble sterols in eight different phycomycetous or *Aspergillus flavus* fungi. However, as Anding *et al.* (1972) suggests, the presence of water-soluble sterols must be "systematically included" in all studies on phytosterols.

Idler and Safe (1972) have recently proposed a modification of the Vroman and Cohen (1967) method for separating complex sterol mixtures using thin-layer chromatography (TLC). Idler and Safe substituted thin-layer plates impregnated with silica gel HF_{254} and HF_{254} plus 366 silver nitrate (5:1) and developed twice in hexane-benzene (5:2) for the silica gel H-silver nitrate impregnated columns used by Vroman and Cohen to separate sterol acetates. The various sterol acetate bonds were readily visible in long-wave ultraviolet light. They state that this method greatly aided in the identification of mollusc sterols found in complex mixtures that differed only in the number and/or position of alkyl groups of side-chain double bonds. Another advantage of this method is that the time involved in separation by thin-layer plates is less than that using column separation. Reports in the literature on improved methods for isolation and identification appear with increasing frequency.

III. Role of Sterols

Although Schönheimer *et al.* (1930) stated that phytosterols are waste products, Heftmann (1971) reviewed the function of phytosterols and suggested that they probably have the same functions as animal sterols i.e., they act as membrane components, as hormones, and as steroid precursors.

A. Membrane Components

Grunwald studied the role of sterols as components of membranes of higher plants. In an early paper he reported that cholesterol was more effective than $CaCl_2$ in preventing the leakage of β-cyanin from red beet (*Beta vulgaris*) root cells treated with methanol (Grunwald, 1968). Other sterols such as β-sitosterol and stigmasterol, were less effective and he suggested that only sterols with a flat molecular configuration, similar to cholesterol, could enter the phospholipids of the membranes and be active. These results support the membrane model proposed by Finean (1953) and Vandenheuvel (1963) which states that the micelle arrangement in the membrane could be changed by compounds having a hydroxyl group which would interact with the phospholipids of the membrane and thus alter its permeability. The insertion of an extra methyl group in the side chain reduces the ability of a sterol to enter the phospholipids of the membrane and the insertion of an ethyl group would reduce it even further. Edwards and Green (1972) compared *"in vitro"* the ability of phytosterols to enter liposomes and erythrocyte membranes; cholesterol entered more rapidly than sitosterol, whereas campesterol was intermediate which is additional evidence that the insertion of an extra methyl or ethyl group in the side chain reduces the ability of a sterol to enter the membrane phospholipids. Edwards and Green also stated that since ergosterol and stigmasterol are not well absorbed into membranes, the presence of the double bond in the side chain of these sterols reduces its flexibility and also results in a reduction in the ability of the sterol to pack into the phospholipid molecules.

In 1971 Grunwald, using barley roots (*Hordeum vulgare*), compared free sterols with the other forms of sterols found in plants, i.e., steryl esters, steryl glycosides, and acetylated steryl glycosides for their membrane stabilizing effectiveness. He found that cholesteryl palmitate and cholesteryl glucoside which do not have a free hydroxyl group at the C-3 position of the cholestene nucleus, did not change the rate of electrolyte leakage from cells whereas cholesterol, which has a free hydroxyl group at the C-3 position, was effective in preventing leakage. Kemp *et al.* (1967) reported that the level of free sterols in rapidly developing corn shoots increased during the germination period, which you would expect if free sterols are involved in membrane structures. The level of sterol esters, however, did not change in the shoot and root during germination, whereas there was a threefold increase in sterol esters in the scutellum.

If free sterols are involved in membrane structure, what then is the function of sterol esters or sterol glycosides in the plant? Kemp *et al.* (1967) suggested that sterols may be transported intracellularly from their site of synthesis to other organelles as esters and recently Grunwald (1970) investigated the distribution of sterols in intracellular organelles from tobacco (*Nicotiana tabacum*) leaves and found that all membrane-containing fractions contained free sterols, sterol glycosides, and sterol esters. Furthermore, when cholesterol-^{14}C was added to the isolation medium it became distributed intracellularly which led Grunwald to conclude that most of the sterols in plants (free sterols, esters, and glycosides) are associated with membrane-containing organelles.

Evidence for the role of sterols in membrane structures in lower plants, i.e., the fungi, is also available. The most conclusive studies which support the theory that sterols are important as fungal membrane constituents have been done using polyene antibiotics which inhibit sterol incorporation into membranes. In 1968, Siestma and Haskins and Child *et al.* (1968) demonstrated that members of the Pythiaceae fungi which do not synthesize cholesterol, could incorporate exogenous cholesterol into protoplasmic membranes unchanged. As a result there was more leakage of material such as nucleotides, nitrogen, and proteins from mycelia grown without cholesterol. With the addition of polyene antibiotics to the medium, a greater loss of intracellular components occurred as compared to mycelia grown on sterol-amended medium without the antibiotics. They also found that when the cell wall, protoplasmic membrane, and intracellular membrane fractions of *Pythium* spp. were separated and tested for sterol composition, most of the cholesterol was found in the protoplasmic membrane and the remainder was present in the intracellular membrane. Siestma and Haskins (1968) concluded that cholesterol and closely related sterols are taken up by *Pythium* spp. and incorporated into membranes resulting in changes in membrane permeability. A more recent study by Siestma (1971) reports on changes in the metabolism of *Pythium* spp. which he suggests are the result of changes in cell permeability. For example, sexual body formation by *Pythium* spp. is normally initiated after the third day provided that cholesterol or closely related sterols are present in the medium and a high carbon: nitrogen ratio exists. Siestma found that a number of enzymes in the mycelia also showed peak activity after 3–4 days which may have triggered fruiting after they were released into the medium.

Other reported indirect effects of sterols in altering membrane permeability are the increase in tolerance of *Pythium* spp. to high temperatures when grown on sterol-amended medium (Haskins, 1965), an increase in tolerance of *Fusarium roseum* spores, when grown on medium containing ergosterol, to long periods of storage in distilled water (Tillman and Bean, 1970), and the recovery of the yeast *Candida albicans* from UV-induced lethal damage by postirradiation growth on sterol-amended medium (Sarachek and Higgins, 1972). In the later study, the authors proposed that the sterols were being incorporated into the membrane which had been damaged by irradiation.

B. HORMONES

A second major function of sterols, proposed by Heftmann (1971) is their role as hormones. Probably the best understood sterol hormone is that produced by the water molds *Achlya bisexualis* and *A. ambisexualis* (Barksdale, 1969). A steroid having 3-β and 22 hydroxyl groups, $\Delta^{5,\ 24:28}$-double bonds, a keto group on carbon-7, and a lactone group with the ethylene side chain and designated "antheridiol" by Barksdale is secreted by the female strain which stimulates the formation of antheridial branches in the male. Antheridiol also stimulates the male strain to se-

crete a different hormone which induces the formation of sex organs by
the female and is followed by conjugation of male and female organs.
The concentration of the steroid hormone determines both the amount
of elapsed time occurring between the addition of hormone and formation
of branches, and the number of antheridial branches formed. Although
Hendrix (1970) questions whether a hormone controlling sexualism exists
in the pythiaceous fungi, recently Child and Haskins (1971) stimulated
a sexual reaction between heterothallic *Pythium* spp. by growing them on
synthetic medium which contained cholesterol. They were also able to
induce oospore formation in unisexual strains which suggests that a steroid
hormone may be involved in the sexual process of fungi other than
Achyla spp.

Studies on steroid hormones in the higher plants have been largely
concerned with their role in the insect molting process. In reviewing the
subject in 1970, Heftmann states that the C_{27} insect molting hormone
probably originates from cholesterol which would explain its widespread
distribution in the plant kingdom; all contain an $\alpha\beta$ unsaturated carboxyl
group and a 14α hydroxyl group and all are water soluble. A suggested
mode of action of the insect molting hormone is as follows: the hormone,
after ingestion by the insect activates genes within the insect which then
activate ribonucleic acids which direct the synthesis of enzymes controlling insect metamorphosis. Heftmann (1970) stated that, because of the
similarity of gene regulation in plants and animals, the insect molting
hormones may also be involved in plant metamorphosis. Bonner *et al.*
(1963) were able to prevent floral initiation and Bae and Mercer (1970)
prevented potato tuber formation by applying a sterol inhibitor to plants;
however, Heftmann (1970) was unable to stimulate flowering by treating
plants with ecdysone, the steroid insect hormone. Of further interest is
the importance of molting sterols to insects which are unable to synthesize the steroid nucleus and thus require an external supply which will
be discussed later on in this paper.

C. Steroid Precursors

A third major function of sterols in plants is their role as steroid precursors. Cholesterol is undoubtedly the most important sterol in the biosynthesis of plant steroids, and when metabolized it produces C_{27} sapogenins such as tomatidine and solanidine which are involved in plant
disease resistance, ecdysterone which is the insect molting hormone and
other sapogenins important to the pharmaceutical industry. Cholesterol
may also convert to pregnenolone which serves as the source of C_{21}
steroids or to progesterone which has endocrine properties in animals, yet

its role in plant metabolism is as yet unknown. The C_{28} and C_{29} plant sterols probably originate from a precursor to cholesterol such as sitosterol which may serve as the primary reserve supply of sterol which the plant uses to produce other sterols and steroids. The reader is again directed to the excellent review articles by Goad (1967), Heftmann (1968), and others for additional information on phytosterol biosynthesis.

D. OTHER ROLES

Phytosterols also have functions other than what has been discussed i.e., membrane component, hormonal and steroid precursors. For example, the role of sterols in growth and reproduction of fungi is well substantiated. The genera *Pythium* and *Phytophthora* in the family Pythiaceae require exogenous sterols for both sexual and asexual reproduction. Hendrix (1970) lists other fungi such as *Trichophyton rubrum, Aspergillus niger, Colletotrichum lagenarium,* and *Piricularia oryzae* which can grow in the absence of sterols yet exhibit a growth stimulation when they are added to the medium.

An analogous situation occurs in phytophagous insects which require an exogenous source of sterol for growth. The dependence of *Drosophila pachea,* on the Senita cactus (*Lophocereus schottii*), is an example (Kircher and Heed, 1970). Kircher and Heed studied the distribution of *Drosophila* species among different species of cacti and found varying degrees of specificity between insect and plant species and hypothesized that both may have co-evolved. The most evolved of these insect-plant relationships is the limitation of *D. pachea* to the Senita cactus. A study of the nutritional requirements of *D. pachea* and the nutrients available in the cactus revealed that *D. pachea* had a specific dietary sterol requirement which was provided by the Senita cactus. The sterols present in the Senita cactus were 4α-methyl-Δ^7-cholesten-3β-ol (lophenol) and Δ^7-stigmasten-3β-ol (schottenol) which were not found in any other cactus species. In addition, the Senita cactus contained a level of alkaloids that was toxic to all *Drosophila* species but *D. pachea* (Kircher and Heed, 1970).

It has also been suggested that sterols could be used to control insects. Salama and El-Sharaby (1972) found that growing the cotton leafworm insect (*Spodoptera littoralis*) on medium containing β-sitosterol, resulted in insect sterility and they proposed the use of naturally occurring plant substances such as β-sitosterol as a means of biological control.

Other workers have used sterol synthesis inhibitors to demonstrate the importance of sterols in the metabolism of fungi. *Cochliobulus carbonum* was prevented from forming sexually produced perithecia by the sterol inhibitor SKF 3301-A (Nelson *et al.*, 1967). With *Gibberella fujikori,* a sterol inhibitor stimulated sterol synthesis and reproduction (Reid, 1969) whereas with the Ascomycete *Sordaria,* SKF 3301-A stimulated perithecia production at low concentrations and inhibited perithecia production at high concentrations (Elliott, 1969). Aaronson (1971) reported that the yeast *Saccharomyces cerevisiae* is inhibited from multiplication by the hypocholesteremic compounds benzmalecene and triparanol but the inhibition was reversed by addition of oleic acid, lauric acid, ergosterol, and squalene whereas the following lipids were ineffective: mevalonic acid, lanosterol, cholesterol, β-sitosterol, myristic, palmitic, and stearic acid. Aaronson states that the hypocholesteramic compounds may also be interfering with fatty acid synthesis in some organisms which may account for the reported diversity in response of microorganisms to this group of chemicals (Hendrix, 1970).

Reports also show that sterols may cause an inhibition in growth and reproduction of some fungi. Elliott (1968) compared the effect of cholesterol and cholestanol on growth and reproduction by *Phytophthora cactorum.* Although both sterols stimulated mycelia growth, their influence on reproduction was different. Cholesterol normally stimulates oospore formation, cholestanol inhibits oospore formation, but when both sterols were added to the medium together, at a low concentration, the oospore number was increased. However, when a high concentration of cholesterol was added along with cholestanol, then oospore formation was decreased. Elliott suggests two sites in the cellular structure of the fungus controlling vegetative growth and oospore development which can be occupied by either cholesterol or cholestanol. He also postulated that one of the sites has a "higher affinity for more active molecules" so that above a critical level of cholesterol, the addition of cholestanol replaces cholesterol from the site controlling oospore development and the oospore number is decreased. Likewise, below this critical concentration of cholesterol, the cholestanol molecule can also occupy controlling oospore development and the oospore number is increased.

The presence of sterols in plant tissues which are inhibitory to some microorganisms and stimulatory to others, thus resulting in resistance or susceptibility of the plant, has only recently received the attention it deserves. Several studies suggesting that sterols could play a role in disease resistance or susceptibility are as follows: Allen and Kuć (1968) report that the immunity of white potato tubers (*Solanum tuberosum*) to *Helminthosporium carbonum* was probably due to the presence of the steroid glycoalkaloids α-solanine and α-chaconine in the potato peel. Arneson and Durbin (1968) found the steroid glycoalkaloid tomatine more toxic to nonpathogens of tomato than to pathogens and suggested that tomatine reacts with the sterols of the nonpathogens thus preventing them from infecting tomato tissue. Jennings *et al.* (1970) studied sterol changes in corn leaves infected with *H. carbonum.* Although the percentage of campesterol did not change in the resistant reaction, the percentage of stigmasterol increased and β-sitosterol decreased as compared to the controls. In the susceptible reactions, there was a large increase in stigmasterol and a large decrease in β-sitosterol. The authors proposed that the fungus could be producing a toxin which is interfering with sterols in the host, thus causing a change in plant cell permeability resulting in increased loss of sterols.

Elliott and Knights (1969) proposed that the relative different amounts of sterols in the plants may be more important than the level of any one sterol in conferring resistance or susceptibility in a plant. They found that in potato varieties the ratio of precursor sterols to sterols was directly proportional to the degree of resistance to *Phytophthora* and *Pythium.* The plant and fungus are both competing for the same sterol precursors and the result is that the sterol-requiring fungus has reduced sporulation and pathogenicity.

Knights (1970) investigated the sterols present in resting spores of the root gall fungus *Plasmodiophora brassicae* which causes the clubroot disease of Cruciferae. In an earlier paper Ingram *et al.* (1968) reported that sterols in the Cruciferae vary in proportion during growth and physiological development of the plant and specifically that 28-isofucosterol occurred at a high level in seeds, but 2 weeks after germination it had virtually disappeared. When spores of *P. brassicae* were analyzed for sterols, Knights (1970) found 28-isofucosterol, but it was not present in healthy roots indicating that the fungus had derived part of its sterol from the plant during early stages of development. Knights also compared the relative amounts of sterols in Cruciferae during different stages of growth; β-sitosterol level rises during vegetative growth of the plant up to flowering and then decreases whereas campesterol falls during vegetative growth and increases after flowering. He found that the percentage of campesterol in healthy root tissue was lower than in spores, so that the fungus had obtained sterols from the roots at a time when the campesterol level was highest in the plant. This led Knights to conclude that the parasite is probably using the host as its source of sterols which suggests that the manipulation of the host sterol content either by breeding or by application of sterol-inhibiting compounds may be possible thus resulting in increased resistance to the plant pathogens. Surprisingly only a few studies have been done in this area.

IV. Changes in Sterols during Plant Growth

Elsewhere in this chapter is a list of plants, the sterols that they contain, and their locations within the plants. However, of greater interest are those studies on the qualitative and quantitative changes in sterols that occur during plant growth. Kemp *et al.* (1967), studied the sterols in the shoot, root, scutellum, and endosperm of 4-, 6-, 9-, 11-, and 13-day-old corn seedlings. The free sterols increased in the shoot and root but remained the same in the other fractions, whereas the level of sterol esters remained the same except for a rise in Δ^5-sterol esters in the scutellum. They also found that as the level of stigmasterol increased, in root tissues, the level of β-sitosterol decreased. In 1968 Kemp and Mercer (1968b), studied the sterol esters of 10-day-old corn seedlings and found a greater proportion of esterified cholesterol in the shoots than in all other plant parts.

Other workers have investigated intracellular sterols. For example, Mercer and Treharne (1966) isolated chloroplasts from dwarf-bean (*Phaseolus vulgaris*) using carbon tetrachloride–hexane and found that cholesterol constituted more than 80% of the sterol fraction. They noted that after five hexane washings, acetone could still remove additional sterols. Chloroplasts from spinach (*Spinacia oleracea*) also contained cholesterol in addition to β-spinasterol and stigmast-7-enol (Eichenberger and Menke, 1966). Kemp and Mercer (1968a) investigated the sterols of the intracellular organelles of corn shoots and found that the microsomal and mitochondrial fractions contained the greatest amount of sterols, whereas the greatest proportion of cholesterol was found in the nuclear fraction. When the chloroplasts were examined, two fractions were identified; in the esterified sterol fraction, cholesterol was 50% of the mixture and β-sitosterol 35%, whereas in the unesterified fraction, cholesterol was 2–3%, campesterol 13%, stigmasterol 26%, and β-sitosterol 59%.

Knights (1971) recently compared the sterols in the chloroplasts of eight plant species and also found evidence for two qualitatively distinct forms. The chloroplasts were extracted sequentially with petroleum ether and acetone. Although cholesterol was extracted with both solvents there was more present in the acetone fraction than in the petroleum ether fraction. Knights (1971) found a lower level of sterols in beans reported by Mercer and Treharne in their early paper (1966), yet the ratio of sterols in the two fractions was very similar; Knights' study also supports the earlier work of Kemp and Mercer (1968a) with corn.

Work with the alga *E. gracilis* strain Z suggests that sterols may exist in four forms, i.e., unesterified, esterified, water-soluble–acid-hydrolyzable, and water-soluble–alkaline-pyrogallol labile forms. When grown in light *E. gracilis* is photosynthetic, green, and autotrophic, whereas in dark it is nonphotosynthetic, white, heterotrophic, and does not contain chloroplasts. Brandt *et al.* (1970) studied sterol metabolism during cell growth and division of *E. gracilis* under light and dark conditions. A number of differences were observed. Three types of sterols were found, i.e., Δ^7, Δ^5, and $\Delta^{5,7}$; the Δ^7-sterols were found only in free form, whereas bound sterols contained only Δ^5. In light-grown cultures, Δ^7-sterols were 65% of the total sterol and 98% of the free sterols, whereas in dark-grown cultures, Δ^7-sterols represented only 5% of the total sterol and 47% of the free sterols. As Brandt *et al.* (1970) point out, this is to be expected since Δ^7-sterols are precursors to Δ^5 sterols with $\Delta^{5,7}$ sterols as the intermediates. Chondrillasterol was present in light-grown cultures but absent in dark-grown cultures. Although the total amounts of free and bound sterols are similar in light- and dark-grown culture, there were more free sterols in light-grown cultures and a high level of bound sterols in dark-grown cultures, which the authors state may indicate a "sterol reserve function" for bound sterols.

The quantities of the two water soluble sterol fractions previously discussed in yeast (Adams and Parks, 1967, 1968), and in *Kalanchoe blossfeldiana* (Pryce, 1971) were the same in light and dark cultures. Brandt *et al.* (1970) suggest that the presence of water-soluble sterols in plants may be a means by which sterols could be eliminated by the organism into the culture medium, since water-soluble forms have been found in the culture medium and their composition is the same as the water-soluble sterols within the cell.

The influence of light on the sterols of higher plants has also been investigated. Bae and Mercer (1970) studied the levels of free sterol, sterol esters, and glycosides in the leaves of potato (*Solanum andigena*) when plants were transferred from long-day to short-day conditions. There is an initial decrease in the level of β-sitosterol and cycloartenol and an increase in the level of cholesterol. After 2–3 weeks, however, the sterol levels return to those within long-day leaves. Bae and Mercer proposed that the change in cholesterol level may be involved with tuber formation which occurs under short-day conditions. If cholesterol serves as a precursor to the hormone controlling tuber formation then there should be an initial increase in cholesterol which is followed by a decrease in cholesterol as tuberization is completed.

Davis (1971) investigated the influence of light, maturation, and curing phase on the sterols in tobacco. Stigmasterol increased with increasing amount of shading; i.e., the plant base and leaves had the highest amount; β-sitosterol decreased with increasing shade whereas campesterol and cholesterol increased slightly from the base of the plant to the apex. During maturation and curing there was a general decrease in total sterol with little change in the percentages of different sterols. Davis found no evidence for upward translocation of sterols into other leaves, but suggested that sterols may be translocated into the stalk during air-curing. Grunwald *et al.* (1971), also working with tobacco, found no difference in the recovery of sterols from air-dried and oven-dried tobacco and also reported that nitrogen fertilization level had no influence on the amounts of sterols present.

Other workers have investigated the sterols in green and etiolated leaves. Hirayama and Suzuki (1968) found that etiolated corn leaves had about 60% more free sterol than green tissue, whereas Bush *et al.* (1971) reported that etiolated barley shoots had 38% more free sterols than green tissue which they claim may be the result of the methods used to determine cholesterol equivalents. Although Gaunt and Stowe (1967) interpreted their data to mean that there was not a change in level of unsaturated free sterol during greening of etiolated pea plants (*Pisum sativum*) during a 24-hour period, Bush *et al.* (1971) looked at the same results and stated that there was a 12–15% decrease in sterol content during this period. In their study with etiolated barley shoots, Bush *et al.* (1971) observed that the difference in total sterol content between green and etiolated tissue, 2.87 and 3.20 mg per gram dry weight respectively, was the result of the difference in the level of free sterols, and the sterol ester and glycoside plus acylated sterol glycoside content of green and etiolated tissue was the same. Etiolated barley tissue had twice the amount of β-sitosterol as stigmasterol, whereas green tissues had the same amount. The authors also investigated possible intracellular changes in sterols that occur during actual greening of etiolated leaves. Although free campesterol and cholesterol content did not change, the stigmasterol content increased while the β-sitosterol content decreased in the chloroplasts and throughout the cell.

To explain the changes in biosynthesis of terpenoids (including phytosterols) that occur during greening of etiolated leaves and seedling development, Rogers *et al.* (1968) have proposed a theory of "compartmentation" which states that terpenoid biosynthesis occurs within the cell as a result of enzyme segregation and the impermeability of intracellular membranes to terpenoids and their precursors, which means that terpenoid biosynthesis is directed during various stages of plant development.

"Compartmentation" may occur as follows: Mevalonic acid is formed from food reserves during seed germination and is used in the formation of sterols that are necessary for membranes. Although mevalonic acid is unable to enter the chloroplasts to form pigments, pigments are not needed by the plant at this time. After emergence of seedlings from the soil, the chloroplasts develop, carbon dioxide is fixed, and mevalonate is formed which is then used in the synthesis of chloroplast terpenoids. The mevalonate is now unable to leave the chloroplast and be used in sterol synthesis, but upon maturity of the chloroplasts, phosphoglyceric acid moves out of the plastid, is converted to mevalonate which is now needed for formation of sterols for further growth of the plant. The authors also present a great deal of evidence to support their theory.

Other environmental factors, such as pollutants, have been studied as to their influence on phytosterols. Tomlinson and Rich (1971) reported that the pollutant ozone changed the sterols and sterol derivatives in bean plants, resulting in a loss of cellular contents into intracellular spaces which is the first symptom of ozone damage. They found that ozonated leaves contained 25% less free sterol, 100–150% more acylated sterol glycosides and 50% more sterol glycosides. Apparently the free sterols are being converted to acylated sterol glycosides and sterol glycosides which results in a change in cell wall permeability and leakage of intracellular liquids.

V. Sterols and Their Location in Plants

It would be difficult to summarize the information in Tables I and II on sterol distribution in the plant kingdom. First of all, the distribution of some sterols, such as β-sitosterol, is uniform throughout the plant kingdom, whereas others, such as 22-dehydrocholesterol, have been found in only one fungus, i.e., *Rhizophylyctis rosea*. In addition, only a small number of species in a relatively few plant families have been studied, and therefore any generalizations would have to be based to a great extent on speculation and might prove to be erroneous as has happened in the past. For example, prior to the discovery of cholesterol in phycomycetous fungi by McCorkindale *et al.* (1969) it was assumed that ergosterol was the characteristic sterol of fungi. Furthermore when we compared four fungi taxonomically related to those studied by McCorkindale *et al.*, cholesterol was only present in two of the fungi, whereas ergosterol, its precursors, or metabolites could not be detected (Bean *et al.*, 1972). The belief that bacteria and blue-green algae do not contain sterols has also been recently found to be erroneous and probably resulted from earlier improper procedures in sterol extraction (Carr and Craig, 1970). Although a proposed "chemotaxonomic classification" of plants utilizing information on their phytosterols composition may eventually be possible, a great number of additional plant families and species within the same family should first be studied before any attempts are made at proposing either relationships or evolutionary trends in the plant kingdom.

Table I

STEROLS FOUND IN PLANTS

Plants	Sterol[a]	Location	Reference
A. Angiosperms			
Betulaceae			
Alnus glutinosa	29	Pollen	Barbier, 1970
Corulus avellana	29	Pollen	Barbier, 1970
Bromeliaceae			
Tillandsia usnacoides	22, 24, 29, 33, 35, 36, 43	Leaves	Atallah and Nicholas, 1971
Cactaceae			
Carnegias gigantea	23	Pollen	Barbier, 1970
Lophocereus schottii	6, 25	—	Kircher, 1969a
Cheirodendron gaudichaudii	24, 29	—	Kircher, 1969b
Chenopodiaceae			
Spinacia oleracea	22, 25	Chloroplasts	Grunwald, 1970
Compositae			
Aster baccharoides	32	Leaves	Hui *et al.*, 1971
Baccharis viminea	29	Pollen	Barbier, 1970
Helianthus annuus	29	Pollen	Barbier, 1970
Hypochoeris radicata	22	Pollen	Barbier, 1970
Lactuca sativa	9, 24, 29, 33	Leaves, seed	Knapp *et al.*, 1968; Knights and Middleditch, 1972
Taraxacum officinale	29	Pollen	Barbier, 1970
Crassulaceae			
Kalanchoe blossfeldiana	9, 22, 24, 29, 33	Leaves	Pryce, 1971
Cruciferae			
See Knights, 1970b		Roots	
See Knights and Berrie, 1971		Seeds	

		Chloroplasts Pollen	
See Knights, 1971			
See Barbier, 1970			
Cucurbitaceae			
Bryonia dioca	44	Leaves	Gonzalez and Panzio, 1969
Bryonia verrucosa	44	Leaves	Gonzalez and Panzio, 1969
Cucurbita pepo	32	Leaves	Sucrow and Raduchel, 1970
Ecballium elaterium	44	Leaves	Gonzales and Panzio, 1967
Dioscoreaceae			
Dioscorea tokoro	22, 24, 29, 33	Tissue cultures	Tomita *et al.*, 1970a
Ericaceae			
Arbutus menziesii	29	Bark	Robinson and McCaig, 1971
Calluna vulgaris	24	Pollen	Barbier, 1970
Euphorbiaceae			
Euphorbia peplus	8, 9, 22, 24, 29, 33	Leaves	Basted, 1969
Graminaceae			
Avena spp.		Leaves	See Knights, 1968; Knights and Laurie, 1967
Hordeum vulgare	22, 29, 33	Leaves	Bush *et al.*, 1971
Phleum pratense	33	Pollen	Barbier, 1970
Secale cereale	33	Pollen	Barbier, 1970
Triticum aestivum	22, 24, 29, 33	Leaves	Nowak *et al.*, 1972
Zea mays	22, 24, 29, 33, 35, 36	Leaves, roots, intracellular	Kemp and Mercer, 1968a,b; Kemp *et al.*, 1967
Hippocastanaceae			
Aesculus hippocastanum	29	Pollen	Barbier, 1970
Hydrocharitaceae			
Halophila engelmanni	24, 29, 33	Leaves	Attaway *et al.*, 1971
Thalassia testudinum	24, 29, 33	Leaves	Attaway *et al.*, 1971
Hydrophyllaceae			
Hydrophyllum capitatum	29	Pollen	Barbier, 1970

(Continued)

Table I (*Continued*)

Plants	Sterol[a]	Location	Reference
Leguminosae			
Cassia jahnii	29	Leaves	Mendez, 1970
Erythrina suberosa	22, 24, 29, 33	Bark	Singh *et al.*, 1970
Phaseolus multiflorus	29	Seed	Pryce, 1971
Phaseolus vulgaris	22, 24, 29	Intracellular	Mercer and Treharne, 1966; Knapp *et al.*, 1969
Trifolium pratense	23	Pollen	Barbier, 1970
Musaceae			
Musa sapientum	24, 29, 33, 35, 36, 43	Stalks, leaves, peel, rhizome, pulp	Knapp and Nicholas, 1969a,b,c
Myrtaceae			
Eucalyptus microcorys	29, 35, 36, 43	Leaves	Bottari *et al.*, 1972
Palmaceae			
Phoenix dactylifera	22	Leaves	Bennett *et al.*, 1965
Polygonaceae			
Polygonum spp.	29	Leaves	Barbier, 1970
Rosaceae			
Malus sylvestris	22, 23	Seed, pollen	Gawienowski and Gibbs, 1968; Barbier, 1970
Rubiaceae			
Coffea arabica	35, 36	Oil	Alcaide *et al.*, 1971
Ruppiaceae			
Ruppia maritama	24, 29, 33	Leaves	Attaway *et al.*, 1971
Rutaceae			
Citrus spp.	10	Peel	Yokayama and White, 1968
Citrus paradisi	4, 5, 24, 29, 33, 35, 36, 43	Peel	Williams *et al.*, 1967
Citrus sinensis	22, 23, 24, 29, 33, 38, 43	Juice sacs	Nagy and Nordby, 1971

Salicaceae			
Populus nigra	29	Pollen	Barbier, 1970
Solanaceae			
Lycopersicon esculentum	24	Leaves	Bennett and Heftmann, 1961
Nicotiana spp.	5, 22, 24, 29, 33, 35, 36	Leaves	Bolt and Clarke, 1970; Cheng et al., 1971a,b; Davis, 1971
Nicotiana langsdorffii	22, 24, 29, 33	Leaves	Cheng et al., 1971a
Nicotiana suaveolens	22, 24, 29, 33	Leaves	Cheng et al., 1971a
Nicotiana tabacum	22, 24, 29, 33	Intracellular	Grunwald, 1970
Solanum andigena	22, 29, 36	Leaves	Bae and Mercer, 1970
Solanum tuberosum	4, 5, 6, 18, 22, 24, 29, 33, 35, 36	Leaves	Rees et al., 1968
Solanum xanthorcarpum	29	Leaves	Heble et al., 1971
Verbenaceae			
Clerodendron campbellii	4, 19, 20, 35, 36, 42, 43	Leaves	Bolger et al., 1970
Zannichelliaceae			
Diplanthera wrightii	24, 29, 33	Leaves	Attaway et al., 1971
Syringodium filiforme	24, 29, 33	Leaves	Attaway et al., 1971
B. Gymnosperms			
Cupressaceae			
Juniperus utahensis	29	Pollen	Barbier, 1970
Ginkgoaceae			
Ginkgo biloba	24, 29	Leaves	Kircher, 1970
Pinaceae			
Larix decidua	4, 5, 29, 33, 35, 36	Leaves	Goad and Goodwin, 1967
Pinus sylvestris	29	Pollen	Barbier, 1970
Pinus sativum	9, 29, 33	Leaves	Buisted, 1971
C. Ferns			
Polypodiaceae			
Polypodium vulgare	29, 34	Leaves	de Souza et al., 1970
Polystichum filix mas	22	Leaves	Duperon et al., 1964

(*Continued*)

Table I (*Continued*)

Plants	Sterol[a]	Location	Reference
D. Mosses			
Sphagnaceae			
Sphagnum spp.	27, 29	Leaves	Ives and O'Neill, 1958
See Huneck, 1971			
E. Algae			
See Patterson, 1971b			
Chlorophyta			
Chlorella ellipsoidea	10, 24		Tomita *et al.*, 1971
Chlorella vulgaris	21, 25, 41		Tomita *et al.*, 1970b
Oocystis polymorpha	21, 22, 25, 41		Orcutt and Richardson, 1970
Euglenophyta			
Euglena gracilis	11, 15, 21, 22, 23, 24, 25, 30, 37, 39, 40, 41		Brandt *et al.*, 1970
Rhodophyta			
Porphyridium cruentum	22, 31, 36	—	Beastall *et al.*, 1971
F. Fungi			
I. Fungi Imperfecti			
Aspergillus flavus	2, 10, 12	—	G. A. Bean, unpublished; Vacheron and Michel, 1968
Aspergillus fumigatus	1, 10	—	Goulston *et al.*, 1967; Osman *et al.*, 1969
Aspergillus niger	10, 13	—	Mostafa *et al.*, 1969; Barton and Bruun, 1951
Fusarium moniliforme	10	—	Serebryakov *et al.*, 1970
Fusarium oxysporum	2, 10	—	Starratt and Madhosingh, 1967
Fusarium solani	10	—	Kok *et al.*, 1970
Mucor genevensis	10, 24	—	Gordon *et al.*, 1970
Mucor fragilis	10	—	Mostafa *et al.*, 1969

Species		Numbers	Reference
Penicillium funiculosum		22	Chen and Haskins, 1962
Phycomyces blakesleeanus		1, 7, 10	Chenovda, 1970; Goulstonand Mercer, 1969
Rhizoctonia solani	—	10	Schlosser *et al.*, 1969
Rhizopus arrhizus	—	11, 21	Weete *et al.*, 1973
Stemphylium consortiale	—	10	Mostafa *et al.*, 1969
Zalerion maritima	—	10	Kirk, 1970
II. Phycomycetes			
Allomyces macrogynus	—	22, 29, 33	Bean *et al.*, 1972
Hyphochytrium catenoides	—	24, 29, 33	Bean *et al.*, 1972
Plasmodiophora brassicae	—	9, 22, 24, 29, 34, 38	Knights, 1970
Rhizidiomyces apophysatus	—	29, 33	Bean *et al.*, 1972
Rhizophlyctis rosea	—	22, 31	Bean *et al.*, 1972
Aquatic Phycomcetes	—	—	See McCorkindale *et al.*, 1669
III. Ascomycetes			
Claviceps purpurea	—	11	Barton and Cox, 1948
Coriosporopsis halima	—	10	Kirk, 1970
Corollospora maritima	—	10	Kirk, 1970
Corollospora trifurcata	—	10	Kirk, 1970
Neurospora crassa	—	10	Tsuda and Tatum, 1963
Saccharomyces cerevisiae	—	3, 10, 14	Adams and Parks, 1968; Barton *et al.*, 1968; Parks *et al.*, 1972
Yeast species			
See El-Refai and El-Kady, 1968			
IV. Basidiomycetes			
Coprinus lagopus	—	10, 12	Défago *et al.*, 1971
Daedalea quercina	—	10, 11	Tanahashi and Takahashi, 1966
Fomes applanatus	—	11	Holtz and Schisler, 1972
Ganoderma applandatum	—	15, 21	Strgina *et al.*, 1971
Melampsora lini	—	25, 26, 28	Jackson and Frear, 1968
Polyporus paragamenus	—	12	Alt and Barton, 1952

(*Continued*)

Table I (*Continued*)

Plants	Sterol[a]	Location	Reference
Polyporus pinicola	11	—	Halsall and Sayer, 1959
Puccinia graminis	21, 22, 25	—	Nowak *et al.*, 1972; Hougen *et al.*, 1958
Schizophyllum commune	10	—	Mokady and Koltin, 1971
Ustilago maydis	10	—	Ragsdale and Sisler, 1972
V. Myxomycetes			
Physarum polycephalum	22, 24, 27, 29, 33, 34	—	Lenfant *et al.*, 1970
VI. Lichens			
Xanthoria parietina	10	—	Solberg, 1971
G. Bacteria			
See Carr and Craig, 1970			
Mathylococcus capsulatus	16, 17	—	Bird *et al.*, 1971

[a] See Table II for sterol identification.

Table II
KEY TO STEROL IDENTIFICATION

Number (as in Table I, col. 2)	Sterol
1	Lanosterol (lanosta-$\Delta^{8,24}$-dienol)
2	Cerevisterol
3	4α-Methyl-24-methylene-24-dihydrozymasterol
4	24-Methylenelophenol
5	Citrostadienol (24-ethylidene lophenol)
6	Lophenol
7	Fucosterol (ergosta-$\Delta^{5,7,24(28)}$-trienol)
8	Δ^7-Isofucosterol
9	28-Isofucosterol (Δ^5-avenasterol)
10	Ergosterol
11	5-Dihydroergosterol (ergosta-$\Delta^{7,22}$-dienol)
12	22-Dihydroergosterol (ergosta-$\Delta^{5,7}$-dienol)
13	14-Dehydroergosterol (ergosta-5,7,11,22-tetraenol)
14	Ergosta-$\Delta^{8(9),22}$-dienol
15	Ergosta-$\Delta^{7,16,24(28)}$-dienol (episterol)
16	4,4-Dimethyl-5α-cholest-8(9)-en-3β-ol
17	4,4-Dimethyl-5α-cholesta-8(9), 24-dien-3β-ol
18	4α-14α-Dimethylcholesta-8,24-diem-3β-ol
19	24α-Ethyl cholesta-5,22,25-triene-3β-ol
20	24-Ethyl-4α-methyl-5α-cholesta-7,25-dien-3β-ol
21	24α-Methyl-5α-cholesta-7-ene-3β-ol (Δ^7-ergostenol) (fungisterol)
22	Cholesterol
23	24-Methylene cholesterol (chalinasterol)
24	Stigmasterol (24α-ethyl-$\Delta^{5,22}$-cholestadien-3β-ol)
25	Δ^7-Stigmastenol (schottenol) (Δ^7-chondrillastenol) (24-ethyl-Δ^7-Cholestanol)
26	Stigmasta-5,7-dienol (7-dehydrositosterol)
27	Stigmastanol
28	5α-(24Z)Ethylidene-cholesta-7,24(28)-dien-3β-ol (stigmasta-7,24(28)-dienol)
29	β-Sitosterol (24α-ethyl cholesterol)
30	7-Dehydrocholesterol ($\Delta^{5,7}$-cholestadienol)
31	22-Dehydrocholesterol
32	α-Spinasterol
33	Campesterol (24α-methyl cholesterol)
34	Campestanol
35	24-Methylene cycloartenol
36	Cycloartenol
37	Δ^5-Ergostenol (22-dihydrobrassicasterol)
38	Brassicasterol (24α-methyl-$\Delta^{5,22}$-cholestadien-3β-ol)
39	Δ^7-Cholestenol
40	$\Delta^{5,7}$-Chondrillasterol
41	Chondrillasterol
42	Obtusifoliol
43	Cycloeucalenol (24-ethylidene cholesterol)
44	Elasterol (stigmasta-7,16,25(26)-trien-3β-ol)

VI. Conclusions

The study of phytosterols is still in its infancy if we consider the application of GLC in the identification of sterols (1960) as the beginning point of current phytosterol research. Because of increasing interest and availability of instrumentation for the extraction and identification of phytosterols there will undoubtedly be a voluminous amount of information available on the occurrence of sterols in the plant kingdom. This information will be looked upon by some as an invaluable aid in understanding evolutionary trends in plants; others will concentrate on the probable biosynthetic pathways that have produced those sterols, whereas some may attempt to manipulate sterols in order to produce plants which are more productive as well as resistant to insects and diseases.

ACKNOWLEDGMENTS

I am very grateful to my colleague Dr. G. Patterson for his assistance in the preparation of this manuscript. I also thank Messrs M. Fusco and R. Blum who aided in the collection of data on phytosterol distribution in plants.

References

Aaronson, S. (1971). *Proc. Soc. Exp. Biol. Med.* **136**, 61.

Adams, B. G., and Parks, L. W. (1967). *Biochem. Biophys. Res. Commun.* **28**, 490.

Adams, B. G., and Parks, L. W. (1968). *J. Lipid Res.* **9**, 8.

Alcaide, A., Devys, M., Barbier, M., Kaufman, H. P., and Sen Gupta, A. K. (1971). *Phytochemistry* **10**, 209.

Allen, E. H., and Kuć, J. (1968). *Phytopathology* **58**, 776.

Alt, G. H., and Barton, D. H. R. (1952). *Chem. Ind. (London)* **45**, 1103.

Anding, C., Brandt, R. D., Ourisson, G., Pryce, R. J., and Rohmer, M. (1972). *Proc. Roy. Soc., Ser. B* **180**, 115.

Arneson, P. A., and Durbin, R. D. (1968). *Phytopathology* **58**, 536.

Atallah, A. M., and Nicholas, H. J. (1971). *Phytochemistry* **10**, 3139.

Attaway, D. H., Hang, P., and Parker, P. L. (1971). *Lipids* **6**, 687.

Bae, M., and Mercer, E. I. (1970). *Phytochemistry* **9**, 63.

Baisted, D. J. (1969). *Phytochemistry* **8**, 1697.

Baisted, D. J. (1971). *Biochem. J.* **124**, 375.

Barbier, M. (1970). *Progr. Phytochem.* **2**, 1.

Barksdale, A. W. (1969). *Science* **166**, 831.

Barton, D. H. R., and Brunn, T. (1951). *J. Chem. Soc., London* p. 2728.

Barton, D. H. R., and Cox, J. D. (1948). *J. Chem. Soc., London* p. 1354.

Barton, D. H. R., Harrison, D. M., and Widdowson, D. A. (1968). *Chem. Commun.* p. 17.

Bean, G. A., Patterson, G. W., and Motta, J. J. (1972). *Comp. Biochem. Physiol.* **43B**, 935.

Beastall, G. H., Rees, H. H., and Goodwin, T. W. (1971). *Tetrahedron Lett.* **52**, 4935.

Beerthius, R. K., and Recourt, J. H. (1960). *Nature (London)* **186**, 372.

Bennett, R. D., and Heftmann, E. (1961). *Science* **134**, 671.

Bennett, R. D., Ko, S.-T., and Heftmann, E. (1965). *Phytochemistry* **5**, 231.

Bird, C. W., Lynch, J. M., Pirt, F. J., Reid, W. W., Brooks, C. J. W., and Middleditch, B. S. (1971). *Nature (London)* **230**, 473.

Bolger, L. M., Rees, H. H., Ghisalberti, E. L., Goad, L. J., and Goodwin, T. W. (1970). *Tetrahedron Lett.* **35**, 3043.

Bolt, A. J. N., and Clarke, R. E. (1970). *Phytochemistry* **9**, 819.

Bonner, J., Heftmann, E., and Zeevaart, J. A. D. (1963). *Plant Physiol.* **38**, 81.

Bottari, F., Marsili, A., and Morelli, I. (1972). *Phytochemistry* **11**, 2120.

Brandt, R. D., Ourisson, G., and Pryce, R. J. (1969). *Biochem. Biophys. Res. Commun.* **37**, 399.

Brandt, R. D., Pryce, R. J., Anding, C., and Ourisson, G. (1970). *Eur. J. Biochem.* **17**, 344.

Bush, B., Grunwald, C., and Davis, D. L. (1971). *Plant Physiol.* **47**, 745.

Carr, N. G., and Craig, I. W. (1970). *In* "Phytochemical Phylogeny" (J. B. Harborne, ed.), pp. 119–143. Academic Press, New York.

Chen, Y. S., and Haskins, R. H. (1962). *Can. J. Chem.* **41**, 1647.

Cheng, A. L. S., Kasperbauer, M. J., and Rice, L. G. (1971a). *Phytochemistry* **10**, 1481.

Cheng, A. L. S., Tso, T. C., and Chaplin, J. F. (1971b). *Crop Sci.* **11**, 580.

Chenovda, M. S. (1970). *J. Gen. Appl. Microbiol.* **16**, 501.

Child, J. J., and Haskins, R. H. (1971). *Can. J. Bot.* **49**, 329.

Child, J. J., Défago, G., and Haskins, R. H. (1968). *Can. J. Microbiol.* **15**, 599.

Davis, D. L. (1971). *Phytochemistry* **11**, 489.

Défago, G., Fazeli, A., and Schneizer, H. (1971). *Zentralbl. Bakteriol., Parasitenk., Infektimskr. Hyg., Abt. 2* **126**, 1.

de Souza, N. J., Ghisalberti, E. L., Rees, H. H., and Goodwin, T. W. (1970). *Phytochemistry* **9**, 1247.

Duperon, P., Vetter, W., and Barbier, M. (1964). *Phytochemistry* **3**, 89.

Edwards, P. A., and Green, C. (1972). *FEBS Lett.* **20**, 97.

Eichenberger, W., and Menke, W. (1966). *Z. Naturforsch. B* **21**, 859.

Elliott, C. G. (1968). *J. Gen. Microbiol.* **51**, 137.

Elliott, C. G. (1969). *J. Gen. Microbiol.* **56**, 331.

Elliott, C. G., and Knights, B. A. (1969). *J. Sci. Food Agri.* **20**, 406.

El-Refai, A. H., and El-Kady, I. A. (1968). *Z. Allg. Mikrobiol.* **8**, 355.

Enroth, P., Hellström, K., and Ryhage, R. (1964). *J. Lipid Res.* **5**, 245.

Fieser, L. F., and Fieser, M. (1959). "Steroids," Van Nostrand-Reinhold, Princeton, New Jersey.

Finean, J. B. (1953). *Experientia* **9**, 17.

Gaunt, J. K., and Stowe, B. B. (1967). *Plant Physiol.* **42**, 851.

Gawienowski, A. M., and Gibbs, C. C. (1968). *Steroids* **12**, 545.

Goad, L. J. (1967). *In* "Terpenoids in Plants" (J. B. Pridham, ed.), pp. 159–190. Academic Press, New York.

Goad, L. J., and Goodwin, T. W. (1966). *Biochem. J.* **99**, 735.

Goad, L. J., and Goodwin, T. W. (1967). *Eur. J. Biochem.* **1**, 357.

Gonzalez, B., and Panzio, F. M. (1967). *Estos Anales* **63b**, 1123.

Gonzalez, B., and Panzio, F. M. (1969). *An. Quim.* **65**, 1139.

Gordon, P. A., Stewart, P. R., Walker, D., and Clarke, G. (1970). *J. Bacteriol.* **107,** 114.

Goulston, G., and Mercer, E. I. (1969). *Phytochemistry* **8,** 1945.

Goulston, G., Goad, L. J., and Goodwin, T. W. (1967). *Biochem. J.* **102,** 15c.

Grunwald, C. (1968). *Plant Physiol.* **43,** 484.

Grunwald, C. (1970). *Plant Physiol.* **45,** 663.

Grunwald, C. (1971). *Plant Physiol.* **48,** 653.

Grunwald, C., Bush, L. P., and Keller, C. J. (1971). *J. Agr. Food Chem.* **19,** 216.

Halsall, T. G., and Sayer, G. C. (1959). *J. Chem. Soc., London* p. 2031.

Haskins, R. H. (1965). *Science* **150,** 1615.

Heble, M. R., Narayanaswami, S., and Chadha, M. S. (1971). *Phytochemistry* **10,** 2393.

Heftmann, E. (1963). *Annu. Rev. Plant Physiol.* **14,** 225.

Heftmann, E. (1968). *Lloydia* **31,** 293.

Heftmann, E. (1970). *Recent Advan. Phytochem.* **3,** 211–227.

Heftmann, E. (1971). *Lipids* **6,** 128.

Hendrix, J. W. (1970). *Annu. Rev. Phytopathol.* **8,** 111.

Hirayama, O., and Suzuki, T. (1968). *Agr. Biol. Chem.* **32,** 549.

Holtz, R. B., and Schisler, L. C. (1972). *Lipids* **7,** 251.

Hougen, F. W., Craig, B. M., and Ledingham, G. A. (1958). *Can. J. Microbiol.* **4,** 521.

Hui, W. H., Lam, W. K., and Tye, S. M. (1971). *Phytochemistry* **10,** 903.

Huneck, S. (1971). *Phytochemistry* **10,** 3282.

Idler, D. R., and Safe, L. M. (1972). *Steroids* **19,** 315.

Ingram, D. S., Knights, B. A., McEvoy, I. J., and McKay, P. (1968). *Phytochemistry* **7,** 1241.

Ives, D. A. J., and O'Neill, A. N. (1958). *Can. J. Chem.* **36,** 434.

Jackson, L. L., and Frear, D. S. (1968). *Phytochemistry* **7,** 651.

Jennings, P. H., Zscheite, F. P., and Brannaman, B. L. (1970). *Plant Physiol.* **45,** 634.

Kemp, R. J., and Mercer, E. I. (1968a). *Biochem. J.* **110,** 111.

Kemp, R. J., and Mercer, E. I. (1968b). *Biochem. J.* **110,** 119.

Kemp, R. J., Goad, L. J., and Mercer, E. I. (1967). *Phytochemistry* **6,** 1609.

Kircher, H. W. (1969a). *Phytochemistry* **8,** 1481.

Kircher, H. W. (1969b). *J. Insect Physiol.* **15,** 1167.

Kircher, H. W. (1970). *Phytochemistry* **9,** 1879.

Kircher, H. W., and Heed, W. B. (1970). *Recent Advan. Phytochem.* **3,** 191.

Kirk, P. W., Jr. (1970). *Phytochemistry* **9,** 595.

Knapp, F., and Nicholas, H. J. (1969a). *Phytochemistry* **8,** 2091.

Knapp, F., and Nicholas, H. J. (1969b). *Phytochemistry* **8,** 207.

Knapp, F., and Nicholas, H. J. (1969c). *J. Food Sci.* **34,** 584.

Knapp, F., Aexel, R., and Nicholas, H. J. (1968). *J. Food Sci.* **33,** 159.

Knapp, F., Aexel, R., and Nicholas, H. J. (1969). *Plant Physiol.* **44,** 442.

Knights, B. A. (1967). *J. Gas Chromatogr.* **5,** 273.

Knights, B. A. (1968). *Phytochemistry* **7,** 2067.

Knights, B. A. (1970). *Phytochemistry* **9,** 701.

Knights, B. A. (1971). *Lipids* **6,** 215.

Knights, B. A., and Berrie, A. M. M. (1971). *Phytochemistry* **10,** 131.

Knights, B. A., and Laurie, W. (1967). *Phytochemistry* **6,** 404.

Knights, B. A., and Middleditch, B. S. (1972). *Phytochemistry* 11, 1177.

Kok, L. T., Norris, D. M., and Chu, H. M. (1970). *Nature (London)* 225, 661.

Lenfant, M., Lecompte, M. F., and Farrugia, G. (1970). *Phytochemistry* 9, 2529.

McCorkindale, N. J., Hutchinson, S. A., Pursey, B. A., Scott, W. T., and Wheeler, R. (1969). *Phytochemistry* 8, 861.

Mendez, A. (1970). *Phytochemistry* 10, 2255.

Mercer, E. I., and Treharne, K. J. (1966). *In* "The Biochemistry of Chloroplasts" (T. W. Goodwin, ed.), Vol. 1, pp. 181–185. Academic Press, New York.

Mokady, S., and Koltin, Y. (1971). *Phytochemistry* 10, 2035.

Mostafa, M. A., Taha, E. M., and El-Refai, A. H. (1969). *J. Bot. UAR* 12, 81.

Nagy, S., and Nordby, H. E. (1971). *Lipids* 6, 826.

Nelson, R. R., Huisingh, D., and Webster, R. K. (1967). *Phytopathology* 57, 1081.

Nowak, R., Kim, W. K., and Rohringer, R. (1972). *Can. J. Bot.* 50, 185.

Orcutt, D. M., and Richardson, B. (1970). *Steroids* 16, 429.

Osman, H. G., Abdel-Aziz, M., and El-Refai, A. H. (1969). *J. Chem. UAR* 12, 99.

Parks, L. W., Bond, F. T., Thompson, E. D., and Staee, P. R. (1972). *J. Lipid Res.* 13, 311.

Patterson, G. W. (1971a). *Anal. Chem.* 43, 1165.

Patterson, G. W. (1971b). *Lipids* 6, 120.

Pryce, R. J. (1971). *Phytochemistry* 10, 1303.

Rees, H. H., Goad, L. J., and Goodwin, T. W. (1968). *Phytochemistry* 7, 1875.

Ragsdale, N. N., and Sisler, H. D. (1972). *Biochem. Biophys. Res. Commun.* 46, 2048.

Reid, W. W. (1969). *Biochem. J.* 113, 37.

Robinson, F. P., Jr., and McCalg, T. N. (1971). *Phytochemistry* 10, 3307.

Rogers, L. J., Shah, S. P. J., and Goodwin, T. W. (1968). *Photosynthetica* 2, 184.

Salama, H. S., and El-Sharaby, A. M. (1972). *Experientia* 28, 413.

Sarachek, A., and Higgins, N. P. (1972). *Arch. Mikrobiol.* 82, 38.

Schlosser, E., Shaw, P. D., and Gottlieb, D. (1969). *Arch. Mikrobiol.* 66, 147.

Schonheimer, R., von Behring, H., and Hummel, R. (1930). *Hoppe-Seyler's Z. Physiol. Chem.* 192, 93.

Serebryakov, E. P., Simolin, A. V., and Kucherov, V. F. (1970). *Tetrahedron* 26, 5215.

Sietsma, J. H. (1971). *Biochim. Biophys. Acta* 244, 178.

Sietsma, J. H., and Haskins, R. H. (1968). *Can. J. Biochem.* 46, 813.

Singh, H., Chawla, A. S., Rowe, J. W., and Toda, J. K. (1970). *Phytochemistry* 9, 1673.

Solberg, Y. J. (1971). *Bryologist* 74, 144.

Starratt, A. N., and Madhosingh, C. (1967). *Can. J. Microbiol.* 13, 1351.

Strigina, L. I., Elkin, Y. N., and Elyakov, G. B. (1971). *Phytochemistry* 10, 2361.

Sucrow, W., and Raduchel, B. (1970). *Phytochemistry* 9, 2003.

Tanahashi, Y., and Takahashi, T. (1966). *Bull. Chem. Soc. Jap.* 39, 848.

Thompson, M. J., Dutky, S. R., and Patterson, G. W. (1972). *Phytochemistry* 11, 1781.

Tillman, R. W., and Bean, G. A. (1970). *Mycologia* 62, 428.

Tomita, Y., Uomori, A., and Minato, H. (1970a). *Phytochemistry* 9, 111.

Tomita, Y., Uomori, A., and Minato, H. (1970b). *Phytochemistry* 9, 555.

Tomita, Y., Uomori, A., and Sakurai, E. (1971). *Phytochemistry* 10, 573.

Tomlinson, H., and Rich, S. (1971). *Phytopathology* 61, 1404.

Tsuda, S., and Tatum, E. L. (1963). *J. Biophys. Biochem. Cytol.* **11**, 171.
Vacheron, M., and Michel, G. (1968). *Phytochemistry* **7**, 1645.
Vandenheuvel, F. A. (1963). *J. Amer. Oil Chem. Soc.* **40**, 455.
Vroman, H. E., and Cohen, C. F. (1967). *J. Lipid Res.* **8**, 150.
Weete, J. D., Lasetar, J. L., and Lawler, G. C. (1973). *Arch. Biochem. Biophys.* **154** (in press).
Williams, B. L., Goad, L. J., and Goodwin, T. W. (1967). *Phytochemistry* **6**, 1137.
Windaus, A., and Vibrig, C. (1914). *Ber. Deut. Chem. Ges.* **47**, 2384.
Yokoyama, H., and White, M. J. (1968). *Phytochemistry* **7**, 493.

Metabolism of Steroids in Insects

M. J. THOMPSON, J. N. KAPLANIS, W. E. ROBBINS,
AND J. A. SVOBODA

Insect Physiology Laboratory, Plant Protection Institute, ARS, USDA,
Agricultural Research Center, Beltsville, Maryland

I. Introduction

Insects require a dietary or exogenous source of sterol for normal growth, metamorphosis, and reproduction and the only known exceptions to this are those species in which a sterol source may be attributed to associated symbiotes. This sterol requirement has been conclusively established by extensive nutritional experimentation and has been shown through biochemical research to result from a lack in insects of the sterol biosynthetic mechanism. Thus, insects, along with certain related arthropods and some other invertebrates, differ from most plants and vertebrates which fulfill their sterol requirement through endogenous sterol biogenesis. Although incapable of *de novo* sterol biosynthesis, insects do metabolize dietary sterols and these metabolic modifications

219

serve to provide steroid structures that are appropriate to the specific physiological and biochemical functions of sterols. In insects, as in mammals, the sterols serve a dual role—as structural components of cells and tissues and as precursors for essential steroid metabolites and regulators such as the molting hormones or ecdysones.

Current knowledge on the utilization, metabolism, and function of steroids in insects has been discussed and summarized in a number of comprehensive reviews (Clayton, 1964; Gilbert, 1967; Ritter and Wientjens, 1967; Dadd, 1970; Robbins *et al.*, 1971a; Thompson *et al.*, 1972) including two that are concerned specifically with the ecdysones (Horn, 1971; Rees, 1971). The main topic of the present chapter will be a summarization of the metabolic transformations of steroids that occur in insects and a discussion of how these transformations fit into the known biochemical pathways and relate to the physiological functions of steroids in insects.

II. Metabolic Modifications of Sterols and Steroids

Information on the metabolic transformation of steroids in insects currently is derived primarily from *in vivo* studies. Because of the pitfalls that may result and the precautions that must be observed in attempting to place a biochemical interpretation on the results of *in vivo* nutritional studies in insects (see the reviews), only those transformations will be considered and discussed where a direct precursor-metabolite relationship has been demonstrated to occur. These examples involve the use of highly purified steroid preparations—particularly radiolabeled steroids—and specific physical and chemical methods of steroid analysis, usually when these were employed in combination with semidefined artificial insect diets. An attempt has been made to include in the tables examples of each type of steroid modification known to occur in insects. However, each species in which a modification has been reported has not in every case been included and certain of the transformations, such as the esterification of sterols and the hydrolysis of sterol esters, have been treated rather generally.

A. Esterification and Hydrolysis

Although little research has been done on defining the function(s) of sterol esters in insects, it is well established that insects readily esterify free sterols and hydrolyze sterol esters (Table I) (Casida *et al.*, 1957; Kaplanis *et al.*, 1960; Robbins *et al.*, 1961; Clayton and Edwards, 1961;

Table I

ESTERIFICATION AND HYDROLYSIS

Compound	Product(s)	Insect	Reference
Esterification			
Cholesterol-4-^{14}C	Cholesterol 18:1 ester (76%)	*Musca domestica*	Dutky et al., 1963
	Cholesterol 16:1 ester (16%)	(eggs)	
Cholesterol-4-^{14}C	Cholesterol oleate	*Eurycotis floridana*	Bade and Clayton, 1963
Hydrolysis			
Cholesterol-4-^{14}C—	Cholesterol	*Eurycotis floridana*	Clayton et al., 1964
Acetate			
Laurate			
Palmitate			
Stearate			
Oleate			

Clayton *et al.*, 1964; Ishii *et al.*, 1963; Dutky *et al.*, 1963; Bade and Clayton, 1963; Monroe *et al.*, 1967). Long-term studies with the adult American cockroach, *Periplaneta americana*, following injection or feeding of cholesterol-4-^{14}C (Ishii *et al.*, 1963; Vroman *et al.*, 1964) have indicated a widespread distribution of sterol esters throughout the tissues and that the establishment of an equilibrium between free and ester sterol in this insect is a very slow process.

Not only are sterol esters present in larval and adult tissues, but Kaplanis *et al.* (1960) also showed that the adult female housefly, *Musca domestica*, utilized the cholesterol-^{14}C in egg production and that this sterol and its major metabolite, 7-dehydrocholesterol, were present in both the free and esterified form. The percentage of sterol esters in housefly eggs may be as high as 41% of the total sterols-4-^{14}C and analyses of these esters showed that greater than 92% of the fatty acid moieties were monounsaturated C_{16} and C_{18} fatty acids (Dutky *et al.*, 1963). In the housefly eggs, the 18:1 acids account for about 76% and 16:1 acids another 16% of the sterol esters (Dutky *et al.*, 1963) whereas 18:2 was the major fatty acid moiety of sterol esters from eggs from wild populations of the grasshopper *Aulocara elliotti* (Svoboda *et al.*, 1966). Cholesterol oleate has been reported to be the major sterol ester in the cockroach *Eurycotis floridana* (Bade and Clayton, 1963), and this and the two studies with insect eggs are the only reports in which the fatty acid moieties of the sterol esters of insects have been examined (Table I).

The role of esterification in the intestinal absorption of cholesterol has been carefully studied in the roach *E. floridana* (Clayton *et al.*, 1964) but, according to the authors, it still remains undefined. They concluded, however, that even though their results suggest that sterol esterification is not obligatory for the absorption of sterols, it may facilitate the absorption of certain sterols when they are present at low dietary concentrations. The function of sterol esters in insects is still not well understood. The report by Monroe *et al.* (1967) indicates that the sterol esters in houseflies compose a very minor fraction of the total sterols during larval growth but increase progressively in the pupa and the adult and reach a maximum concentration in the first group of eggs. This report, taken with the previous studies of Kaplanis *et al.* (1960) correlating cholesterol esterification and oogenesis, suggests that in the housefly sterol esterification is related to the storage and utilization of sterols. The finding that approximately 80% of the sterol esters in housefly eggs were converted to free sterol(s) during embryonic development (Robbins, 1963) certainly supports the premise that sterol esters function in the storage of sterols and indicates that hydrolysis provides the insect with free sterols for structural components of cells and tissues during periods of rapid growth and development when an exogenous source of sterol may be either insufficient or unavailable.

B. REDUCTION

Reductions of the double bonds are biochemical adaptations which permit insects to use available exogenous sterols by modifying them to provide steroid structures for specific physiological and biochemical functions and these reductions mainly involve the Δ^7-, Δ^{22}-, and Δ^{24}-bonds (Table II). The report of the reduction of cholestanone to cholestanol by the housefly (Dutky *et al.*, 1967) indicates that insects can also reduce a ketosteroid to its corresponding alcohol.

The reduction of the Δ^7-bond during the oxidative-reductive conversion of ergosterol-^{14}C to 22-dehydrocholesterol-^{14}C by the German cockroach, *Blattella germanica* (Clark and Bloch, 1959), provided the first biochemical evidence for a sterol reduction in an insect. Further studies on the mechanism of the dealkylation process demonstrated that desmosterol was the terminal intermediate in the conversion of plant sterols to cholesterol in insects (Svoboda *et al.*, 1967; Svoboda and Robbins, 1971). This led to the discovery in insects of a Δ^{24}-sterol reductase enzyme system that converts desmosterol to cholesterol and *in vitro* studies showed that this reductase in the tobacco hornworm, *Manduca sexta*, is primarily present in midgut tissue (Svoboda *et al.*, 1969b).

Although reduction of the Δ^{24}-bond of desmosterol proceeds directly to form cholesterol, the presence of the Δ^{24}-bond is required for reduction of the Δ^{22}-bond in the conversion of 22-*trans*-5,22,24-cholestatrien-3β-ol to cholesterol (Fig. 2) by the tobacco hornworm. Studies with 22-dehydrocholesterol as the dietary sterol for the hornworm showed little, if any, conversion of this sterol to cholesterol, indicating that the enzyme that reduces the Δ^{22}-bond is highly specific for a $\Delta^{22,24}$-sterol substrate. It is also likely that the conjugated $\Delta^{5,7}$-diene system may be a prerequisite for the reduction of Δ^7-bond by insects.

C. OXIDATION

The oxidative biotransformations of sterols and steroids that occur in insects are apparently similar to those reported for vertebrates, namely oxidation, dehydrogenation, and peroxidation. The oxidative modifications of sterols and steroids by insects are summarized in Table III.

The demonstration that the German cockroach converts ergosterol-^{14}C

Table II

REDUCTION

Compound	Position(s) reduced	Product(s)	Insect	Reference
Ergosterol-^{14}C	Δ^7	22-Dehydrocholesterol	*Blattella germanica*	Clark and Bloch, 1959
7-Dehydrocholesterol-^{3}H	Δ^7	Cholesterol	*Tribolium confusum*	Svoboda *et al.*, 1972b
5,22,24-Cholestatrien-3β-ol-^{3}H	Δ^{22}	Desmosterol	*Manduca sexta*	Svoboda *et al.*, 1969a
	Δ^{22}, Δ^{24}	Cholesterol	*Manduca sexta*	Svoboda *et al.*, 1969a
Desmosterol-^{3}H	Δ^{24}	Cholesterol	*Manduca sexta*	Svoboda *et al.*, 1967
Cholestanone-^{14}C	3-Keto	Cholestanol	*Musca domestica*	Dutky *et al.*, 1967

Table III

OXIDATION

Compound	Position	Product(s)	Insect	Reference
Introduction of double bond				
Cholestanol-^{14}C	Δ^5	Cholesterol	*Thermobia domestica*	S. C. Joyner, W. E. Robbins, and R. C. Dutky, unpublished observations
Lathosterol	Δ^5	7-Dehydrocholesterol	*Drosophila pachae*	Goodnight and Kircher, 1971
Cholesterol-^{14}C	Δ^7	7-Dehydrocholesterol	*Blatella germanica*	Robbins *et al.*, 1964
			Musca domestica	Kaplanis *et al.*, 1960
			Periplaneta americana	Ishii *et al.*, 1963
Cholestanol-^{14}C	Δ^7	Lathosterol	*Biatella germanica*	Louloudes *et al.*, 1962
Cholestanol-^{3}H	Δ^7	Lathosterol	*Eurycotis floridana*	Clayton and Edwards, 1963
			Blatella germanica	Clayton and Edwards, 1963
Sitosterol-^{3}H	$\Delta^{24(28)}$	Fucosterol	*Manduca sexta*	Svoboda *et al.*, 1971
	Δ^{24}	Desmosterol		
Introduction of keto group				
Cholesterol-^{3}H	C-6	α-Ecdysone	*Calliphora erythro-cephala (= vicina)*	Karlson and Hoffmeister, 1963
Testosterone-^{14}C	C-17	4-Androsten-3,17-dione	*Gryllus domesticus*	Lehoux and Sandor, 1969

to 22-dehydrocholesterol-^{14}C led Clark and Bloch (1959) to postulate that demethylation is initiated by a dehydrogenation between C-24 and C-28 in the sterol side chain. This assumption was proven to be correct a number of years later when fucosterol and 24-methylenecholesterol were identified as primary intermediates in the conversion of sitosterol and campesterol, respectively, to cholesterol (Svoboda *et al.*, 1971, 1972a).

The conversions of cholestanol to lathosterol by *Eurycotis floridana* and the German cockroach, *Blattella germanica* (Clayton and Edwards, 1962, 1963; Louloudes *et al.*, 1962), cholestanol to cholesterol by the firebrat, *Thermobia domestica* (S. C. Joyner, W. E. Robbins, and R. C. Dutky, unpublished observations), and cholesterol to 7-dehydrocholesterol by a number of insects (Kaplanis *et al.*, 1960; Robbins *et al.*, 1961, 1964; Svoboda *et al.*, 1972b) are additional examples of steroid oxidation by insects (Table III). The function of these oxidations will become obvious in their discussion in relation to the pathways of steroid metabolism in Section III.

The biosynthesis of the insect ecdysones requires the introduction of a keto group at C-6 and the elucidation of the molting hormone structure provided the first indication that steroids are oxidized to ketosteroids by an insect. Related oxidations are necessary to produce those ketosteroids found to be biosynthesized by a dytiscid water beetle (Section III,E). The *in vitro* conversions of testosterone-4-^{14}C to 4-androsten-3,17-dione and 17β-estradiol to estrone by male gonad preparations of the house cricket, *Gryllus domesticus*, are examples of a hydroxysteroid dehydrogenase system in insects (Lehoux and Sandor, 1969, 1970) and the reported complete conversion of these substrates suggests that formation of a ketosteroid in an insect may proceed through a combination of hydroxylation and dehydrogenation.

D. HYDROXYLATION

Hydroxylation of steroids is a most important biochemical transformation in insects. It is an essential mechanism in the biosynthesis of the molting hormones from cholesterol and in the inactivation and excretion of certain of the inhibitory synthetic analogs of α-ecdysone (Section III,C). Interestingly, there has been no report on the isolation of dihydroxy- or trihydroxysteroids from insects such as 20-hydroxycholesterol, 25-hydroxycholesterol, 26-hydroxycholesterol, or 20,22-dihydroxycholesterol even though certain insects hydroxylate these side-chain positions during the biosynthesis of the ecdysones. All of the C_{27} steroids hydroxylated beyond the C-3 position thus far isolated from insects contain the

Table IV

Hydroxylation

Compound	Position(s) hydroxylated	Product(s)	Insect	References
Cholesterol	2, 14, 22, 25	α-Ecdysone	*Calliphora erythrocephala* (= *vicina*)	Karlson and Hoffmeister, 1963
Cholesterol; 7-Dehydrocholesterol	2, 14, 20, 22, 25	20-Hydroxyecdysone	*Calliphora stygia*	Galbraith *et al.*, 1970
22,25-Dideoxyecdysone	25	22-Deoxyecdysone	*Manduca sexta*	Kaplanis *et al.*, 1971; Kaplanis *et al.*, 1972; King, 1972b
			Calliphora stygia	Thomson *et al.*, 1971
22,25-Dideoxyecdysone	20, 22, 25, 26	α-Ecdysone	*Manduca sexta*	Kaplanis *et al.*, 1969; King, 1972b
		20-Hydroxyecdysone	*Manduca sexta*	Kaplanis *et al.*, 1969; King, 1972b
		20,26-Dihydroxyecdysone	*Manduca sexta*	Kaplanis *et al.*, 1969; King, 1972b
Cholesterol	21	21-Hydroxy-4-pregnen-3,20-dione	*Acilius sulcatus*	Schildknecht, 1970

5β-configuration (A/B ring *cis*) and a 7-en-6-one system in the B ring. Thus, in the insect an A/B ring *cis* system and a 7-en-6-one system appear to be prerequisites for the hydroxylation of a C_{27} steroid substrate. With the appropriate C_{27} substrate the insect is capable of hydroxylating the steroid nucleus at positions 2 and 14 and the side chain at positions 20, 22, 25, and 26 as indicated (Table IV) in the conversion of cholesterol to α-ecdysone and 20-hydroxyecdysone and the conversion of 22,25-dideoxyecdysone and 22-deoxyecdysone to α-ecdysone, 20-hydroxyecdysone, and 20,26-dihydroxyecdysone.

In the biosynthesis of the insect ecdysones, the hydroxylation most likely proceeds in an orderly sequence. However, depending on the insect species, developmental stage, the nature of the substrate, and its mode of administration, hydroxylations may also occur randomly at the normal positions, producing steroids with various combinations of hydroxyl groups. This phenomenon and the role of hydroxylation in ecdysteroid biosynthesis and metabolism will be discussed in Section III,C.

A number of C_{18}, C_{19}, and C_{21} steroids with hydroxyl groups at carbons 12, 15, 17, 20, and 21 have been isolated from dytiscid water beetles. While cholesterol-^{14}C has been demonstrated as a precursor only for the C_{21} steroids with hydroxyl groups at C-20 and C-21 in *Acilius sulcatus* (Tables IV and VI), it is likely that the steroids with the hydroxyl groups at the other positions are also biosynthesized by dytiscid beetles (Section III,E). Since these steroids with keto groups at C-20 have been isolated from these beetles, it is possible that the hydroxyl groups result from both an oxidation and a reduction reaction (Section III,E).

E. DEALKYLATION

The dealkylation of sterols in insects involves the removal of C-24 alkyl substituents from C_{28} and C_{29} plant sterols to provide the insect with cholesterol. Some of the intermediates formed during these dealkylations have structural features similar or identical to certain of the intermediates known to occur in the pathways of the biosynthesis of the C_{28} and C_{29} sterols in plants (Fig. 2). In alkylation in plants, the carbons of the ethyl group are introduced via a two-step process, whereas in dealkylation in insects it appears that a two-carbon moiety is eliminated. Dealkylation proceeds through oxidation-reduction reactions and involves several steps as evidenced by the metabolites and intermediates isolated and identified thus far (Fig. 2). The biochemical mechanism for the conversion of plant sterols to cholesterol is available to a number of phytophagous and omnivorous insects (Table V) and the process appears to be irreversible.

Table V

DEALKYLATION OF C-24 SUBSTITUENTS

Compound	Group removed	Final product	Insect	Reference
Ergosterol-[14]C	CH_3-	22-Dehydrocholesterol	*Blattella germanica*	Clark and Bloch, 1959
Campesterol-[3]H	CH_3-	Cholesterol	*Manduca sexta*	Svoboda *et al.*, 1972a
24-Methylenecholesterol-[3]H	$CH_2=$	Cholesterol	*Manduca sexta*	Svoboda *et al.*, 1972a
Sitosterol-[3]H	CH_3CH_2-	Cholesterol	*Blattella germanica*	Robbins *et al.*, 1962
			Neodiprion pratti	Schaefer *et al.*, 1965
			Bombyx mori	Ikekawa *et al.*, 1966
			Manduca sexta	Svoboda *et al.*, 1967
			Eurycotis floridana	Ritter and Wientjens, 1967
Stigmasterol-[3]H	CH_3CH_2-	Cholesterol	*Manduca sexta*	Svoboda *et al.*, 1969a
Fucosterol-[3]H	$CH_3CH=$	Cholesterol	*Manduca sexta*	Svoboda *et al.*, 1971

Table VI

SIDE-CHAIN CLEAVAGE

Compound	Product(s)	Insect	Reference
Cholesterol-4-^{14}C	21-Hydroxy-4-pregnen-3,20-dione 20α-Hydroxy-4-pregnen-3-one 20α-Hydroxy-4,6-pregnadien-3-one 21-Hydroxy-4,6-pregnadien-3,20-dione 4,6-Pregnadien-3,20-dione	*Acilius sulcatus*	Schildknecht, 1970
20-Hydroxyecdysone-^{3}H Ponasterone-^{3}H A	4-Hydroxy-4-methylpentanoic acid Poststerone	*Calliphora stygia* *Bombyx mori*	Galbraith *et al.*, 1969a Hikino *et al.*, 1971

Thus far, the complete dealkylation process has not been demonstrated in *in vitro* system(s). Future research on dealkylation should be concentrated on the enzymes involved in these processes.

F. Side-Chain Cleavage

Other than the dealkylation of alkane or alkene substituents from C-24, side-chain cleavage of sterols has not thus far been found to be a widespread metabolic modification in insects. Side-chain cleavage has been shown to occur with the two ecdysteroids, 20-hydroxyecdysone (Galbraith *et al.*, 1969a) and ponasterone A (Hikino *et al.*, 1971). The scission takes place at the 20-22-bond, where vicinal hydroxyl groups are located, and in this respect it resembles the conversion of 20,22-dihydroxycholesterol to pregnenolone in vertebrates. In addition, a number of C_{18}, C_{19}, and C_{21} steroids, similar or identical to the vertebrate steroid hormones, have been isolated from the thoracic bladders of several species of dytiscid beetles (Schildknecht, 1970) and cholesterol-4-^{14}C has been shown to be a precursor for the C_{21} steroids listed in Table VI. The C_{18}, C_{19}, and C_{21} steroids in insects will be further discussed in Section III,E.

G. Conjugation

During the 1960's, considerable effort was spent in studying the utilization and metabolism of radioactive sterols in insects, and while the procedures of isolation employed in these studies demonstrated the presence of radiolabeled polar steroid metabolites, these polar compounds were never identified. Hutchins and Kaplanis (1969) were the first to characterize polar steroids from an insect when they isolated and identified the sulfates of cholesterol, sitosterol, and campesterol from the meconium of the tobacco hornworm (Table VII). This first identification of sterol conjugates from an insect meconium indicates that the sterol sulfates may serve as a means of sterol excretion in insects. One year later, Heinrich and Hoffmeister (1970) reported that the insect ecdysone, 20-hydroxyecdysone, and the phytoecdysone, ponasterone A, are metabolized to 3β-(α-glucoside) derivatives by the fat body of immature *Calliphora vicina*. In our experiments on the metabolism of a synthetic ecdysone analog by houseflies, we obtained, in addition to free ecdysteroids, a mixture of ecdysteroid sulfate and glucoside conjugates (Kaplanis *et al.*, 1971; Thompson *et al.*, 1972). Ecdysteroid conjugates have since been isolated from a number of insects, and conjugation is an important metabolic modification in insects that plays a vital role in ecdysone metabolism, inactivation, and excretion (Section III,C and D).

Table VII

CONJUGATION

Compound	Product(s)	Insect	Reference
Sulfates			
Cholesterol-¹⁴C	Cholesterol	*Manduca sexta*	Hutchins and Kaplanis, 1969
Campesterol	Campesterol	*Manduca sexta*	Hutchins and Kaplanis, 1969
Sitosterol	Sitosterol	*Manduca sexta*	Hutchins and Kaplanis, 1969
22-Deoxyecdysone-³H	α-Ecdysone	*Manduca sexta*	King, 1972b
	20-Hydroxyecdysone	*Manduca sexta*	King, 1972b
	20,26-Dihydroxyecdysone	*Manduca sexta*	King, 1972b
α-Glucosides			
20-Hydroxyecdysone	20-Hydroxyecdysone-3β	*Calliphora vicina*	Heinrich and Hoffmeister, 1970
Ponasterone³H A	Ponasterone A-3β		
Sulfates and glucosides			
22,25-Dideoxyecdysone-¹⁴C	22,25-Dideoxyecdysone	*Musca domestica*	Kaplanis *et al.*, 1971
	Tetrahydroxy steroids	*Musca domestica*	Kaplanis *et al.*, 1971
22,25-Dideoxyecdysone-³H	22,25-Dideoxyecdysone	*Manduca sexta*	Kaplanis *et al.*, 1971
	α-Ecdysone	*Manduca sexta*	Kaplanis *et al.*, 1971
	20-Hydroxyecdysone	*Manduca sexta*	Kaplanis *et al.*, 1971
22,25-Dideoxyecdysone-¹⁴C	22,25-Dideoxyecdysone	*Manduca sexta*	Kaplanis *et al.*, 1972
	22-Deoxyecdysone	*Manduca sexta*	Kaplanis *et al.*, 1972
	Pentahydroxy steroids	*Manduca sexta*	Kaplanis *et al.*, 1972

III. Pathways of Steroid Metabolism

A. Conversion of Plant Sterols to Cholesterol

Cholesterol fulfills the dietary sterol requirement of all the insects studied thus far, with two exceptions (Heed and Kircher, 1965; Chu *et al.*, 1970), and many phytophagous and omnivorous species of insects convert certain C_{28} and C_{29} phytosterols to cholesterol in order to satisfy their need for this essential sterol. The formation of cholesterol from these plant sterols involves the dealkylation of a one- or two-carbon moiety from the 24-position of the phytosterol side chain, and for many years the only evidence for this conversion was that obtained indirectly from nutritional studies. The first direct conclusive proof for dealkylation of a plant sterol by an insect was provided by the classic study of Clark and Bloch (1959) in which ergosterol-^{14}C was fed to the German cockroach and shown to be converted to 22-dehydrocholesterol-^{14}C through the dealkylation of the 24-methyl group and reduction of the Δ^7-bond. Three years later Robbins *et al.* (1962) provided the first direct proof for the dealkylation and conversion of a phytosterol to cholesterol in an insect. In the latter work, the German cockroach was shown to dealkylate sitosterol-^{3}H (remove the 24-ethyl group) to produce cholesterol-^{3}H. Subsequently, this conversion —sitosterol to cholesterol—has been shown to occur in a number of species of insects including the pine sawfly, *Neodiprion pratti* (Schaefer *et al.*, 1965); the silkworm, *Bombyx mori* (Ikekawa *et al.*, 1966); the boll weevil, *Anthonomus grandis* (Earle *et al.*, 1967); the tobacco hornworm (Svoboda *et al.*, 1967); a cockroach, *Eurycotis floridana* (Ritter and Wientjens, 1967); a locust, *Locusta migratoria* (Allais and Barbier, 1971); and the honeybee, *Apis mellifera* (Allais *et al.*, 1971). However, not all insects are capable of converting C_{28} and C_{29} plant sterols to cholesterol. For example, both the larva and adult of the housefly are unable to convert sitosterol to cholesterol (Kaplanis *et al.*, 1963, 1965) and thus it must rely entirely on a dietary source of cholesterol to satisfy its requirement for this sterol.

The biochemical mechanism for the conversion of sitosterol and other phytosterols to cholesterol is not unique to insects. An insect-parasitic nematode, as well as a free-living nematode, both of which require an exogenous or dietary sterol for normal growth, development, and reproduction (Cole and Dutky, 1969; Dutky *et al.*, 1967), have been shown to convert sitosterol to cholesterol (Cole and Krusberg, 1968; Dutky, 1968). Perhaps this metabolic transformation is quite widespread in invertebrates, particularly among those that lack the capacity for *de novo* bio-synthesis of sterols (Ritter and Wientjens, 1967).

The omnivorous German cockroach was used in earlier biochemical studies on the conversion of plant sterols to cholesterol but most of the recent research on phytosterol metabolism has been primarily with a phytophagous insect, the oligophagous tobacco hornworm (Svoboda and Robbins, 1967, 1968; Svoboda *et al.*, 1967, 1968, 1969a, 1971, 1972a). The hornworm with its rapid growth rate and low incidence of cannibalism, has proven to be a most useful test organism. The tobacco hornworm is also biochemically efficient and versatile in that it converts a variety of C_{28} and C_{29} plant sterols (Fig. 1) to cholesterol (Svoboda and Robbins, 1968). This insect can dealkylate the 24α-ethyl from sitosterol and stigmasterol, the 24α-methyl from campesterol, and the 24β-methyl of brassicasterol or 22,23-dihydrobrassicasterol. In addition to the dealkylation of alkane substituents from the C-24 position, the hornworm also removed alkene substituents—the methylene of 24-methylenecholesterol and the 24-ethylidene of fucosterol. Apparently, however, there is some degree of specificity in the dealkylation process in that the 24β-methyls of brassicasterol and 22,23-dihydrobrassicasterol were not as efficiently dealkylated as the 24α-alkyls of sitosterol, campesterol, and stigmasterol. This selectivity may well be an adaptation of the hornworm to the sterols of tobacco, the major host plant of this insect, in which the latter three are

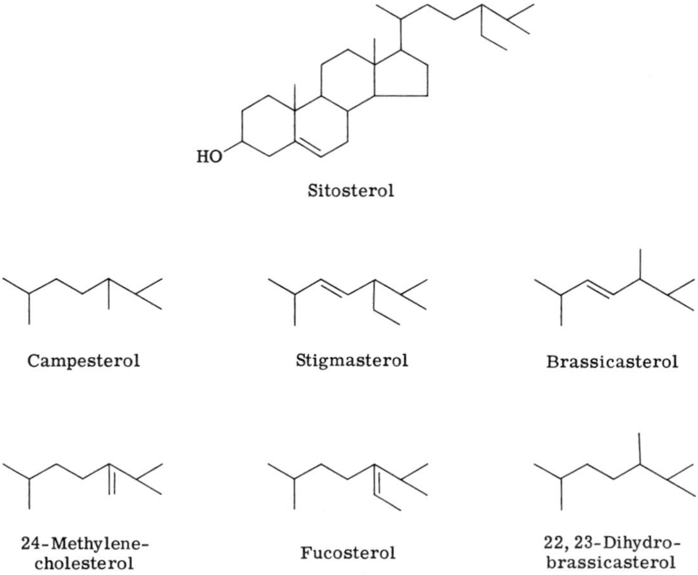

Sitosterol

Campesterol

Stigmasterol

Brassicasterol

24-Methylene-cholesterol

Fucosterol

22, 23-Dihydro-brassicasterol

FIG. 1. C_{28} and C_{29} Plant sterols.

the predominant sterols. The hornworm also reduces the Δ^{22}-bond of stigmasterol and brassicasterol, a biochemical conversion unavailable to the German cockroach (Clark and Bloch, 1959).

Radiolabeled sitosterol, campesterol, and stigmasterol are all efficiently utilized and converted to cholesterol and 7-dehydrocholesterol by larvae of the confused flour beetle, *Tribolium confusum* (Svoboda et al., 1972b), an insect that is rather exceptional in that 7-dehydrocholesterol comprises over half of its total tissue sterols (Beck and Kapadia, 1957). When any of these phytosterols was used as the dietary source of sterol, the quantity of 7-dehydrocholesterol exceeded the cholesterol content in sterol samples from *Tribolium* larvae in each case, indicating an equilibrium between cholesterol and 7-dehydrocholesterol in the tissues of this insect. 7-Dehydrocholesterol is a minor component of the tissue sterols in a number of insects; however, the significance of the large quantity of 7-dehydrocholesterol in this phytophagous insect is unknown.

B. Intermediates of Plant Sterol Metabolism

1. *Fucosterol*

A primary step in sitosterol metabolism in the tobacco hornworm was elucidated when fucosterol-^{3}H was isolated and identified as a metabolite of sitosterol-^{3}H and shown to be a probable intermediate in the conversion of sitosterol to cholesterol (Fig. 2) (Svoboda et al., 1971). Positive identification of fucosterol-^{3}H was achieved by analysis of the sterol and several of its derivatives by mass spectrometry, gas-liquid chromatography (GLC), and thin-layer chromatography (TLC). Fucosterol, although accounting for less than 1% of the total sterols-[3]H (Svoboda et al., 1971), is a constant minor metabolite of sitosterol-^{3}H in the hornworm and as previously pointed out, it is readily utilized and converted to cholesterol in this insect (Svoboda and Robbins, 1968). Recent metabolic studies have shown that fucosterol also occupies a similar position in the conversion of sitosterol-^{3}H to 7-dehydrocholesterol and cholesterol in *Tribolium* (Fig. 3) (Svoboda et al., 1972b). The occurrence of fucosterol as a metabolite and possible intermediate had been suggested by its tentative identification, solely on the basis of GLC analysis, from the German cockroach and *Eurycotis floridana* (Ritter and Wientjens, 1967).

2. *24-Methylenecholesterol*

Biochemical and nutritional studies with campesterol-^{3}H and 24-methylenecholesterol-[3]H (Fig. 2) in the tobacco hornworm have shown that a metabolic transformation analogous to the conversion of sitosterol to

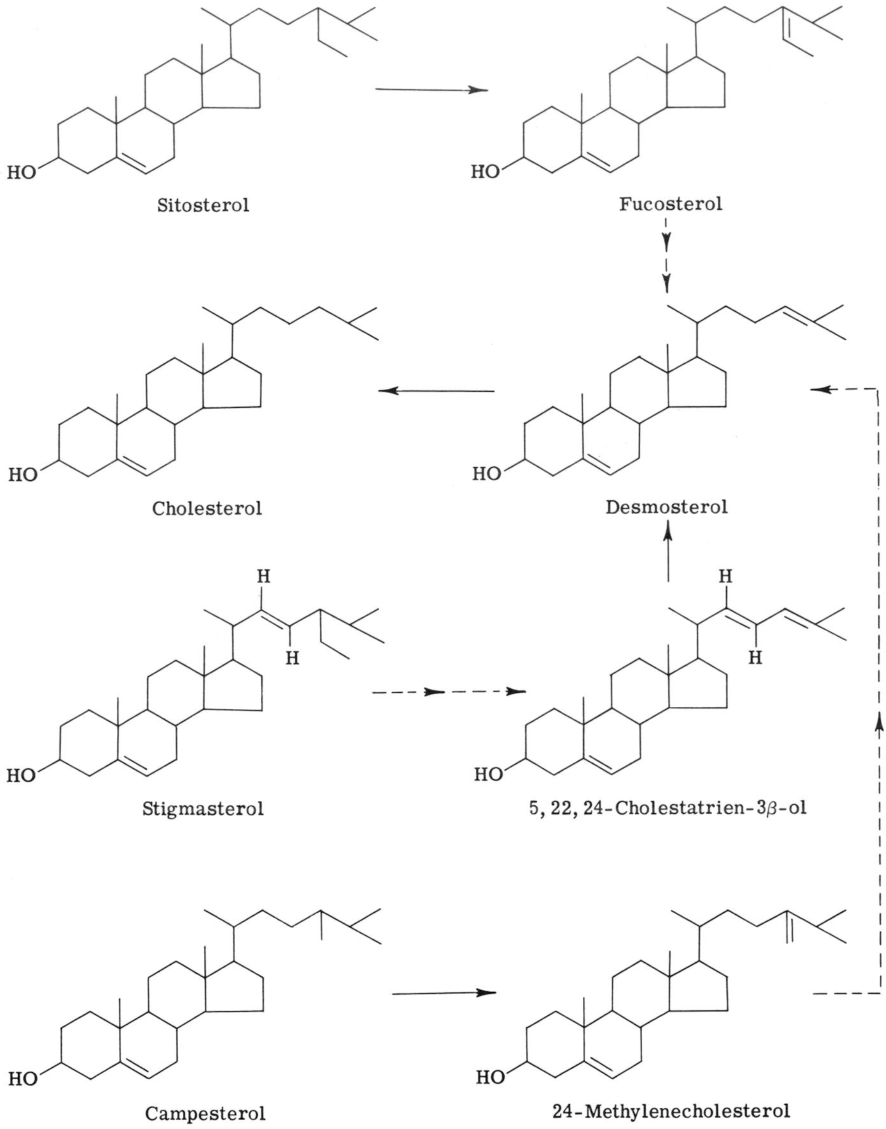

FIG. 2. Conversion of sitosterol, stigmasterol, and campesterol to cholesterol in insects.

cholesterol also occurs in the pathway of conversion of campesterol to cholesterol. 24-Methylenecholesterol was positively identified as an intermediate in the dealkylation and conversion of campesterol to cholesterol in this insect (Svoboda et al., 1972a; Thompson et al., 1972), indicating that 24-alkene intermediates are involved in the dealkylation of both 24-methyl and 24-ethyl groups from the phytosterol side chain. These findings strongly suggest that a 24-ethylidene metabolite may also be an intermediate in the dealkylation of stigmasterol in insects (Thompson *et al.*, 1972). Studies with dihydrobrassicasterol as the dietary sterol have shown that 24-methylenecholesterol is also a metabolite and an intermediate in the conversion of this C_{28} sterol to cholesterol and thus is involved in the dealkylation of 24β- as well as 24α-methyl substituents of phytosterols (Svoboda *et al.*, 1972a).

3. *22-Trans-5,22,24-cholestatrien-3β-ol*

Another intermediate of sterol metabolism in insects was discovered in the sterols isolated from tobacco hornworm larvae that had been fed stigmasterol in combination with the azasteroid inhibitor, 20,25-diazacholesterol (Section III,F). The new sterol 22-*trans*-5,22,24-cholestatrien-3β-ol accumulated in these inhibited larvae and was later shown to be a normal intermediate in the conversion of stigmasterol to cholesterol (Fig. 2) (Svoboda *et al.*, 1969a; Hutchins *et al.*, 1970). It was firmly established that the metabolic sequence is as shown in Fig. 2 by feeding 22-*trans*-5,22,24-cholestatrien-3β-ol alone and in combination with a diazasterol (Svoboda *et al.*, 1969a). No 22-dehydrocholesterol was detected in the sterols from either the noninhibited or inhibited insects, indicating that the Δ^{22}-bond is reduced before the Δ^{24}-bond. When *trans*-22-dehydrocholesterol is used as the dietary sterol, there is little if any conversion of this sterol to cholesterol, indicating that the presence of a Δ^{24}-bond is necessary for reduction of the Δ^{22}-bond of 22-*trans*-5,22,24-cholestatrien-3β-ol by the hornworm. An *in vitro* preparation of hornworm midgut tissue that converts desmosterol to cholesterol also reduces 22-*trans*-5,22,24-cholestatrien-3β-ol-^{3}H to desmosterol and cholesterol (Svoboda *et al.*, 1969a).

In the dealkylation and conversion of stigmasterol to cholesterol and 7-dehydrocholesterol in *Tribolium*, 22-*trans*-5,22,24-cholestatrien-3β-ol was also a normal intermediate (Fig. 3) (Svoboda *et al.*, 1972b), revealing yet another similarity in the sterol metabolism of *Tribolium* and the tobacco hornworm. This metabolite and intermediate in stigmasterol metabolism has also been isolated from the German cockroach and from the corn earworm, *Heliothis zea* (Svoboda *et al.*, 1969a).

4. *5,7,24-Cholestatrien-3β-ol and 5,7,22,24-Cholestatetraen-3β-ol*

Recent metabolic studies with *Tribolium* have resulted in the isolation and identification of two new sterol metabolites from insects (Svoboda *et al.*, 1972b). When either sitosterol-^{3}H, campesterol-^{3}H, stigmasterol-^{3}H,

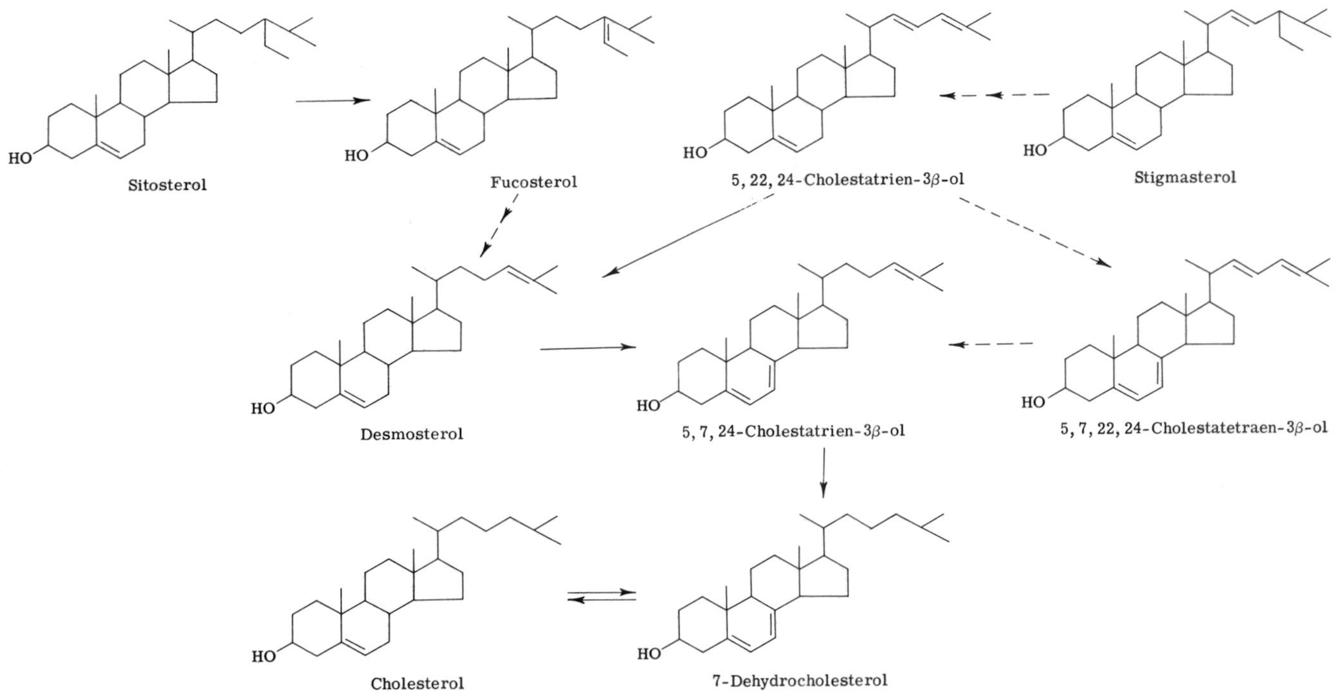

FIG. 3. Conversion of sitosterol and stigmasterol to cholesterol in the confused flour beetle, *Tribolium confusum*.

or desmosterol-^{14}C was fed in diets in combination with an azasteroid inhibitor (Section III,F) to *Tribolium,* an unknown radiolabeled metabolite accumulated in the tissues of the inhibited larvae in every case. The unknown sterol was identified as 5,7,24-cholestatrien-3β-ol (Fig. 3) and was subsequently found to be a constant normal metabolite of each of the four dietary sterols. This intermediate represents a major difference in the sterol metabolism of *Tribolium* as compared to the hornworm and certain other species.

A new metabolite of stigmasterol also was discovered during the course of studies with *Tribolium* (Svoboda *et al.,* 1972b). Feeding stigmasterol-^{3}H in combination with a diazasterol inhibitor resulted in the accumulation of the sterol-^{3}H, 5,7,22,24-cholestatetraen-3β-ol (Fig. 3). However, this sterol is found only in trace amounts in normal insects and thus may not be a true intermediate in the metabolism of stigmasterol in *Tribolium.* Apparently, in the presence of the inhibitor that prevents the reduction of $\Delta^{22,24}$-bonds of the 5,22,24-cholestatrien-3β-ol and results in its accumulation, a Δ^7-bond is then introduced to give the 5,7,22,24-cholestetraen-3β-ol, even though this sterol may not be the normal intermediate.

5. *Desmosterol*

During the course of studies on the utilization and metabolism of sitosterol-^{3}H in the tobacco hornworm, desmosterol-^{3}H was isolated and identified as the first known intermediate in the conversion of sitosterol to cholesterol (Fig. 2) (Svoboda *et al.,* 1967). Desmosterol was found to be a constant metabolite of sitosterol-^{3}H, normally comprising less than 1.4% of the total tissue sterols. Furthermore, when desmosterol-^{14}C was used as the dietary sterol, the hornworms grew and developed normally and there was near complete conversion of desmosterol to cholesterol, thus substantiating desmosterol as the terminal intermediate in this pathway (Fig. 2). Subsequently, desmosterol has been identified as an intermediate in the conversion of sitosterol to cholesterol in a number of other insects including the firebrat, the German cockroach, the American cockroach, the corn earworm, and the fall armyworm, *Spodoptera frugiperda* (Svoboda and Robbins, 1971). More recently, desmosterol has been shown to be an intermediate in the conversion of sitosterol to 7-dehydrocholesterol and cholesterol in *Tribolium* (Fig. 3) indicating again that the steroid metabolic pathways in insects may be similar even when the final composition of tissue sterols is quite different, as in the tobacco hornworm and *Tribolium* (Svoboda *et al.,* 1972b). Feeding desmosterol in combination with an azasteroid results in a large accumulation of 5,7,24-cholestatrien-3β-ol and a greatly reduced production of 7-dehydrocholesterol and cholesterol in *Tribolium,* indicating the metabolic sequence for these sterols to be as shown in Fig. 3. Since sterols with only a Δ^{22}-bond in the side chain were not produced from stigmasterol in *Tribolium*, then the Δ^{22}-bond must be reduced before the Δ^{24}-bond, as was found in the tobacco hornworm (Svoboda *et al.*, 1969a). Although other metabolic pathways may exist, the scheme in Fig. 3 is based on identified intermediates and metabolites and shows the major known pathways of plant sterol metabolism in *Tribolium*.

That desmosterol is an intermediate in the formation of cholesterol from phytosterols in insects is of interest from a comparative biochemical standpoint: Desmosterol is a terminal intermediate in *de novo* biosynthesis of cholesterol in vertebrates (Steinberg and Avigan, 1960; Stokes and Fish, 1960), and in plants a Δ^{24}-sterol intermediate is involved in a primary step in which alkylation at the C-24 position of the side chain occurs in the biosynthesis of C_{28} and C_{29} plant sterols (Goad, 1967). Since fucosterol and desmosterol are the first and terminal intermediates, respectively, in the major pathways of conversion of sitosterol to cholesterol in the hornworm and certain other insects, dealkylation in insects then may well be, in part, the reverse of the alkylation process as outlined for phytosterol biosynthesis in plants (Goad, 1967).

The conversion of desmosterol-^{14}C to cholesterol has been studied with insect tissue preparations patterned after the *in vitro* system used for the Δ^{24}-sterol reductase enzyme(s) of vertebrates (Steinberg and Avigan, 1969). A preparation of tobacco hornworm midgut tissue efficiently converted desmosterol-^{14}C to cholesterol, whereas preparations utilizing other tissues were essentially inactive (Svoboda *et al.*, 1969b). Similar *in vitro* preparations of American cockroach tissues had very low levels of Δ^{24}-sterol reductase activity compared to the hornworm (J. A. Svoboda, W. E. Robbins, and M. J. Thompson, unpublished observations), indicating a significant difference in titer or kinetics of the reductases of these two species. The Δ^{24}-sterol reductase activity of tobacco hornworm midgut tissue is associated with the microsomal fraction and NADPH is a necessary cofactor. This is the first *in vitro* system available for studying a specific sterol-metabolizing enzyme from an insect.

The conversion of desmosterol to cholesterol in the hornworm is blocked by certain vertebrate hypocholesterolemic agents (Fig. 6) (Svoboda and Robbins, 1967) and these inhibitors, when fed in combination with sitosterol, cause an accumulation of desmosterol and unchanged sitosterol at the expense of cholesterol formation. Certain of these inhibitors have proven to be valuable tools in studying the utilization and metabolism of phytosterols in insects. Azasteroids were used to demonstrate that desmosterol is a common intermediate in the conversion of a number of different C_{28} and C_{29} plant sterols (Fig. 1) to cholesterol in the hornworm (Svoboda and Robbins, 1968) and that desmosterol is also an intermediate in the conversion of sitosterol to cholesterol in several species of insects (Svoboda and Robbins, 1971). These inhibitors, which have been discussed thus far only in regard to the isolation and identification of metabolites and intermediates, are treated in some detail in Section III,F.

With the exception of *Tribolium*, the omnivorous and phytophagous species of insects that have been examined critically appear to possess similar pathways for dealkylation and conversion of phytosterols to cholesterol. The presence of 5,7,24-cholestatrien-3β-ol as an intermediate in the conversion of plant sterols to cholesterol and 7-dehydrocholesterol in *Tribolium* is a variation from that observed in other insects but perhaps some such difference in the pathway should be expected because of the high level of 7-dehydrocholesterol in this insect. Considering the diversity of ecological niches occupied by insects and their evolutionary adaptations, one might well expect many more such interesting differences to surface and as we broaden our knowledge of steroid metabolism and function in insects, there will no doubt be discovered additional unique facets of this important area of insect biochemistry.

C. Ecdysone Biosynthesis and Metabolism

1. *The Molting Hormones*

a. Insects. Molting is a characteristic feature of insect growth and development and three types of hormones control molting and metamorphosis in insects: the brain hormone, the molting hormones or ecdysones, and the juvenile hormones (Fig. 4). The brain hormone, secreted by neurosecretory cells in the insect brain, activates the prothoracic glands or ecdysial glands. In turn, the activation of these glands brings about the secretion of one or more closely related steroids, the ecdysones, which cause the insect to molt and shed its old cuticle or exoskeleton. The kind of molt that the insect undergoes is controlled by the third type of hormones, the juvenile hormones which are secreted by the corpora allata. The presence of juvenile hormones in the immature insect causes the larva to molt to a larger larva and thus prevents it from differentiating into an adult. In the absence of the juvenile hormone at the time of the molt, differentiation does occur, and the nymphs of hemimetabolous insects molt into adults and the larvae of holometabolous insects molt into pupae and then into adults. In summation then, the steroid molting hormones or ecdysones are the true growth and differentiation hormones of insects and possibly of arthropods generally (Krishnakumaran and Schneiderman, 1968, 1969, 1970).

Thus far, three molting hormones—α-ecdysone, 20-hydroxyecdysone,

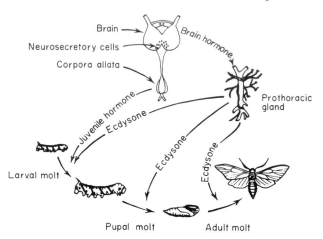

Fig. 4. Schematic diagram of the hormonal control of molting and metamorphosis in an insect.

and 20,26-dihydroxyecdysone—have been isolated from insects in highly purified or crystalline form and conclusively identified by their physical and spectral properties. The first molting hormone, α-ecdysone (Fig. 5) isolated from pupae of the silkworm (Butenandt and Karlson, 1954), was identified by chemical methods (Karlson *et al.*, 1963) and X-ray diffraction spectroscopy (Huber and Hoppe, 1965) as the pentahydroxy steroid, $2\beta,3\beta,14\alpha,22R,25$-pentahydroxy-$5\beta$-cholest-7-en-6-one. A second molting hormone, more polar than α-ecdysone, was also initially isolated from pupae of the silkworm (Karlson, 1956) and assigned the name of β-ecdysone. However, β-ecdysone was not characterized until after its isolation from another member of the Arthropoda, a seawater crayfish *Jasus lalandei* (Hampshire and Horn, 1966). Since this hormone was isolated and identified from a crustacean, it was given the name crustecdysone. Crustecdysone differs structurally from α-ecdysone only in the presence of an additional hydroxyl group at the C-20 position. This hexahydroxy steroid ($2\beta,3\beta,14\alpha,20R,22R,25$-hexahydroxy-$5\beta$-cholest-7-en-6-one), which is the predominant molting hormone in the majority of insects thus far examined, was independently identified from different insects by several laboratories and is referred to by several different designations. Thus, crustecdysone isolated from the oak silkmoth, *Antheraea pernyi* (Horn *et al.*, 1966), β-ecdysone (Karlson, 1956), ecdysterone (Hoffmeister and Grützmacher, 1966), and 20-hydroxyecdysone (Hocks and Wiechert, 1966) isolated from the silkworm, and THE-1 (Kaplanis *et al.*, 1966) isolated from the tobacco hornworm are one and the same compound. The name 20-hydroxyecdysone (Fig. 5) immediately relates the compound structurally to α-ecdysone and will be used throughout the chapter for the sake of uniformity and to avoid confusion. The third molting hormone 20,26-dihydroxyecdysone (Thompson *et al.*, 1967) (Fig. 5), thus far isolated and identified only from the tobacco hornworm during pupal-adult development, differs from α-ecdysone by the presence of two additional hydroxyl groups located at the C-20 and C-26 position. Since all three of the insect ecdysones, α-ecdysone, 20-hydroxyecdysone, and 20,26-dihydroxyecdysone have been isolated from the tobacco hornworm during pupal-adult development at peak ecdysone titer, it has been proposed that these steroids are intermediates in the biosynthetic-degradative scheme of the ecdysones (Thompson *et al.*, 1967).

b. *Phytoecdysones and Other Zooecdysones.* The molting hormones, α-ecdysone and 20-hydroxyecdysone are not restricted to insects or related arthropods since these two hormones, *per se,* have also been isolated and identified from plants (Horn, 1971; Rees, 1971). In addition, approximately thirty-five ecdysone analogs have been isolated and characterized from a wide variety of plant species representing all three major classes of the Pteropsida (Okauchi, 1969; Horn, 1971; Rees, 1971; Nakanishi, 1971; Heftmann, 1970). Ponasterone A, inokosterone, cyasterone, makisterone A, rubrosterone, and poststerone (Fig. 5) are but a few examples of the ecdysone analogs isolated and identified from plants. A detailed account of the distribution, chemistry, and metabolism of the phytoecdysones is beyond the scope of this chapter and for this information the reader is referred to the excellent reviews cited above.

Other molting hormones isolated from arthropods include 2-deoxy crustecdysone (Fig. 5) from the seawater crayfish, *Jasus lalandei* (Galbraith *et al.*, 1968), and two ecdysones first reported from plants, inokosterone (= callinecdysone A) and the C-28 steroid, makisterone A (= callinecdysone B) (Fig. 5) from the marine crab *Callinectus sapidus* (Faux *et al.*, 1969). Whether or not the arthropods specifically, or invertebrates generally also possess the diversity of ecdysone-like steroids found in plants is conjectural at this time. However, such a possibility certainly exists as unidentified substances with molting hormone activity have been reported from the mussel *Mytilus edulis* (Takemoto *et al.*, 1967), a snail, *Australorbis glabratus* (Muftic, 1969), and a polychaete annelid, *Nereis* sp. (King, 1972a).

Steroids with molting hormone activity have not as yet been detected in or isolated from the Vertebrata. Although assays of extracts from a number of human tissues for molting hormone activity have yielded negative results (Burdette, 1962), a systematic search for ecdysones or ecdysone-like compounds as has been carried out for plants has not to the authors knowledge been done with vertebrates. Thus, it would be

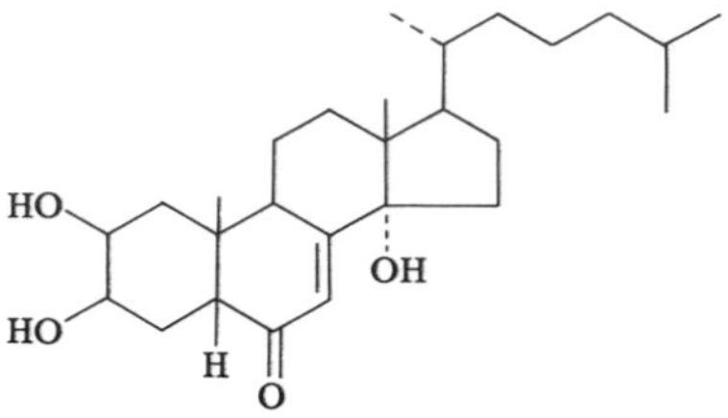

22, 25-Dideoxyecdysone

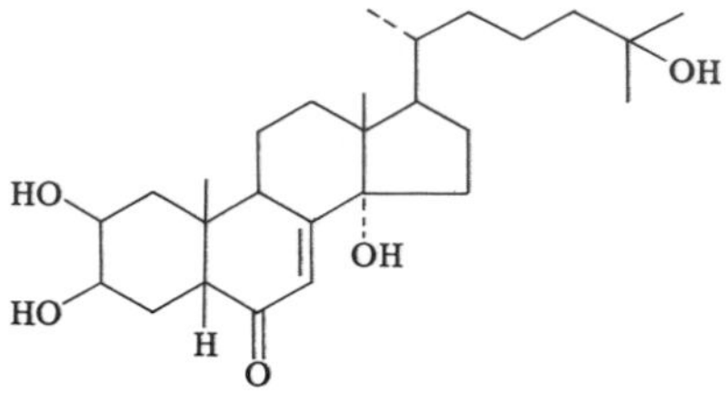

22-Deoxyecdysone

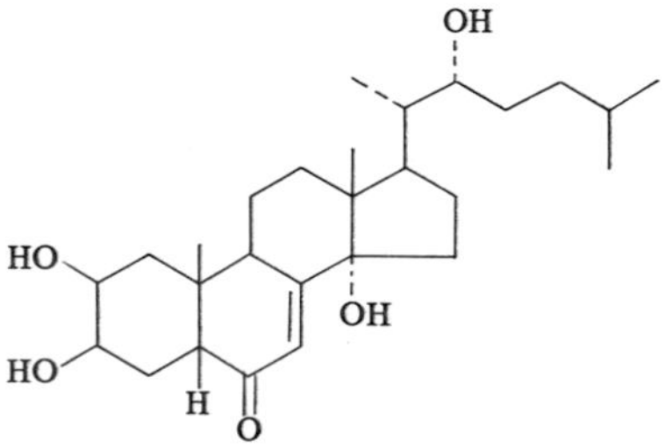

25-Deoxyecdysone

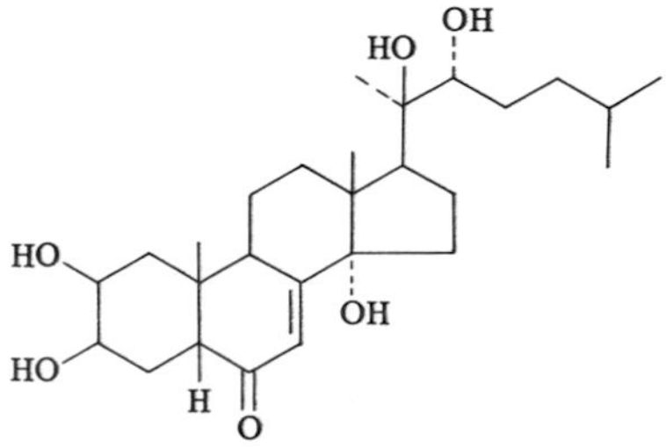

Ponasterone A

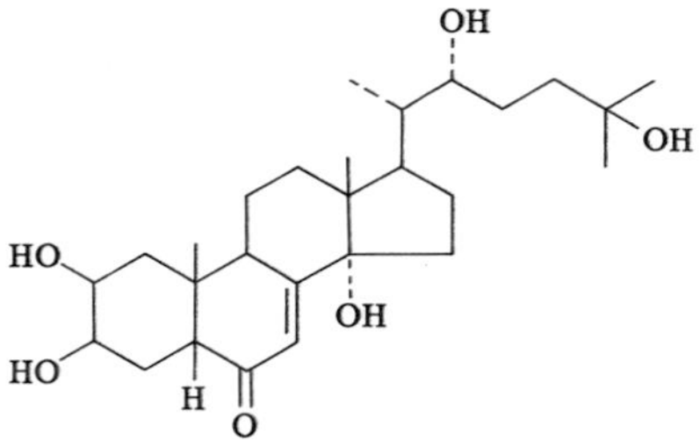

α-Ecdysone

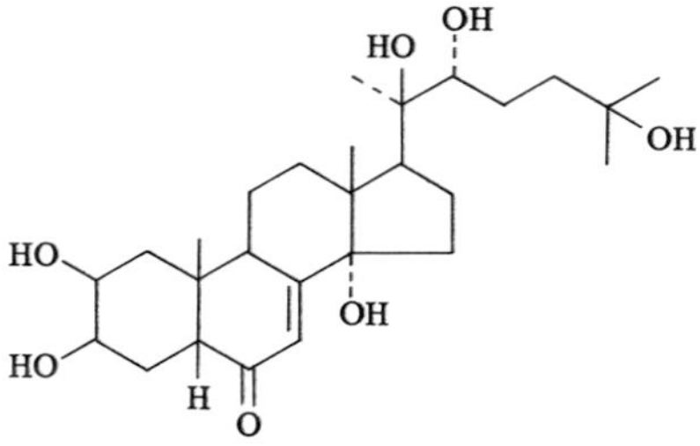

20-Hydroxyecdysone

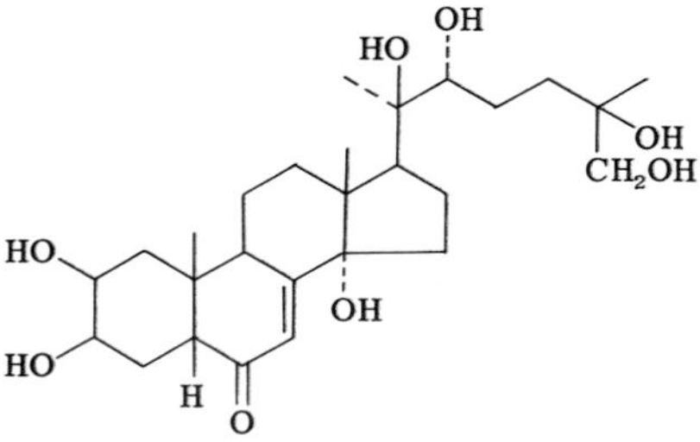

20, 26-Dihydroxyecdysone

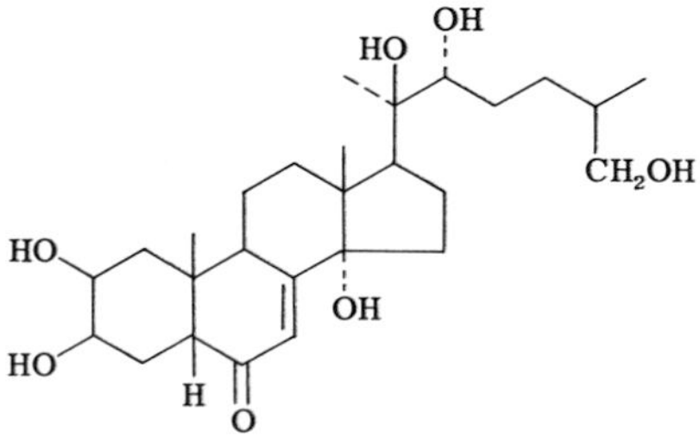

Inokosterone

FIG. 5.   Ecdysones and analogs.

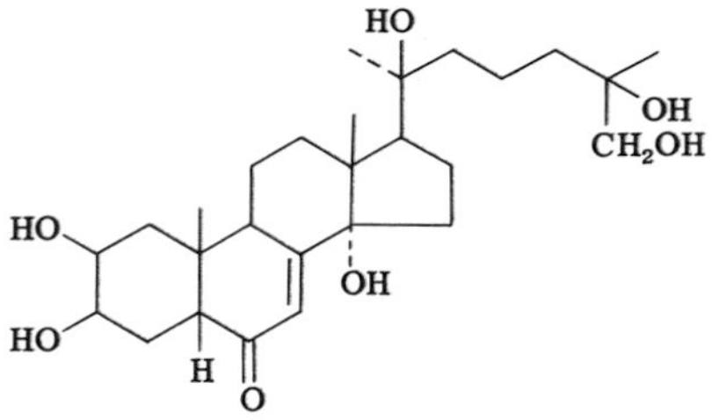

22-Deoxy-26-hydroxyecdysone

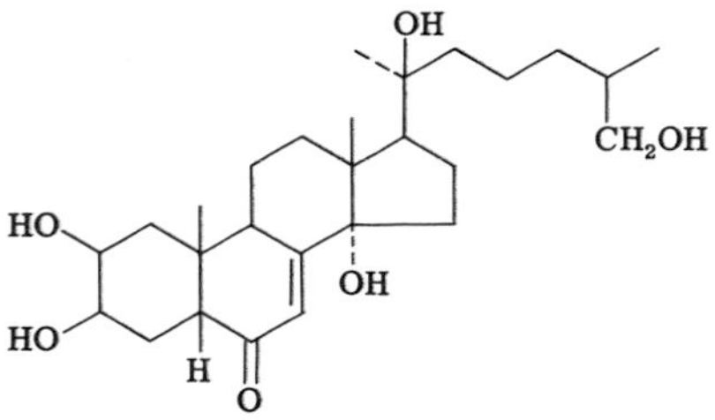

22-Deoxyinokosterone

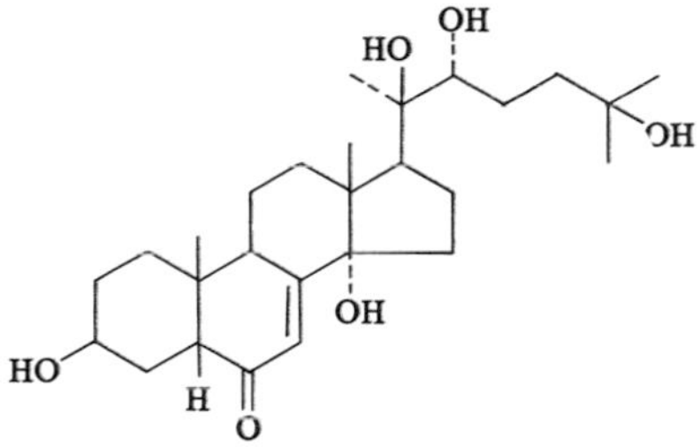

2-Deoxycrustecdysone

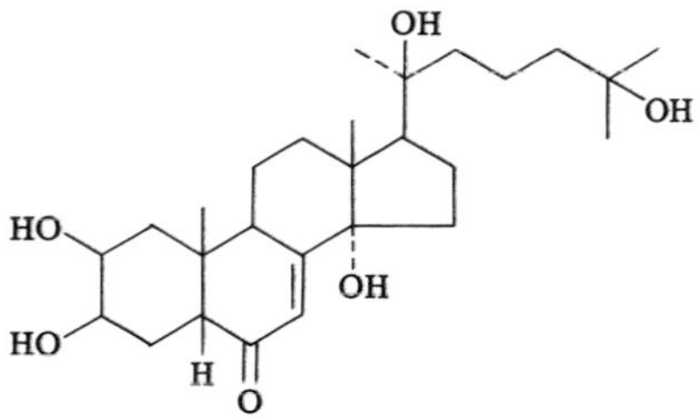

22-Deoxy-20-hydroxyecdysone

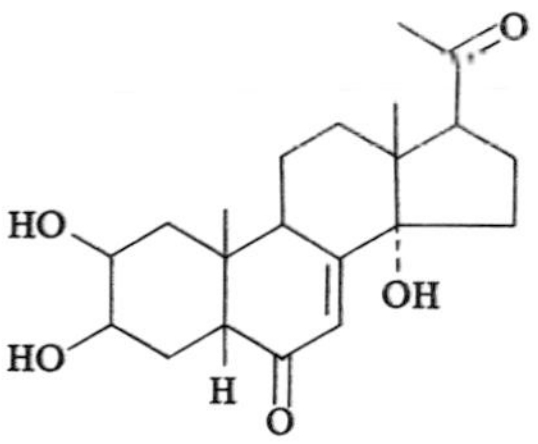

Poststerone

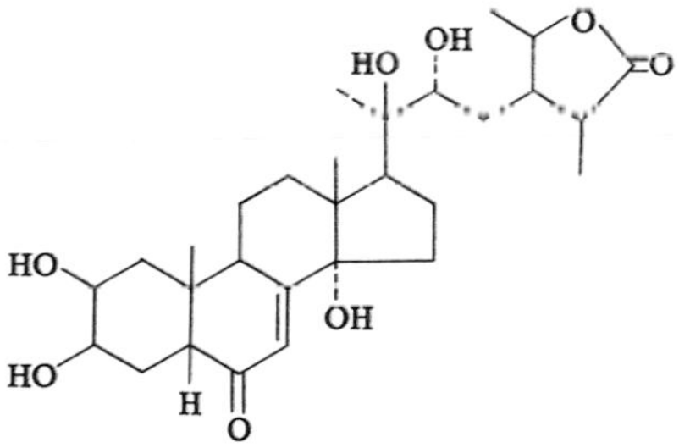

Cyasterone

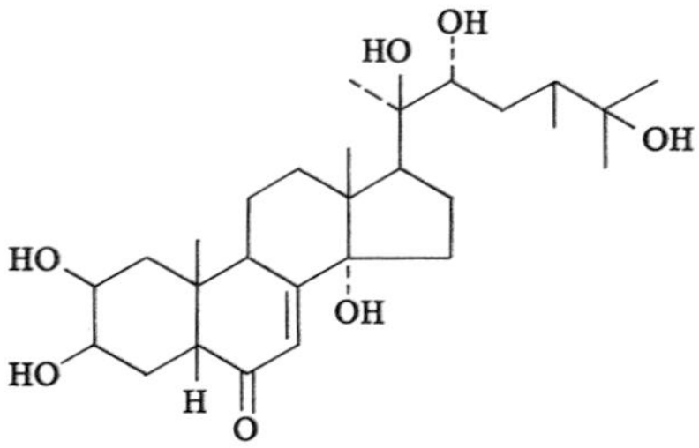

Makisterone A

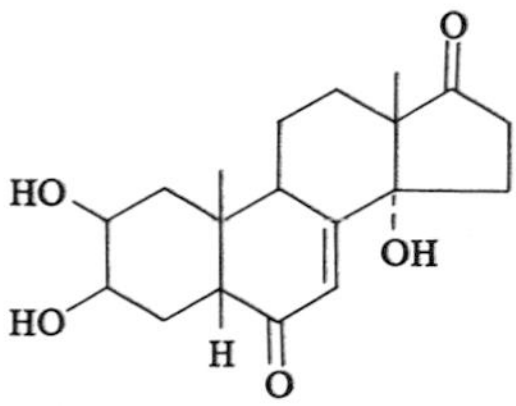

Rubrosterone

Fig. 5 (*Continued*).

premature at this time to rule out the possibility that such steroids also occur in vertebrates.

2. Precursors and Intermediates for the Insect Molting Hormones

a. Cholesterol. The conversion of cholesterol-^{3}H to α-ecdysone was first shown by Karlson and Hoffmeister (1963) in *Calliphora erythrocephala* (= *vicina*) and in this insect, about 0.0001% of the cholesterol-^{3}H injected into the larvae was converted into α-ecdysone. Galbraith *et al.* (1970) reported that injected cholesterol-^{3}H was incorporated into 20-hydroxyecdysone but not into α-ecdysone by *Calliphora stygia,* and in this study, 0.015% of the cholesterol-^{3}H was converted to 20-hydroxyecdysone. Recently, Willig *et al.* (1971) showed the conversion of cholesterol-4-^{14}C into both α-ecdysone and 20-hydroxyecdysone by *C. erythrocephala* (1). About 0.018 and 0.035% of the injected cholesterol was converted to α-ecdysone and 20-hydroxyecdysone respectively. The more efficient conversion of the labeled cholesterol into both α-ecdysone and 20-hydroxyecdysone in this latter study could be attributed to the proper developmental stage or physiological state of the organism at the time of treatment and analysis.

Nakanishi *et al.* (1972) demonstrated that cholesterol-4-^{14}C injected into the isolated abdomens of 5th instar larvae of the silkworm was about equally utilized (0.0008%) for the synthesis of α-ecdysone and 20-hydroxyecdysone. These very interesting results indicate that the entire complex of enzymes necessary for the conversion of cholesterol to the ecdysones resides in the abdomen, and that the ecdysial glands are not essential for any of the steps in ecdysone biosynthesis. When the brain-ring gland complex from *Calliphora erythrocephala* was incubated with cholesterol-4-^{14}C there was no conversion of the cholesterol to either α-ecdysone or 20-hydroxyecdysone in either their free, esterified, or conjugated forms (Willig *et al.,* 1971). However, these workers did find hormonally active metabolites of cholesterol following hydrolyses of the inactive fraction with either an esterase or a glucosidase. Thus, in *C. erythrocephala,* the brain-ring gland complex, which includes the ecdysial glands, produces steroidal substances from cholesterol with molting hormone activity that are not the known insect molting hormones but may be intermediates in ecdysone biosynthesis.

$$\text{cholesterol} \rightarrow \alpha\text{-ecdysone} \rightarrow 20\text{-hydroxyecdysone} \tag{1}$$

b. 7-Dehydrocholesterol. A likely candidate for a precursor and an intermediate in the biosynthetic pathway of the molting hormones in insects is the $\Delta^{5,7}$ sterol, 7-dehydrocholesterol. The conversion of labeled cholesterol to 7-dehydrocholesterol in insects is well documented

(Kaplanis *et al.,* 1960; Robbins *et al.,* 1961; Ishii *et al.,* 1963; Robbins *et al.,* 1964; Schaefer *et al.,* 1965; Monroe *et al.,* 1967; Svoboda *et al.,* 1972b), and this conversion is independent of the action of intestinal microorganisms (Robbins *et al.,* 1964; Monroe *et al.,* 1967). Certain of the above reports (Kaplanis *et al.,* 1960; Robbins, 1963; Monroe *et al.,* 1967) further show that the concentration of the 7-dehydrocholesterol-4-^{14}C varies within a species from none or barely detectable quantities to as high as 36% of the total sterols of the insect depending on the developmental stage. Similarly, the quantity of 7-dehydrocholesterol may differ among species from less than 1%, as in the American cockroach (Ishii *et al.,* 1963; D. Chen, J. N. Kaplanis, and W. E. Robbins, unpublished observations) and the tobacco hornworm (S. Chen and J. N. Kaplanis, unpublished observations), to as much as 70% in *Tribolium* (Beck and Kapadia, 1957; Svoboda *et al.,* 1972b). However, not all insects are able to introduce the Δ^7-bond; two species of insects have been shown to require an exogenous source of a sterol that contains a Δ^7-bond (Heed and Kircher, 1965; Chu *et al.,* 1970) and thus must rely on a dietary sterol with a Δ^7- or $\Delta^{5,7}$-bond to serve as precursors for the molting hormones.

The apparent absence or lack of detectable quantities of 7-dehydro cholesterol in a developmental stage of an insect may not necessarily indicate, however, that either the species or the stage of development lacks the ability to dehydrogenate cholesterol at the C-7 position. For example, sterol analyses of a number of individual tissues from two widely differing insect species—the hemimetabolous American cockroach (D. Chen, J. N. Kaplanis, and W. E. Robbins, unpublished observations) and the holometabolous tobacco hornworm (S. Chen and J. N. Kaplanis, unpublished observations)—reveal that only the ecdysial glands possess a large percentage of 7-dehydrocholesterol. Only in this tissue of the American cockroach and the tobacco hornworm does 7-dehydrocholesterol account for as much as 25% and 60% of the total sterol, respectively (Tables VIII and IX), whereas other tissues contain only a few percent at most, thus, implicating the ecdysial gland as a site of synthesis or storage of 7-dehydrocholesterol. The Δ^7-bond that is common to 7-dehydrocholesterol and the ecdysones further suggests that this sterol is an intermediate in molting hormone biosynthesis. Indeed, Galbraith *et al.* (1970) have shown that 7-dehydrocholesterol-^{3}H, like cholesterol-^{3}H, is metabolized to 20-hydroxyecdysone-^{3}H, in *Calliphora stygia* (2). Particularly noteworthy was that the incorporation of 7-dehydrocholesterol-^{3}H into 20-hydroxyecdysone was nearly twice that of cholesterol-^{3}H.

$$\text{7-dehydrocholesterol} \rightarrow \text{20-hydroxyecdysone} \qquad (2)$$

Table VIII

STEROLS OF PROTHORACIC GLANDS OF THE AMERICAN COCKROACH,
Periplaneta americana[a]

	Sterols[b]	
Stage	Cholesterol (%)	7-Dehydrocholesterol (%)
Last instar nymph		
I[c]	90	10
II[d]	75	25
III[e]	81	19
Adult	93	7

[a] D. Chen, J. N. Kaplanis, and W. E. Robbins (unpublished observations).
[b] Analyses by GLC and UV spectroscopy of sterol fractions following purification by adsorption chromatography.
[c] Nymphs with definitive wing bud patterns and abdomen not distended.
[d] Nymphs with definitive wing bud patterns and fully distended abdomens.
[e] Nymphs with swollen wing buds and fully distended abdomens.

c. 22,25-Dideoxyecdysone. The scheme of ecdysone biosynthesis from such precursors as cholesterol and 7-dehydrocholesterol to α-ecdysone is not currently known. In the search for intermediates in the biosynthesis of the molting hormones, 22,25-dideoxyecdysone ($2\beta,3\beta,14\alpha$,trihydroxy-5β-cholest-7-en-6-one) (Fig. 5) has served to elucidate the sequence of hydroxylation of the side chain of the ecdysones. This synthetic analog has all of the structural features of the ecdysone nucleus but lacks the hydroxyl groups on the side chain. In addition to molting hormone activity, the analog exhibits a variety of biological activities (Robbins *et al.*,

Table IX

STEROLS OF PROTHORACIC GLANDS OF TOBACCO HORNWORM (*Manduca sexta*) PUPAE[a]

	Sterols[b]	
Age[c] (days)	Cholesterol (%)	7-Dehydro-cholesterol (%)
0[c]	40	60
1	60	40
4	80	20

[a] S. Chen and J. N. Kaplanis (unpublished observations).
[b] Analyses by GLC and UV spectroscopy of sterol fractions following purification by adsorption chromatography.
[c] Zero time—when the prepupal skin is shed.

1970) including the termination of pupal diapause in the tobacco horn-worm (Kaplanis *et al.*, 1969). When its metabolism was examined in relation to termination of pupal diapause in male diapausing tobacco horn-worm pupae, the 22,25-dideoxyecdysone-³H was efficiently converted into α-ecdysone and 20-hydroxyecdysone (Kaplanis *et al.*, 1969). The specific activity of each of the crystalline ecdysones was approximately one-half that of theoretical indicating that one-half originated from endogenous sterol precursors and the other half from the ecdysone analog. In addition to α-ecdysone and 20-hydroxyecdysone, the third insect ecdysone, 20-26-dihydroxyecdysone, was also detected. Since the 22,25-dideoxyecdysone readily entered the steroid pool and was so efficiently incorporated into the insect ecdysones (3), it was concluded that this compound may be a normal intermediate in the biosynthesis of the molting hormones in the tobacco hornworm (Kaplanis *et al.*, 1969).

$$22,25\text{-dideoxyecdysone} \rightarrow \alpha\text{-ecdysone} \rightarrow 20\text{-hydroxyecdysone}$$
$$\downarrow$$
$$20,26\text{-dihydroxyecdysone} \qquad (3)$$

The metabolism of 22,25-dideoxyecdysone-³H was also studied *in vivo* (by injection) and *in vitro* in the prepupae of the tobacco hornworm (King, 1972a,b) and here again at this earlier stage of development, the compound was efficiently converted (4) to α-ecdysone, 20-hydroxy-ecdysone, and 20,26-dihydroxyecdysone via the intermediate, 22-deoxy-ecdysone (Fig. 5). The *in vitro* work further demonstrated that while the fat body and Malpighian tubules convert the 22,25-dideoxyecdysone ³H to the three insect ecdysones the ecdysial glands do not metabolize the compound beyond α-ecdysone. The prepupae of *Calliphora stygia* also efficiently convert the 22,25-dideoxyecdysone to α-ecdysone and 20-hydroxyecdysone (Thomson *et al.*, 1971).

$$22,25\text{-dideoxyecdysone} \rightarrow 22\text{-deoxyecdysone} \rightarrow \alpha\text{-ecdysone} \rightarrow 20\text{-hydroxyecdysone} \rightarrow$$
$$20,26\text{-dihydroxyecdysone} \quad (4)$$

However, unlike the normal sequence of side-chain hydroxylation of 22,25-dideoxyecdysone to the insect ecdysones found to occur in pre-pupae of *Calliphora stygia* and in the prepupae and during pupal-adult development of the tobacco hornworm, the metabolism of the compound proceeds quite differently during the earlier stages of development in the latter insect. When newly hatched tobacco hornworm larvae were reared to the early prepupal stage on a diet containing the 22,25-dideoxyecdy-sone-4-¹⁴C the major radioactive metabolites isolated and identified from larval frass and early prepupae consisted of a complex mixture of steroid metabolites, the majority of which lacked the hydroxyl group at the C-22 position (Kaplanis *et al.*, 1972). In addition to 22-deoxyecdysone which was the major metabolite, 22-deoxyinokosterone, 22-deoxy-26-hydroxy-ecdysone, and 22-deoxy-20-hydroxyecdysone (Fig. 5) were also isolated and identified. Conversion to α-ecdysone and 20-hydroxyecdysone was a minor pathway since only minute amounts of these two compounds were detected in either the frass or early prepupae. The metabolites of 22,25-dideoxyecdysone from larval frass and early prepupae of the tobacco hornworm are shown in (5).

$$22,25\text{-dideoxyecdysone} \rightarrow 22\text{-deoxyecdysone} \rightarrow \alpha\text{-ecdysone} \rightarrow$$

20-hydroxyecdysone   22-deoxy-20-hydroxyecdysone

22-deoxyinokosterone   22-deoxy-26-hydroxyecdysone   (5)

There are several possible explanations for the observed differences in metabolism of 22,25-dideoxyecdysone in the different developmental stages of the hornworm. During pupal-adult development and prepupal development, the compound is metabolized at a time when the biochemical mechanism(s) necessary for the conversion of the analog to the ecdysones would be expected to be active in the tobacco hornworm since peak titers of molting hormone activity occur in both of these developmental stages (Kaplanis et al., 1966). Thus, the relatively low level of conversion of the analog to α-ecdysone and 20-hydroxyecdysone in the early prepupae as opposed to its more efficient conversion during the period of increased molting hormone titer in hornworm prepupae again points to the importance of the developmental period or time in relation to ecdysone biosynthesis and metabolism. It is also possible that in the earlier immature stages of development there may be differences in the biosynthetic pathways to the ecdysones or even qualitative differences in the ecdysones, per se.

d. 22-Deoxyecdysone. This tetrahydroxy steroid (Fig. 5), which serves as an intermediate in the conversion of 22,25-dideoxyecdysone to α-ecdysone in prepupae of the tobacco hornworm (King, 1972b) and Calliphora stygia (Thomson et al., 1971) and during pupal-adult development in the hornworm (Kaplanis et al., 1972), has also been examined as a precursor to the molting hormones. King (1972b) studied the metabolism of 22-deoxyecdysone-³H in vivo in prepupae of the tobacco hornworm and showed that it was efficiently metabolized to α-ecdysone, 20-hydroxyecdysone, and 20,26-dihydroxyecdysone (6), and Thomson et al. (1971) also found that the 22-deoxyecdysone-³H was rapidly metabolized in C. stygia to α-ecdysone (5%) and 20-hydroxyecdysone (25%) (7). However, King (1972b) in further studies on the metabolism of 22-deoxyecdysone in nymphs of the grasshopper Gastrimargus africanus and larvae of the blowfly, Sarcophaga bullata, found the compound was metabolized into a complex mixture of polar steroids. α-Ecdysone was not detected and only small amounts of what might possibly be 20-hydroxyecdysone ($<5\%$) were detected only in *S. bullata.* From these results it was concluded that 22-deoxyecdysone is not a normal precursor of ecdysones in these two insects. However, in view of its efficient metabolism to the ecdysones in the tobacco hornworm, it is quite probable that this compound as well as 22,25-dideoxyecdysone are normal intermediates in ecdysone biosynthesis in this insect.

$$22\text{-deoxyecdysone} \rightarrow \alpha\text{-ecdysone} \rightarrow 20\text{-hydroxyecdysone}$$
$$\downarrow$$
$$20,26\text{-dihydroxyecdysone} \qquad\qquad (6)$$

$$22\text{-deoxyecdysone} \rightarrow \alpha\text{-ecdysone} \rightarrow 20\text{-hydroxyecdysone} \qquad (7)$$

e. 25-Deoxyecdysone. 25-Deoxyecdysone (Fig. 5) thus far has been examined as a possible precursor for the molting hormones only in *Calliphora stygia* at the time of puparium formation (Thomson *et al.,* 1969). When this compound was injected into 3rd instar larvae and the insects extracted 3 hours later (during puparium formation), a complex mixture of metabolites was obtained including ponasterone A, inokosterone, and 20-hydroxyecdysone (8). Since neither ponasterone A, nor inokosterone were previously detected in large-scale extracts from *C. stygia,* it was concluded that 25-deoxyecdysone is not a normal precursor for the insect ecdysones. However, 22-deoxyecdysone is efficiently converted to α-ecdysone and 20-hydroxyecdysone in *C. stygia* indicating that hydroxylation at C-25 precedes that at C-22 at this period of development, and this could well account for the conversion of 25-deoxyecdysone to ponasterone A and inokosterone. These investigators further contend that neither 22-deoxyecdysone nor 22,25-dideoxyecdysone may be normal precursors of 20-hydroxyecdysone (Thomson *et al.,* 1971) but instead biosynthesis may occur via 2-deoxy-α-ecdysone precursors. However, there is no experimental evidence at this time to support the premise that side-chain hydroxylation precedes hydroxylation at C-2 in the steroid nucleus. A final determination of the normal pathway(s) of ecdysone biosynthesis must await the isolation and identification of the intermediates in highly purified or crystalline form from insects. Meanwhile, possible intermediates such as 25-deoxyecdysone, 22-deoxyecdysone, and 22,25-dideoxyecdysone are fulfilling an important function in elucidating the sequence of side-chain hydroxylation in molting hormone biosynthesis.

$$25\text{-deoxyecdysone} \rightarrow \text{ponasterone A} \rightarrow \text{inokosterone}$$
$$\downarrow$$
$$20\text{-hydroxyecdysone} \qquad\qquad (8)$$

f. α-Ecdysone. The metabolism of labeled α-ecdysone has been studied in several species of insects by a number of investigators and all are in agreement that it is readily converted to 20-hydroxyecdysone (King and

Siddall, 1969; Galbraith *et al.*, 1969b; Moriyama *et al.*, 1970; Cherbas and Cherbas, 1970; Gorell *et al.*, 1972) (9). In two insects, *Calliphora erythrocephala* (=*vicina*) and the silkworm, the conversion of α-ecdysone to 20-hydroxyecdysone has been shown to occur peripheral to the ecdysial glands (King, 1969; Moriyama *et al.*, 1970). The metabolism of α-ecdysone-³H has also been studied *in vitro* (King, 1972a,b) and in these studies 20-hydroxyecdysone was formed from α-ecdysone by the fat body, Malpighian tubules, gut, and body wall but not by the ecdysial glands indicating that this organ does not possess the capacity to hydroxylate at C-20. Since evidence is accumulating to indicate that 20-hydroxyecdysone is considerably more active *in vitro* than α-ecdysone, it has been proposed that α-ecdysone may serve as a "prohormone" and 20-hydroxyecdysone functions as the active hormone (King, 1972a).

$$\alpha\text{-ecdysone} \rightarrow 20\text{-hydroxyecdysone} \tag{9}$$

g. 20-Hydroxyecdysone. The metabolism of 20-hydroxyecdysone-³H has been examined in *Calliphora stygia* following puparium formation (Galbraith *et al.*, 1969a). When injected into this insect for 6 hours after puparium formation, most of the hormone was recovered unchanged. However, when the compound was injected into 20-hour-old puparia and the organisms examined 6 hours later, the major part of the hormone was converted to more polar metabolites. Although there is no direct evidence that 20-hydroxyecdysone serves as a precursor for 20,26-dihydroxyecdysone, the structures of α-ecdysone and 20-hydroxyecdysone point to 20,26-dihydroxyecdysone as an intermediate in the biosynthetic-metabolic scheme of the ecdysones. This is further supported by the fact that α-ecdysone, 20-hydroxyecdysone, and 20,26-dihydroxyecdysone all originate from common precursors such as 22,25-dideoxyecdysone and 22-deoxyecdysone.

3. *Inactivation of the Insect Molting Hormones*

A number of investigations on the rate of disappearance of hormonal activity (Ohtaki *et al.*, 1968; Shaaya, 1969; Karlson and Bode, 1969; Emmerich, 1970; Ohtaki and Williams, 1970) have shown that insects are capable of inactivating the molting hormones and studies with the radiotracer-labeled hormone have in essence corroborated these results. When prepupae of *Calliphora stygia* were injected with 20-hydroxyecdysone-³H 20 hours after puparium formation and analyzed 6 hours later, approximately 10% of the radioactivity was found to be unchanged 20-hydroxyecdysone, whereas the remaining radioactivity was in the form of water-soluble metabolites (Galbraith *et al.*, 1969a). In this study, only 0.3% of the total activity of the polar fraction could be accounted for as ³H-labeled 4-hydroxy-4-methyl-pentanoic acid indicating that 20-22-bond scission is not a major metabolic pathway in this insect. However, when the catabolism of ponasterone-^{3}H A was studied in silkworm larvae (Hikino *et al.*, 1971), 2% of the total administered activity was as the C_{21} steroid poststerone (Fig. 5) indicating that scission of the 20-22-bond occurs to a greater extent in the silkworm. Side-chain scission at the 17-20-bond to form rubrosterone was not observed in this study.

In addition to side-chain scission, which to date appears to be a minor route of inactivation, other pathways of inactivation include hydroxylation, the formation of apolar metabolites (a decrease in the number of hydroxyl groups), esterification, and conjugation. Hydroxylation has been proposed as a possible means of inactivation in the hornworm because of the lower biological activity of 20,26-dihydroxyecdysone as compared to that of α-ecdysone and 20-hydroxyecdysone (Thompson *et al.*, 1967). On the other hand, Karlson (1970) in studies on inactivation with radiolabeled α-ecdysone reported two radioactive metabolites less polar than α-ecdysone suggesting there may be a decrease in the number of hydroxyl groups present. In studies on several species of insects, King (1972b) found apolar metabolites only in homogenates from fat body of *Sarcophaga bullata* and from housefly microsome preparations. However, the biological significance and structure of these apolar compounds are unknown.

Willig *et al.* (1971) have shown that hormonally active steroids may occur in the inactive form as esters. These investigators demonstrated the presence of a radiolabeled biologically inactive fraction from brain ring-gland complex of *C. erythrocephala* incubated with cholesterol-4-^{14}C which on hydrolysis with an esterase yielded compounds that gave molting hormone activity. In addition to serving as a possible route of inactivation for the molting hormones, the hormonally inactive derivatives such as esters or conjugates could also serve as prehormones (Baird *et al.*, 1968); they could be stored in the insect and subsequently transported to their site of action and there converted to the active form.

Conjugation may well represent the major route of inactivation of the molting hormones by insects. Heinrich and Hoffmeister (1970) were the first to report *in vitro* conjugation of the ecdysones by insect tissue; both 20-hydroxyecdysone and ponasterone A were rapidly converted into α-glucosides by transglucosylase present in the fat body of *Calliphora erythrocephala*. *In vitro* studies with brain ring-gland complex, with cholesterol-4-^{14}C as the substrate, also yielded a hormonally inactive glucoside fraction which on hydrolysis with α-glucosidase provided hormonally active steroids (Willig *et al.*, 1971). King (1972b) confirmed α-glucosylation in *in vitro* studies using α-ecdysone-^{3}H and the fat body of the tobacco hornworm; however, glucoside conjugates were not detected in the hornworm *in vivo* whereas in *Sarcophaga bullata* glucosides were formed both *in vivo* and *in vitro*. However, when adult houseflies were fed on a diet containing the labeled 22,25-dideoxyecdysone, the analog and its major metabolites were excreted primarily as β-glucoside conjugates (Kaplanis *et al.*, 1972) indicating that the molting hormones and related steroids may be present as either α- or β-glucoside conjugates in insects. Sulfate conjugation of the ecdysones also occurs in insects, and in the tobacco hornworm, sulfates are the predominant conjugates (Kaplanis *et al.*, 1971; Thompson *et al.*, 1972; King, 1972b). When the polar fraction from diapausing tobacco hornworm pupae injected with 22,25-dideoxyecdysone were subjected to enzymatic hydrolysis with a sulfatase preparation, the steroid moieties were found to be 22,25-dideoxyecdysone, α-ecdysone, and 20-hydroxyecdysone. α-Ecdysone was present as a conjugate in much greater quantities than was the 20-hydroxyecdysone, whereas in the free form 20-hydroxyecdysone was the major component suggesting that conjugation may serve as a mechanism for regulating the biosynthesis or the titer of 20-hydroxyecdysone. Whether or not the ecdysone conjugates present in insects are involved in processes other than inactivation, such as the regulation of titer, transport, or storage or even serve as prehormones are areas worthy of intensive research.

D. Steroid Excretory Products

The major metabolic pathways of sterol degradation and excretion in mammals, such as those involved in formation of coprostanol and the bile acids, have not been found to occur in insects. However, following the ingestion or injection of radioactive sterols, unidentified polar steroid metabolites do occur in both the intestinal tract and the excreta of insects (Clayton, 1964; Gilbert, 1967; Ritter and Wientjens, 1967). The first polar steroid metabolites to be characterized were the sulfates of cholesterol, sitosterol, and campesterol which were isolated from the meconium of the tobacco hornworm (Hutchins and Kaplanis, 1969). The large percentage of unmetabolized phytosterol sulfates found in the meconium as compared to the nonconjugated phytosterol content of the meconium or of the insect, suggests the selective elimination of these conjugates during pupal-adult development.

In experiments on the metabolism of 22,25-dideoxyecdysone-^{3}H fed to adult houseflies, the flies and excreta both yielded unmetabolized steroid, unidentified tetrahydroxy and pentahydroxy steroids, and a mixture of sulfate and glucoside conjugates of these ecdysteroids (Kaplanis *et al.*,

1971). The conjugates from the excreta of houseflies fed the ecdysone analog were predominantly glucosides while sulfates were the major conjugate in the excreta from flies treated by injection. In the housefly then, the type of steroid conjugate formed is, in part, dependent on the route of administration. In the tobacco hornworm, approximately one-fourth of the total radioactive steroids present in the frass from hornworm larvae reared to the prepupal stage on a diet containing 22,25-dideoxyecdysone-^{14}C are sulfate and glucoside conjugates of the ecdysone analog and its metabolites (Kaplanis *et al.*, 1972).

Sulfate and glucoside conjugates, then, are the major known steroid excretory products of insects. However, several questions remain to be answered concerning the sterol and ecdysteroid conjugates of insects: In ecdysteroids, does hydroxylation or conjugation occur first? Is there an equilibrium between the conjugates and the free steroids? What is the site(s) of conjugation in the insect? Are there different roles for the different types of conjugates? Until these points are resolved, no definite conclusion can be made as to the role(s) of the sterol and ecdysteroid conjugates; whether they are simply inactivation or excretory products, or whether they also function as prohormones or prehormones in insects as they do in vertebrates (Bernstein and Solomon, 1970; Baird *et al.*, 1968).

E. C_{18}, C_{19}, AND C_{21} STEROIDS

A number of C_{18}, C_{19}, and C_{21} steroids similar or identical to the vertebrate steroid hormones have been isolated from the thoracic bladders of the dytiscid water beetles. Schildknecht *et al.* (1966) first isolated and identified cortexone (21-hydroxy-4-pregnen-3,20-dione) from *Dytiscus marginalis* at the rather high concentration of 0.4 mg per insect and later from *Agabus bipustulatus* and *Acilius sulcatus* (Schildknecht *et al.*, 1967a). Cybisterone (20α-hydroxy-4,6-pregnadien-3-one), which was first discovered in *Cybister lateralimarginalis* (Schildknecht *et al.*, 1967b), was also isolated from *D. marginalis* along with 20α-hydroxy-4-pregnen-3-one (Schildknecht and Hotz, 1967). In addition, 12β,20β-dihydroxy-4,6-pregnadien-3-one was also isolated from *C. lateralimarginalis* (Schildknecht *et al.*, 1967b), whereas in *C. tripunctatus*, 12-hydroxy-4,6-pregnadien-3,20-dione was the principal steroid (Schildknecht and Kornig, 1968). The latter insect, according to Schildknecht, may secrete more than 1 mg of this compound. From *Platambus maculatus*, Schildknecht *et al.* (1969) have isolated 15α,20β-dihydroxy-4-pregnen-3-one. Other C-15 substituted steroids, namely, 15α-isobutyryloxy-4,6-pregnadien-3,20-dione, 15α-hydroxy-4,6-pregnadien-3,20-dione, and 20β-isobutyryloxy-15α-hydroxy-4,6-pregnadien-3-one have been isolated from *Agabus sturmi* (Schildknecht, 1970). Since 1966, a large number of these C_{21} steroids have been isolated from several genera and species of dytiscid beetles (Schildknecht, 1970; Chadha *et al.*, 1970; Sipahimalani *et al.*, 1970). In addition to the C_{21} steroids, small quantities of C_{18} and C_{19} steroids— estrone, 17β-estradiol, 1,2-dehydrotestosterone, and testosterone—have also been isolated from the secretions of dytiscid beetles (Schildknecht, 1970).

Since insects are incapable of *de novo* sterol biosynthesis and require a dietary source of sterol, it is likely that the water beetles synthesize the C_{18}, C_{19}, and C_{21} steroids from exogenous cholesterol or related sterols. Thus, when *Acilius sulcatus* was injected with mevalonolactone-2-^{14}C, cholesterol-4-^{14}C, or progesterone-4-^{14}C, it was demonstrated that 6,7-dehydrocortexone, cortexone, cybisterone, 6,7-dihydrocybisterone, and 6,7-dehydroprogesterone were synthesized by this insect from cholesterol and progesterone but not from mevalonolactone (Schildknecht, 1970). When cholesterol-4-^{14}C was injected, the products were more highly labeled and the rate of incorporation of labeling into the enones and dienones was about equal, whereas when progesterone-4-^{14}C was injected, the dienones were labeled to a lesser extent than the enones. Though the above ^{14}C-labeled C_{21} steroids, thus far, are the only steroids that are known to be synthesized from cholesterol in these beetles, it is likely that either cholesterol or related sterols are also precursors for the other C_{18}, C_{19}, and C_{21} steroids that have been isolated from the dytiscid water beetles.

Several of these C_{21} steroids have been tested for their action on poikilothermous vertebrates and have been shown to cause deep narcosis in fish and an adverse reaction in amphibians. It will be important to determine whether these steroids, which apparently act to protect these beetles against cold-blooded animals, also function in the regulation of certain of the biochemical and physiological processes of these insects.

F. INHIBITORS OF STEROID METABOLISM

As was discussed in Section III,B, certain vertebrate hypocholesterolemic agents have proven to be useful tools in the studies on plant sterol metabolism in insects. Inhibitors such as triparanol (MER-29) or certain azasteroids (Fig. 6) that block the Δ^{24}-sterol reductase enzyme(s) of vertebrates (Avigan *et al.*, 1960; Thompson *et al.*, 1963) were found to also block this enzyme system in insects (Svoboda and Robbins, 1967, 1968; Svoboda *et al.*, 1969a). These studies demonstrated for the first time that sterol utilization and metabolism can be blocked in an insect through

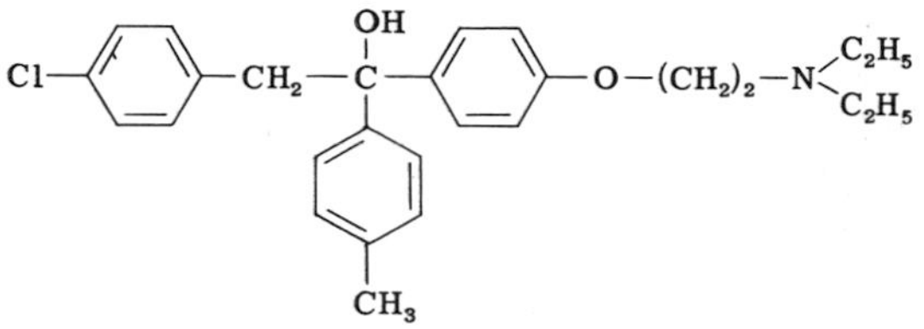

Triparanol (MER-29)

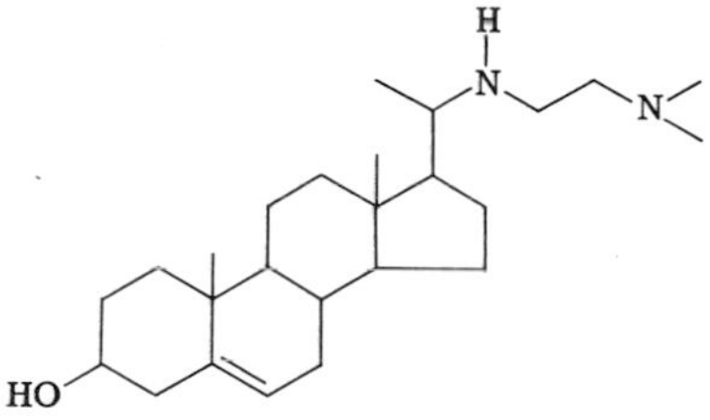

22, 25-Diazacholesterol

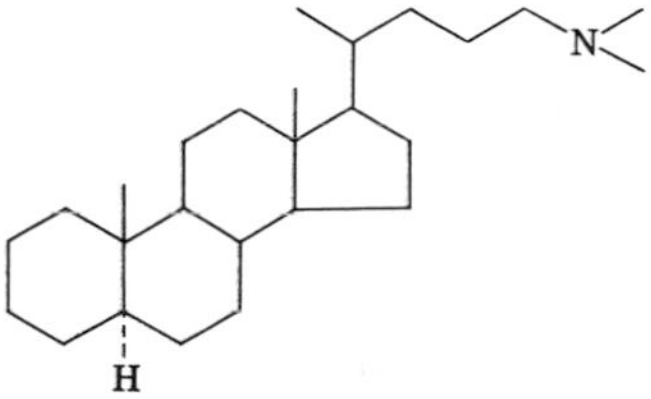

25-Azacholestane

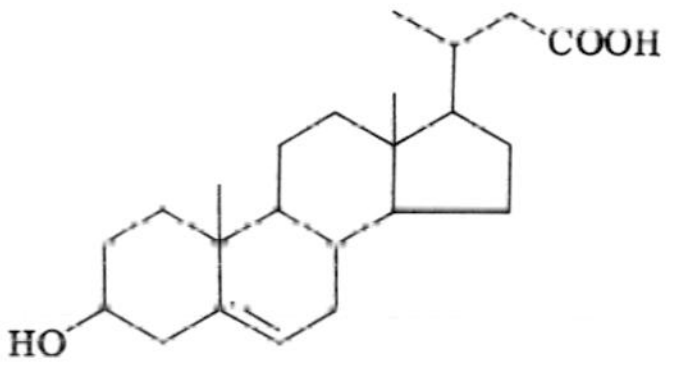

3β-Hydroxy-24-norchol-
5-en-23-oic acid

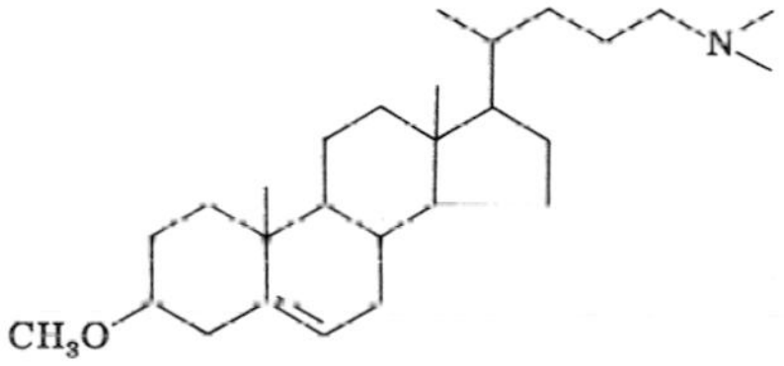

25-Azacholesteryl
methyl ether

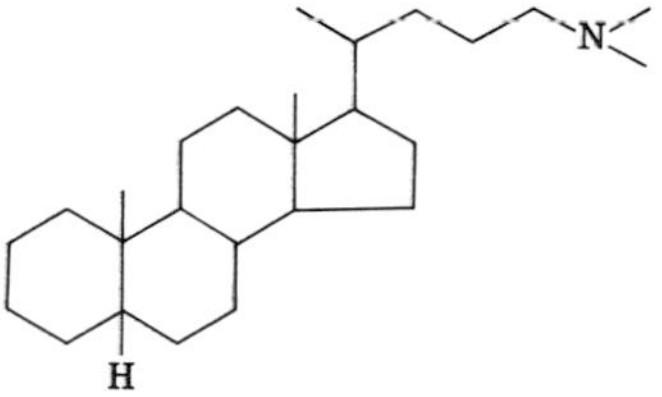

25-Azacoprostane

Fig. 6.   Inhibitors of sterol metabolism.

the inhibition of specific enzyme(s) and that this inhibition can be accompanied by the disruption of growth, development, and metamorphosis. The inhibitors cause a marked decrease in cholesterol formation
from plant sterols; however, a decrease in cholesterol is not in itself suffi-

cient to disrupt larval development, as has been demonstrated with certain of the compounds (Svoboda and Robbins, 1971). The steroidal acid 3β-hydroxy-24-norchol-5-en-23-oic acid (Fig. 6), which was first discovered as an impurity in a commercial sample of sitosterol, is a Δ^{24}-sterol reductase inhibitor both in insects and in a vertebrate (Svoboda et al., 1968, 1969b). Even though this compound blocks the conversion of desmosterol to cholesterol both in vivo and in vitro, it does not affect insect growth and development. Certain azasteroids also greatly reduce the quantity of plant sterol converted to cholesterol in the hornworm without having an effect on the development of the insect (Svoboda and Robbins, 1971).

Studies on the relation of structure to inhibitory activity, with over 30 azasteroids and several species of insects (Svoboda and Robbins, 1971), have made possible the design and synthesis of a number of new and very potent azasteroid inhibitors. Some of these compounds disrupt development or kill certain insects when added to the diet or medium at a fraction of a part per million (Svoboda et al., 1972c). Three of the new azasteroids, 25-azacholesteryl methyl ether, 25-azacholestane, and 25-azacoprostane (Fig. 6), disrupt larval development in the tobacco hornworm and the yellow fever mosquito, Aedes aegypti, at concentrations of less than a part per million in the diet or medium and inhibit development in the fall armyworm, German cockroach, housefly, and the confused flour beetle at somewhat higher concentrations. These new azasteroids are potent Δ^{24}-sterol reductase inhibitors that block the conversion of plant sterols to cholesterol in insects; however, the test diets of both the mosquito and the housefly contained sufficient cholesterol to support normal growth and development. Thus, pathways of steroid metabolism other than those involved in cholesterol production are affected —possibly those pathways related to molting hormone biosynthesis or metabolism. Further evidence for this premise was the characteristic inhibitive effects observed for these azasteroids with each species. As previously found with the hornworm (Svoboda and Robbins, 1971), these effects involved the processes of molting and metamorphosis (Table X) (Robbins et al., 1971b).

To determine whether or not the azasteroids do interfere with the pathways of ecdysone biosynthesis and metabolism, various concentrations of 25-azacholesteryl methyl ether were added in combination with the inhibitory ecdysone analog, 22,25-dideoxyecdysone (Robbins et al., 1970), to the larval diets of Tribolium and the housefly. In Tribolium larvae, the ecdysone analog slightly enhanced the inhibitory activity of the azasteroid suggesting that interaction occurs. However, the response of housefly larvae was quite different; here a concentration of the azasteroid that is

Table X
CHARACTERISTIC EFFECTS OF AZASTEROID INHIBITORS

Insects	Susceptible stages	Effects
Manduca sexta	4th Instar	Precocious prepupa formation-abnormal "4th instar prepupa"
Aedes aegypti	1st and 2nd Instars	Blocks molting, no further development
Tribolium confusum	Last stage larva	Blocks larval to pupal molt
Musca domestica	Puparium and pupa	Blocks pupation or adult emergence

inactive cause an almost complete reversal of the inhibitory effect of the ecdysone analog (Svoboda *et al.*, 1972c). Thus, in the housefly, this azasteroid severely decreases the inhibitive activity of the ecdysone analog—perhaps by blocking its conversion to a more active compound(s). Additional evidence was obtained by the joint administration in the *Tribolium* larval diet of α-ecdysone and 25-azacholesteryl methyl ether. When α-ecdysone is added to the diet with a sufficient concentration of the azasteroid to cause complete inhibition of development or mortality, this insect ecdysone causes approximately a 50% reversal of the inhibitive effect of the azasteroid (Svoboda *et al.*, 1972c).

Although the above-cited results strongly suggest that the azasteroids interfere with the ecdysone biosynthesis and metabolism, proof for this must await biochemical evidence. If our previous experience with the azasteroids in charting the pathways of plant sterol metabolism in insects can be taken as an indicator (Svoboda and Robbins, 1968; Svoboda *et al.*, 1969a), then these compounds should be equally useful in investigating the biosynthesis and metabolism of the ecdysones. These results with the azasteroid inhibitors also conclusively demonstrate the feasibility of disrupting the hormone-mediated processes of insects with simple nonhormonal compounds—possibly by interfering with hormone biosynthesis and metabolism.

IV. Conclusions

In the foregoing discussion, we have first enumerated the types of steroid transformations known to occur in insects and then, where possible, we have attempted to show how these various transformations function and are integrated in the pathways of steroid metabolism in insects. In Fig. 7 an effort has been made to synthesize this information into a scheme, summarizing all the steroid conversions and intermediates known

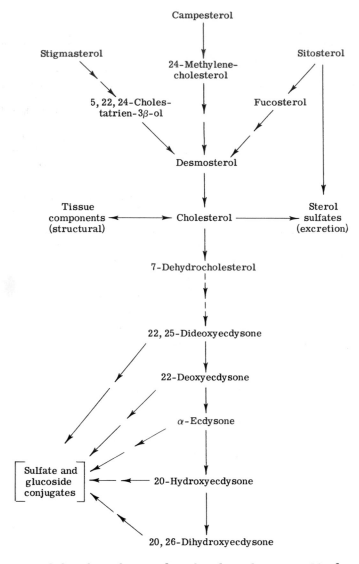

Fig. 7. Metabolic scheme for steroids in the tobacco hornworm, *Manduca sexta*.

to occur in the tobacco hornworm, an insect that has been intensively
studied in relation to most facets of steroid metabolism. The hornworm
utilizes the major sterols of its primary host plant, tobacco—campesterol,
sitosterol, and stigmasterol—through their dealkylation and conversion to
cholesterol. These conversions proceed through a series of oxidation-reduc-
tive steps and a number of the metabolites and intermediates involved have

been characterized. Cholesterol serves both as a structural component of cells and tissues and as a precursor for the ecdysones or molting hormones. Although the early steps in ecdysone biosynthesis are still not known, the latter steps, which involve the sequence of hydroxylation of the side chain, have been elucidated by examining the metabolism of possible intermediates and precursors such as 22,25-dideoxyecdysone and 22-deoxyecdysone and through the isolation and identification of the insect ecdysones. While the sulfate and glucoside conjugates of sterols and ecdysteroids appear to function primarily in the inactivation and excretion of steroids in insects, as previously discussed, these conjugates may have other equally important roles related to the biosynthesis, metabolism, and transport of steroids, or the regulation of hormone titer.

One void in the scheme and in our knowledge of insect steroids is the exact role and position of sterol ester formation and hydrolysis in relation to the other known pathways of steroid utilization and metabolism. An even more serious deficiency is the almost complete lack of information on the enzymes that effect the steroid transformations in insects, and concentrated research effort on these enzymes is essential for continued progress in this area. Another interesting and important facet of steroid metabolism concerns the C_{18}, C_{19}, and C_{21} steroids found in dytiscid water beetles: Are these steroids unique to the dytiscids or do they occur more generally in insects in considerably lower quantities, and do they have specific physiological or biochemical functions in insects analogous to the function of such steroids in vertebrates? Such information, in addition to significantly enhancing our understanding of insect physiology and biochemistry, also contributes to and constitutes an interesting and important aspect of our comparative knowledge of the metabolism and function of this important class of compounds in living systems generally.

References

Allais, J.-P., and Barbier, M. (1971). *Experientia* **27**, 506.
Allais, J.-P., Pain, J., and Barbier, M. (1971). *C. R. Acad. Sci.* **272**, 877.
Avigan, J., Steinberg, D., Thompson, M. J., and Mosettig, E. (1960). *Biochem. Biophys. Res. Commun.* **2**, 63.
Bade, M. L., and Clayton, R. B. (1963). *Nature (London)* **197**, 77.
Baird, D., Horton, R., Longcope, C., and Tait, J. F. (1968). *Perspect. Biol. Med.* 384.
Beck, S. D., and Kapadia, G. G. (1957). *Science* **126**, 258.
Bernstein, S., and Solomon, S. (1970). "Chemical and Biological Aspects of Steroid Conjugation." Springer-Verlag, Berlin and New York.
Burdette, W. J. (1962). *Proc. Soc. Exp. Biol. Med.* **110**, 730.
Butenandt, A., and Karlson, P. (1954). *Z. Naturforsch. B* **9**, 389.
Casida, J. E., Beck, S. D., and Cole, M. J. (1957). *J. Biol. Chem.* **234**, 365.

Chadha, M. S., Joshi, N. K., Mamdapur, V. R., and Sipahimalani, A. T. (1970). *Tetrahedron* **26**, 2061.
Cherbas, L., and Cherbas, P. (1970). *Biol. Bull.* **138**, 115.
Chu, H. M., Norris, D. M., and Kok, L. T. (1970). *J. Insect Physiol.* **16**, 1379.
Clark, A. J., and Bloch, K. (1959). *J. Biol. Chem.* **234**, 2589.
Clayton, R. B. (1964). *J. Lipid Res.* **5**, 3.
Clayton, R. B., and Edwards, A. M. (1961). *Biochem. Biophys. Res. Commun.* **6**, 281.
Clayton, R. B., and Edwards, A. M. (1962). *Fed. Proc., Fed. Amer. Soc. Exp. Biol.* **21**, 297.
Clayton, R. B., and Edwards, A. M. (1963). *J. Biol. Chem.* **238**, 1966.
Clayton, R. B., Hinkle, P. C., Smith, D. A., and Edwards, A. M. (1964). *Comp. Biochem. Physiol.* **11**, 333.
Cole, R. J., and Dutky, S. R. (1969). *J. Nematol.* **1**, 72.
Cole, R. J., and Krusberg, L. R. (1968). *Life Sci.* **7**, 713.
Dadd, R. H. (1970). *In* "Chemical Zoology" (M. Florkin and B. J. Scheer, eds.), Vol. 5, Part A, pp. 35–95. Academic Press, New York.
Dutky, R. C., Robbins, W. E., Kaplanis, J. N., and Shortino, T. J. (1963). *Comp. Biochem. Physiol.* **9**, 251.
Dutky, R. C., Robbins, W. E., Shortino, T. J., Kaplanis, J. N., and Vroman, H. E. (1967). *J. Insect Physiol.* **13**, 1501.
Dutky, S. R. (1968). *Proc. Joint U. S.-Jap. Semin. Microbial Control Insects Pests, 1967* p. 139.
Dutky, S. R., Robbins, W. E., and Thompson, J. V. (1967). *Nematologica* **13**, 140.
Earle, N. W., Lambremont, E. N., Burks, M. L., Slatten, B. H., and Bennet, A. F. (1967). *J. Econ. Entomol.* **60**, 291.
Emmerich, H. (1970). *J. Insect Physiol.* **16**, 725.
Faux, A., Horn, D. H. S., Middleton, E. J., Fales, H. M., and Lowe, M. E. (1969). *Chem. Commun.* p. 175.
Galbraith, M. N., Horn, D. H. S., Middleton, E. J., and Hackney, R. J. (1968). *Chem. Commun.* p. 83.
Galbraith, M. N., Horn, D. H. S., Middleton, E. J., Thomson, J. A., Siddall, J. B., and Hafferl, W. (1969a). *Chem. Commun.* p. 1134.
Galbraith, M. N., Horn, D. H. S., Middleton, E. J., and Hackney, R. J. (1969b). *Aust. J. Chem.* **22**, 1517.
Galbraith, M. N., Horn, D. H. S., Middleton, E. J., and Thomson, J. A. (1970). *Chem. Commun.* p. 179.
Gilbert, L. I. (1967). *Advan. Insect Physiol.* **4**, 69.
Goad, L. J. (1967). *In* "Terpenoids in Plants" (J. B. Pridham, ed.), pp. 159–190. Academic Press, New York.
Goodnight, K. C., and Kircher, H. W. (1971). *Lipids* **6**, 166.
Gorell, T. A., Gilbert, L. I., and Tash, J. (1972). *Insect Biochem.* **2**, 94.
Hampshire, F., and Horn, D. H. S. (1966). *Chem. Commun.* p. 37.
Heed, W. B., and Kircher, H. W. (1965). *Science* **149**, 758.
Heinrich, G., and Hoffmeister, H. (1970). *Z. Naturforsch. B* **25**, 358.
Heftmann, E. (1970). *Recent Advan. Phytochem.* **3**, 211.
Hikino, H., Ohizumi, Y., and Takemoto, T. (1971). *Chem. Commun.* p. 1036.
Hocks, P., and Wiechert, R. (1966). *Tetrahedron Lett.* p. 2989.
Hoffmeister, H., and Grützmacher, H. F. (1966). *Tetrahedron Lett.* p. 4017.

Horn, D. H. S. (1971). *In* "Naturally Occurring Insecticides" (M. Jacobson and D. G. Crosby, eds.), Chapter 9, pp. 333–459. Dekker, New York.

Horn, D. H. S., Middleton, E. J., and Wunderlich, J. A. (1966). *Chem. Commun.* p. 339.

Huber, R., and Hoppe, W. (1965). *Chem. Ber.* **98**, 2403.

Hutchins, R. F. N., and Kaplanis, J. N. (1969). *Steroids* **13**, 605.

Hutchins, R. F. N., Thompson, M. J., and Svoboda, J. A. (1970). *Steroids* **15**, 113.

Ikekawa, N., Suzuki, M., Kobayashi, M., and Tsuda, K. (1966). *Chem. Pharm. Bull.* **14**, 834.

Ishii, S., Kaplanis, J. N., and Robbins, W. E. (1963). *Ann. Entomol. Soc. Amer.* **56**, 115.

Kaplanis, J. N., Robbins, W. E., and Tabor, L. A. (1960). *Ann. Entomol. Soc. Amer.* **53**, 260.

Kaplanis, J. N., Monroe, R. E., Robbins, W. E., and Louloudes, S. J. (1963). *Ann. Entomol. Soc. Amer.* **56**, 198.

Kaplanis, J. N., Robbins, W. E., Monroe, R. E., Shortino, T. J., and Thompson, M. J. (1965). *J. Insect Physiol.* **11**, 251.

Kaplanis, J. N., Thompson, M. J., Yamamoto, R. T., Robbins, W. E., and Louloudes, S. J. (1966). *Steroids* **8**, 605.

Kaplanis, J. N., Robbins, W. E., Thompson, M. J., and Baumhover, A. H. (1969). *Science* **166**, 1540.

Kaplanis, J. N., Dutky, S. R., Robbins, W. E., and Thompson, M. J. (1971). *Proc. Conf. Workshop Hormo. Heterophyly, 1971* (in press).

Kaplanis, J. N., Thompson, M. J., Dutky, S. R., Robbins, W. E., and Lindquist, E. L. (1972). *Steroids* **20**, 105.

Karlson, P. (1956). *Vitam. Horm. (New York)* **14**, 227.

Karlson, P. (1970). *Biochem. Soc. Symp.* **29**, 145.

Karlson, P., and Bode, C. (1969). *J. Insect Physiol.* **15**, 111.

Karlson, P., and Hoffmeister, H. (1963). *Z. Physiol. Chem.* **331**, 208.

Karlson, P., Hoffmeister, H., Hoppe, W., and Huber, R. (1963). *Justus Liebigs Ann. Chem.* **662**, 1.

King, D. S. (1969). *Gen. Comp. Endocrinol.* **13**, 512.

King, D. S. (1972a). *Amer. Zool.* **12**, 343.

King, D. S. (1972b). *Gen. Comp. Endocrinol. Suppl.* **3**, 221.

King, D. S., and Siddall, J. B. (1969). *Nature (London)* **221**, 955.

Krishnakumaran, A., and Schneiderman, H. A. (1968). *Nature (London)* **220**, 601.

Krishnakumaran, A., and Schneiderman, H. A. (1969). *Gen. Comp. Endocrinol.* **12**, 515.

Krishnakumaran, A., and Schneiderman, H. A. (1970). *Biol. Bull.* **139**, 520.

Lehoux, J.-G., and Sandor, T. (1969). *Endocrinology* **84**, 652.

Lehoux, J.-G., and Sandor, T. (1970). *Steroids* **16**, 141.

Louloudes, S. J., Thompson, M. J., Monroe, R. E., and Robbins, W. E. (1962). *Biochem. Biophys. Res. Commun.* **8**, 104.

Monroe, R. E., Hopkins, T. L., and Valder, S. A. (1967). *J. Insect Physiol.* **13**, 219.

Moriyama, H., Nakanishi, K., King, D. S., Okauchi, T., Siddall, J. B., and Hafferl, W. (1970). *Gen. Comp. Endocrinol.* **15**, 80.

Muftic, M. (1969). *Parasitology* **59**, 365.

Nakanishi, K. (1971). *Pure Appl. Chem.* **25**, 167.

Nakanishi, K., Moriyama, H., Okauchi, T., Fujioka, S., and Koreeda, M. (1972). *Science* **176**, 51.

Ohtaki, T., and Williams, C. M. (1970). *Biol. Bull.* **138**, 326.

Ohtaki, T., Milkman, R. D., and Williams, C. M. (1968). *Biol. Bull.* **135**, 322.

Okauchi, T. (1969). *Bochu Kagaku* **34**, 140.

Rees, H. H. (1971). *In* "Aspects of Terpenoid Chemistry and Biochemistry" (T. W. Goodwin, ed.), Chapter 7, pp. 181–222. Academic Press, New York.

Ritter, F. J., and Wientjens, W. H. J. M. (1967). *TNO Nieuws* **22**, 381.

Robbins, W. E. (1963). *In* "Radiation and Radioisotopes Applied to Insects of Agricultural Importance," p. 269. IAEA, Vienna.

Robbins, W. E., Kaplanis, J. N., Monroe, R. E., and Tabor, L. A. (1961). *Ann. Entomol. Soc. Amer.* **54**, 165.

Robbins, W. E., Dutky, R. C., Monroe, R. E., and Kaplanis, J. N. (1962). *Ann. Entomol. Soc. Amer.* **55**, 102.

Robbins, W. E., Thompson, M. J., Kaplanis, J. N., and Shortino, T. J. (1964). *Steroids* **4**, 635.

Robbins, W. E., Kaplanis, J. N., Thompson, M. J., Shortino, T. J., and Joyner, S. C. (1970). *Steroids* **16**, 105.

Robbins, W. E., Kaplanis, J. N., Svoboda, J. A., and Thompson, M. J. (1971a). *Annu. Rev. Entomol.* **16**, 53.

Robbins, W. E., Kaplanis, J. N., Thompson, M. J., and Svoboda, J. A. (1971b). *In* "Chemical Releasers in Insects" (A. S. Tahori, ed.), Vol. III, pp. 1–31. Gordon & Breach, New York.

Schaefer, C. H., Kaplanis, J. N., and Robbins, W. E. (1965). *J. Insect Physiol.* **11**, 1013.

Schildknecht, H. (1970). *Angew. Chem., Int. Ed. Engl.* **9**, 1.

Schildknecht, H., and Hotz, D. (1967). *Angew. Chem., Int. Ed. Engl.* **6**, 881.

Schildknecht, H., and Kornig, W. (1968). *Angew. Chem., Int. Ed. Engl.* **7**, 62.

Schildknecht, H., Siewerdt, R., and Maschwitz, U. (1966). *Angew. Chem., Int. Ed. Engl.* **5**, 421.

Schildknecht, H., Hotz, D., and Maschwitz, U. (1967a). *Z. Naturforsch. B* **22**, 938.

Schildknecht, H., Siewerdt, R., and Maschwitz, U. (1967b). *Justus Liebigs Ann. Chem.* **703**, 182.

Schildknecht, H., Tacheci, H., and Maschwitz, U. (1969). *Naturwissenschaften* **56**, 37.

Shaaya, E. (1969). *Z. Naturforsch. B* **24**, 718.

Sipahimalani, A. T., Mamdapur, V. R., Joshi, N. K., and Chadha, M. S. (1970). *Naturwissenschaften* **57**, 40.

Steinberg, D., and Avigan, J. (1960). *J. Biol. Chem.* **235**, 3127.

Steinberg, D., and Avigan, J. (1969). *In* "Methods in Enzymology" (R. B. Clayton, ed.), Vol. 15, pp. 514–522. Academic Press, New York.

Stokes, W. M., and Fish, W. A. (1960). *J. Biol. Chem.* **235**, 2604.

Svoboda, J. A., and Robbins, W. E. (1967). *Science* **156**, 1637.

Svoboda, J. A., and Robbins, W. E. (1968). *Experientia* **24**, 1131.

Svoboda, J. A., and Robbins, W. E. (1971). *Lipids* **6**, 113.

Svoboda, J. A., Pepper, J. H., and Baker, G. L. (1966). *J. Insect Physiol.* **12**, 1549.

Svoboda, J. A., Thompson, M. J., and Robbins, W. E. (1967). *Life Sci.* **6**, 395.

Svoboda, J. A., Thompson, M. J., and Robbins, W. E. (1968). *Steroids* **12**, 559.

Svoboda, J. A., Hutchins, R. F. N., Thompson, M. J., and Robbins, W. E. (1969a). *Steroids* **14**, 469.

Svoboda, J. A., Womack, M., Thompson, M. J., and Robbins, W. E. (1969b). *Comp. Biochem. Physiol.* **30**, 541.

Svoboda, J. A., Thompson, M. J., and Robbins, W. E. (1971). *Nature* (*London*), *New Biol.* **230**, 57.

Svoboda, J. A., Thompson, M. J., and Robbins, W. E. (1972a). *Lipids* **7**, 156.

Svoboda, J. A., Robbins, W. E., Cohen, C. F., and Shortino, T. J. (1972b). *Conf. Significance Insect Mite Nutr., 1972.*

Svoboda, J. A., Thompson, M. J., and Robbins, W. E. (1972c). *Lipids* **7**, 553.

Takemoto, T., Ogawa, S., Nishimoto, N., and Hoffmeister, H. (1967). *Z. Naturforsch. B* **22**, 681.

Thompson, M. J., Dupont, J., and Robbins, W. E. (1963). *Steroids* **2**, 99.

Thompson, M. J., Kaplanis, J. N., Robbins, W. E., and Yamamoto, R. T. (1967). *Chem. Commun.* p. 650.

Thompson, M. J., Svoboda, J. A., Kaplanis, J. N., and Robbins, W. E. (1972). *Proc. Roy. Soc., Ser. B* **180**, 203.

Thomson, J. A., Siddall, J. B., Galbraith, M. N., Horn, D. H. S., and Middleton, E. J. (1969). *Chem. Comun.* p. 699.

Thomson, J. A., Hafferl, W., Galbraith, M. N., Horn, D. H. S., and Middleton, E. J. (1971). *Chem. Commun.* p. 1023.

Vroman, H. E., Kaplanis, J. N., and Robbins, W. E. (1964). *J. Lipid Res.* **5**, 418.

Willig, A., Rees, H. H., and Goodwin, T. W. (1971). *J. Insect Physiol.* **17**, 2317.

Lipids in Viruses

HERBERT A. BLOUGH AND JOHN M. TIFFANY

*Division of Biochemical Virology and Membrane Research, Scheie Eye
Institute of the Presbyterian—University of Pennsylvania Medical
Center, Philadelphia, Pennsylvania*

I. Introduction

Lipid forms an integral part of many viruses and exists either in the
form of a continuous envelope or in lipoprotein complexes which surround
a nucleoprotein core or helix. In general, the envelope can be described as
a molecular container for the genetic material of the virus. The identification of lipid as a component of viruses was based initially on the loss
or decrease of infectivity observed following exposure to organic solvents

(Andrewes and Horstmann, 1949; Hoyle, 1952). Although a review of lipid-containing viruses has appeared elsewhere (Franklin, 1962), lack of analytical data prevented this from being much more than a catalogue of solvent- or bile salt-sensitive viruses. The relationship of cellular membranes to the biogenesis of enveloped viruses was first pointed out for influenza virus more than 20 years ago by Hoyle (1950); at the time his results were received with some skepticism, primarily because his conclusions were based on dark-field microscopy. With the development of appropriate thin-sectioning techniques, electron microscopy provided the morphological evidence for the assembly of many viruses at cellular membranes (Morgan et al., 1956, 1959, 1961; Hotz and Schäfer, 1955). There are, of course, exceptions: some DNA viruses appear to be synthesized de novo, i.e., without utilizing a preexisting "membrane template" (see Section VI). The application of negative contrast techniques not only demonstrated the symmetry of isometric viruses, but allowed visualization of the fine structure of the envelope; thickness, number and spacing of surface projections, and, in some cases, infrastructure, have been investigated by this means (e.g., Horne et al., 1960; Apostolov and Flewett, 1969). Recently, freeze-etching techniques have been used as a visual probe of the apolar regions of the viral envelope (Bächi et al., 1969; Nermut and Frank, 1971).

The first major compositional analysis of the lipids of influenza virus was performed by Frommhagen et al. (1959), and these studies were extended by Kates et al. (1961) to include the relationship between the lipids of influenza virus and of subcellular fractions of cultured host cells. These and similar studies initiated the present phase of virus research, in which the complex interactions of virus and host are studied as well as simply the lipid composition of the virus. Lipids are found to make up 20–35% by weight of many viruses (Armbruster and Beiss, 1958; Frommhagen et al., 1959; Kates et al., 1961; Pfefferkorn and Hunter, 1963a; Ahmed et al., 1964; Rao et al., 1966; Blough and Lawson, 1968) although there are notable exceptions such as the lipovirus PM2, 15% (Espejo and Canelo, 1968a,b); vaccinia, 5% (Zwartouw, 1964); and insect nuclear polyhedrosis virus, 1.6% (Bergold and Wellington, 1954).

Despite the large amounts of lipid found in some viruses, the status of lipids in the virologists' list of investigative priorities has remained low. This is probably due to a number of factors: the influence of classical bacteriophage genetics in virology, the emphasis in molecular biology on proteins and nucleic acids, and perhaps most importantly, the fact that didactic sessions on lipid biochemistry have not been presented to the young virologist in training. The low priority lipids have received is manifested by one's inability to find lipids as a part of the general taxonomy of viruses (see Wildy, 1971), and many of the current virology texts give only a cursory treatment of these important molecules in the discussion of assembly or in biochemical techniques (e.g., Fenner, 1968; Robinson and Duesberg, 1968). While it is undeniable that this emphasis on the study of the properties of nucleic acids and proteins is justified, since they are the source of virus-specific functions, lipids have an important role in maintaining structural integrity and infectivity of the virion, thereby permitting expression of these functions. Following recent advances in knowledge of the composition and structure of a number of viruses, and the application of more sophisticated techniques of analysis, lipids are now achieving a greater degree of attention than ever before, and it is to be hoped that this interest will lead to a more unified approach to the study and teaching of virology.

With the application of powerful tools such as thin-layer and gas-liquid chromatography and physical techniques such as X-ray diffraction and magnetic resonance spectroscopy, fresh light is being cast on the interactions of the constituent lipid and protein molecules in membranes. Viruses which are assembled at cell membranes, and contain a limited number of protein and lipid species, can serve as relatively simple biological models for study of these activities. The purpose of this review is to provide biochemists, cell biologists, and virologists with insight into the chemical composition of the envelopes of lipid-containing viruses and the effect of these viruses on host cell lipid metabolism. An attempt will be made to explain, by reference to models of membrane systems, how constituent molecules may be arranged and assembled to make up the molecular fabric of the viral envelope.

In many of the following sections, discussion will be found to center primarily on the myxoviruses, and particularly on influenza virus; this in part reflects the authors' own research interests, but also the fact that a large proportion of the work so far done on viral lipids has employed myxoviruses, since their propagation in either embryonated eggs or tissue culture is well established and samples can be obtained in good yield and high purity. The review of literature was substantially completed in March 1972, although a few references later than this have been included.

II. Classification

A. Types of Lipid-Containing Viruses

Viruses may be classified on the basis of their shape and size, type of nucleic acid, and the presence or absence of an envelope (Lwoff *et al.*,

1962). The presence of lipid within a virion does not, however, necessarily imply that the virus is enveloped, since the lipid may complex with protein to form a lipoprotein shell similar to that seen in low density lipoproteins (Pollard *et al.*, 1969), or lipid may associate with the nucleocapsid as in frog virus (E. Houts and M. Gravell, personal communication, 1972). An envelope is essentially a structural feature discernible by electron microscopy, where it may be recognized in one of two ways: (1) by appearing as a coherent shell in positively stained thin sections (when the lipid often stains in the well-known trilamellar pattern) and in negatively stained preparations where the stain has penetrated within the particle; (2) by its independent existence and retention of integrity even after loss of the internal component, or when produced as incomplete particles lacking a core (Almeida and Waterson, 1970).

Lipid-containing viruses are produced in mammalian, avian, bacterial, plant, and insect hosts. They may contain either RNA or DNA, and are characterized by lower densities than those of viruses containing no lipid, e.g., 1.16–1.18 gm cm^{-3} for influenza and murine leukemia viruses (Blough and Merlie, 1970; Johnson and Mora, 1967) up to 1.285 gm cm^{-3} for herpesvirus and iridoviruses (Spear and Roizman, 1967; Spring and Roizman, 1967; E. Houts and M. Gravell, personal communication, 1972); by contrast, the buoyant density of type 5 adenovirus, which contains no lipid, is 1.335 gm cm^{-3} (Wilcox and Ginsberg, 1963). The presence of unique lipids, which might aid in the classification of viruses, has not been reported. The proportions of certain classes of lipid may however differ considerably from those in the host cell (see Section IV).

For simplicity lipid-containing viruses will be divided into those containing RNA and those containing DNA (Table I). The majority of these viruses infect vertebrate and invertebrate hosts, although there are some plant viruses (rhabdoviruses, some iridoviruses, some baculoviruses, and tomato spotted wilt virus), but thus far only two lipid-containing viruses infecting microorganisms, i.e., lipovirus PM2 in *Pseudomonas* BAL-31 and *Mycoplasma laidlawii* type 2 virus (Gourley, 1971). The interested reader is referred to Wildy (1971) for a more comprehensive classification of viruses; even there, however, it will be found that the presence of lipid is in many cases only presumed from the ether sensitivity, without definite chemical proof. Because of this lack of knowledge about the composition of many viruses, we have restricted discussion in this review largely to those examples where electron microscopy, lipid and protein composition, and in some cases other studies such as X-ray diffraction, have all been done.

It will be seen in Table I that rubella virus has been assigned to a

Table I

Classes of Lipid-Containing Viruses and Some Representative Members

Classes	Representative members
1. RNA viruses	
Orthomyxoviruses	Influenza (human, equine, avian, porcine), fowl plague viruses
Paramyxoviruses	Newcastle disease, parainfluenza, mumps viruses
Alphaviruses (Arbovirus group A)	Sindbis, Semliki Forest, equine encephalitis viruses
Arbovirus group B	Yellow fever, dengue, Japanese B encephalitis viruses
Rhabdoviruses	Vesicular stomatitis, rabies, *Drosophila* σ, potato yellow dwarf, Egtved viruses
Leukoviruses	Rous sarcoma, mouse leukemia (e.g., Rauscher, Moloney, Friend), mouse mammary tumor, visna, avian leukosis viruses
Tomato spotted wilt virus	
Coronaviruses	Avian infectious bronchitis, mouse hepatitis, human respiratory viruses
Arenaviruses	Lymphocytic choriomeningitis, Lassa, Parana viruses
Other unclassified enveloped RNA viruses	Rubella virus, measles virus; *Mycoplasma laidlawii* type 2 virus
2. DNA viruses	
Herpesvirus	Herpes simplex, varicella, infectious bovine rhinotracheitis, Epstein-Barr, Marek's disease, pseudorabies viruses
Baculoviruses	*Lymantria* (*Porthetria*) *dispar* nuclear polyhedrosis, *Choristoneura fumiferana* granulosis viruses
Iridoviruses	Amphibian polyhedral cytoplasmic (frog virus FV 3) and some invertebrate iridescent viruses
Lipoviruses	Marine bacteriophage PM2
Poxviruses	Vaccinia, orf, smallpox, fowlpox, Yaba monkey tumor, and entomopoxviruses

group of unclassified enveloped RNA viruses. There is still some controversy as to whether rubella virus belongs to the paramyxoviruses or to the arboviruses; comparison of its morphology and some of its properties with those of a number of arboviruses has led to the suggestion from two groups of workers that it should be reclassified (Holmes and Warburton, 1967; Carver and Marcus, 1968). At the time of writing, no group-specific antigen or arthropod vector has been reported. Measles virus has also been assigned to this unclassified group rather than included in the paramyxoviruses since this virus has not officially been declared to be a paramyxovirus; the particle contains no neuraminidase, but otherwise shares many of the characteristics of the group.

B. Electron Microscopic Observations

This section is intended to provide only a brief review of the morphogenesis of virus particles as revealed by electron microscopy, rather than a detailed description of the morphology of the mature particles, as this has been given in many other texts. Based on the site and mode of assembly, three classes of lipid-containing viruses can be distinguished: (1) those where the virus buds from a preexisting cell membrane following insertion of virus-specific material into the membrane; the membrane is hence used essentially as a "scaffolding" or "template" to support viral material during maturation; (2) a *de novo* form of synthesis, where lipid and protein condense around the viral nucleic acid without utilizing a preexisting membrane; (3) a combination of the "scaffolding" and *de novo* methods for different parts of the virion.

Two terms used to describe structural features of viruses require definition: *capsomers* are morphological units of protein forming the capsid, and *capsid* is the protein structure of the virus which shields the nucleic acid (i.e., all the capsomers together make up the capsid). The capsid may be isometric (icosahedral) or helical (Caspar *et al.*, 1962).

1. RNA Viruses

a. Myxoviruses. These are "template" type viruses assembled at the cell surface membrane and released into the surrounding medium by a budding process (Fig. 1a); they are covered by an array of equidistant projections or spikes on the outer side of the envelope. In certain strains of influenza virus, particularly influenza C, a hexagonal reticular structure appears to exist within the envelope, connecting the bases of the spikes (Apostolov and Flewett, 1969). Extremely regular hexagonal arrays of spikes are also frequently observed (Almeida and Waterson, 1967, 1970). Many myxoviruses are roughly spherical in shape, although distortion may occur during preparation for microscopy, but filamentous strains are also seen, especially of influenza C (Archetti *et al.*, 1967); filamentous particles can also be produced by genotypic (Kilbourne, 1963) or phenotypic means (Blough, 1963) from normally spherical strains. Under conditions of high multiplicity of infection and continued passage, markedly pleomorphic particles of influenza virus are produced which show mor-

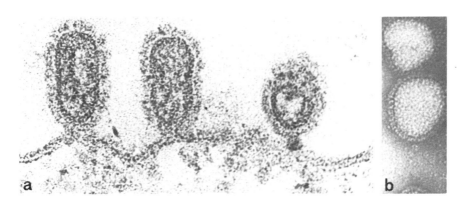

FIG. 1a. Assembly of influenza virus (A₀/PR8/34) at the cell surface membrane ("template" assembly). × 200,000. 1b. Negative contrast micrograph of influenza virus A₀/PR8/34. × 160,000. (H. A. Blough, unpublished micrographs.)

phological defects in the envelope and lack the larger of the pieces of RNA forming the viral genome (Pons and Hirst, 1969). Depending on the method of preparation and staining for electron microscopy, a variety of different structures may be detected within the envelope (Apostolov and Flewett, 1969; Compans and Dimmock, 1969; Nermut, 1970). The paramyxoviruses are larger, contain a continuous genome, and frequently appear pleomorphic; they are also assembled at cell surfaces, although some may be assembled also as single particles within intracytoplasmic vesicles (Blough, 1964).

b. Alphaviruses and Group B Arboviruses. In terms of structural components, these appear to be the simplest of the enveloped viruses. Thus Sindbis virus contains only two envelope glycoproteins and an inner nucleocapsid protein (Schlesinger *et al.*, 1972). They are assembled by budding at the cell surface (Fig. 2a), or by budding from the cytoplasm into intracytoplasmic vesicles by marsupialization of the vesicle wall to form the envelope (Fig. 2b) (Morgan *et al.*, 1961; Grimley and Friedman, 1970).

c. Rhabdoviruses. These viruses are found in plant, vertebrate, and invertebrate hosts, and are characterized by their bacilliform or "bullet shape" (Kitajima and Costa, 1966; Nakai and Howatson, 1968). In some cases, especially with rabies and the plant viruses, the infrastructure of the envelope is visible (Hummeler *et al.*, 1967). The vertebrate rhabdoviruses either bud off the surface membrane ("template" type) or through cytoplasmic membranes into vesicles, but large numbers of particles also appear to be formed *de novo* in the cytoplasm of infected cells (Fig. 3). Plant rhabdoviruses bud off the nuclear membrane or are found within

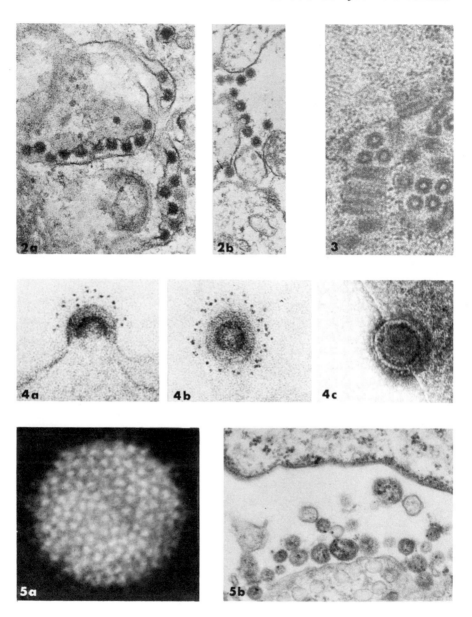

FIG. 2.   Maturation of Semliki Forest virus in mouse neurons. 2a. Intracytoplasmic assembly. × 60,000. 2b. Assembly at the cell surface membrane. × 47,500. (Courtesy of Dr. P. Grimley.)

FIG. 3.   Intracytoplasmic assembly of rabies virus. × 56,000. (Courtesy of Dr. K. Hummeler.)

FIG. 4.   a and b. Maturation of avian myeloblastosis virus at the plasma mem-

intracytoplasmic vesicles derived from the endoplasmic reticulum (Kita-jima and Costa, 1966). Extensive reviews have recently been published on rabies virus (Matsumoto, 1970) and on vesicular stomatitis virus and other rhabdoviruses (Howatson, 1970).

d. Leukoviruses. These are among the most complex of the RNA-containing viruses, and generally exhibit the lowest densities and highest lipid contents (Johnson and Mora, 1967). They appear to contain an inner membrane (possibly containing lipid in addition to protein) sur-rounded by an outer envelope acquired at the cell surface membrane (Fig. 4a–c). The outer envelope of Rous sarcoma virus appears to have a hexagonal subunit structure (Dourmashkin and Simons, 1961). The inner membrane fuses during budding to surround the nucleoid or RNA-containing central core (de Thé and O'Connor, 1966). Some particles of avian myeloblastosis virus have also been found to contain up to 100 molecules of transfer RNA and one or two ribosomes between the nucleoid and the envelope (Říman *et al.*, 1972). Virions are also seen within intracytoplasmic vesicles with certain cell types.

e. Tomato Spotted Wilt Virus. Particles of this virus appear isometric (van Kammen *et al.*, 1966) and are bounded by an envelope with surface projections. Assembly occurs in clusters in intracytoplasmic vacuoles, which may be formed from endoplasmic reticulum (Ie, 1964; Milne, 1970), as well as within the dilated lumen of the nuclear membrane (Kitajima, 1965).

f. Coronaviruses. These are enveloped viruses formed by budding, usu-ally by marsupialization of the bounding membranes of large intracyto-plasmic vacuoles (Becker *et al.*, 1967).

g. Arenaviruses. These are pleomorphic enveloped viruses, variable in size and with conspicuous surface projections. They are assembled at cell surface membranes (Fig. 5) and in intracytoplasmic vacuoles (Murphy *et al.*, 1970).

h. Other Viruses. Rubella virus has in the past proved difficult to ob-tain pure, and preparations examined in the electron microscope have frequently contained large amounts of nonviral material which made it impossible to obtain an accurate picture of the size and construction of the particles (Norrby, 1969). It has been found from purer preparations

brane, labeled with group-specific antigen coupled to ferritin. × 94,000. (Taken from Gelderblom *et al.*, 1972, by courtesy of Dr. H. Bauer and the Editors of *Virology*.) 4c. Negative contrast micrograph of mouse mammary tumor virus budding off a microvillus. × 186,000. (Courtesy of Dr. D. H. Moore.)

Fɪɢ. 5. Arenaviruses. 5a. Negative contrast micrograph of Tacaribe virus. × 413,600. 5b. Pleomorphic particles of Parana virus released at the cell surface membrane. × 42,000. (Courtesy of Dr. F. Murphy.)

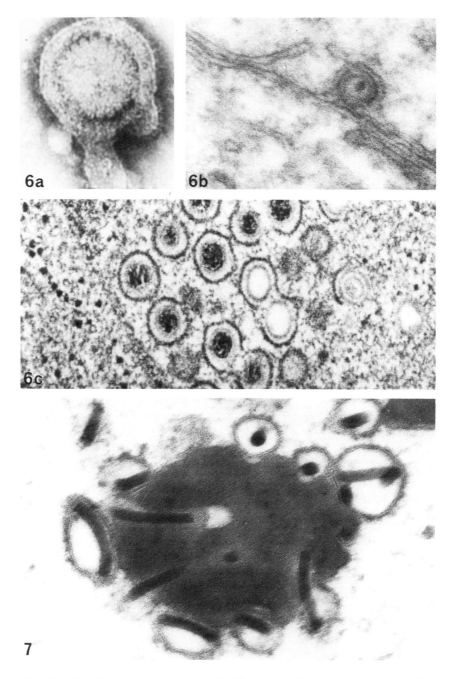

FIG. 6a.   Negative contrast micrograph of herpes simplex virus. Note the envelope surrounding the isometric capsid. × 200,000. (Courtesy of Dr. D. H. Watson.)

that the virus buds largely into intracytoplasmic vesicles (McCombs *et al.*, 1968), specifically at Golgi membranes (Bonissol and Sisman, 1968), although Murphy *et al.* (1968) found that appreciable amounts of virus were produced by budding at the cell surface membrane. Particles generally appear to have a single envelope, although McCombs *et al.* (1968) report particles surrounded by a double membrane as occasionally seen with herpesvirus.

2. DNA Viruses

a. Herpesviruses. In general envelopment proceeds by budding through a membrane; here the inner nuclear membrane is preferred (Siegert and Falke, 1966; Darlington and Moss, 1968). However, any membrane may be used, including the Golgi apparatus, endoplasmic reticulum, and occasionally the plasma membrane; in some cases double membranes are formed. The viral core is icosahedral with a triangulation number of 16, containing 162 capsomers, and is surrounded by a lipoprotein envelope (Fig. 6a) containing 4–5 glycopeptides (Spear and Roizman, 1972). Treatment with phospholipase C suggests that lipid is not only in the envelope but may also be associated with the capsid of "naked" particles (Spring and Roizman, 1968; Asher *et al.*, 1969). Recent electron micrographs of herpesvirus of saimiri (squirrel monkey) (Fig. 6c) suggest that *de novo* synthesis of enveloped particles occurs within the nucleus of owl monkey kidney cells (Heine *et al.*, 1971). The structure of the virion and the usual site of assembly are presented in Figs. 6a and 6b.

b. Baculoviruses. Insect nuclear polyhedrosis viruses develop from a dense "virogenic stroma" to form large crystalline inclusions in the cell nucleus (Smith, 1967); considerable compression of the envelope occurs within the nuclear polyhedral crystals (Fig. 7). *De novo* synthesis of the viral envelope has been suggested in *Lymantria dispar* (= *Porthetria dispar*) and *Aglais urticae* (Harrap, 1969). Multiple genomes may be enclosed within a single envelope, and envelopes possessing different numbers of genomes can be separated by zonal centrifugation (Harrap, 1969). The complex structure of these viruses is indicated in Fig. 27).

c. Iridoviruses. Amphibian viruses such as the cytoplasmic frog virus FV 3 (Fig. 8) appear to be synthesized *de novo* in the cytoplasm of in-

---

6b. Herpes simplex virus acquiring its envelope at the nuclear membrane. × 87,000. (Taken from Morgan *et al.*, 1959, by courtesy of Dr. C. Morgan and the Rockefeller University Press.) 6c. Evidence of *de novo* synthesis of the viral envelope of herpesvirus of saimiri (squirrel monkey) within the nucleus of an owl monkey kidney cell. × 105,000. Taken from Heine *et al.* (1971).

FIG. 7. Development of a nuclear polyhedrosis virus of *Lymantria dispar* within the nucleus of a larval fat cell. × 60,000. (Courtesy of Dr. K. A. Harrap.)

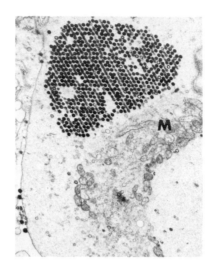

Fig. 8. An intracellular paracrystalline array of frog virus, FV 3 (iridovirus). × 6,000. (Courtesy of Dr. A. Granoff.)

fected cells and frequently appear in paracrystalline arrays (Darlington et al., 1966; Granoff, 1969). Envelopment by budding at cytoplasmic membranes is rare. The lipid of the virion appears to be associated with the nucleocapsid (E. Houts and M. Gravell, personal communication,

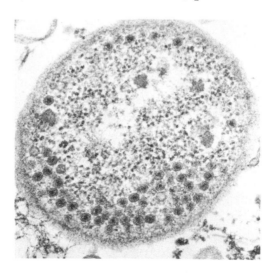

Fig. 9. Assembly of lipovirus PM2 in the marine bacterium *Pseudomonas* BAL-31. Virus particles are found beneath the cell envelope. × 63,000. (Courtesy of Dr. R. M. Franklin.)

1972). Members of this group infecting invertebrate hosts appear to be synthesized in a similar fashion (J. S. Robertson, personal communication, 1972).

d. Lipoviruses. The marine bacteriophage PM2, although assembled in close contact with the plasma membrane of the bacterial host (Fig. 9), appears to develop *de novo* by encapsidation of viral DNA by protein and lipid (Cota-Robles *et al.*, 1968); budding has not been observed (Dahlberg and Franklin, 1970). The virion is found not to contain enough lipid to form a complete bilayer shell (Harrison *et al.*, 1971a). Negative-contrast electron microscopy indicates that the virion is icosahedral.

e. Poxviruses. These are complex particles which are assembled in cytoplasmic "factories," probably *de novo* (Dales and Siminovitch, 1961). These large viruses (3500 × 2800 × 2000 Å) are covered by an outer layer of tubules or "spicules" giving the particle a mulberry-like appearance (Fig. 10a). The DNA is closely associated with protein to form a biconcave structure, and two lateral bodies can also be seen (Peters and Müller, 1963). Immature forms of the virus appear as membranous structures which probably contain DNA-protein complexes (Fig. 10b). Immature particles accumulate when protein synthesis is inhibited by 5-fluorodeoxyuridine or isatin β-thiosemicarbazone (Woodson and Joklik, 1965); on removal of the block, synthesis of mature particles proceeds normally (Dales and Mosbach, 1968). The viral envelope is assembled *de novo* (Dales and Mosbach, 1968; White *et al.*, 1968) in mammalian and avian

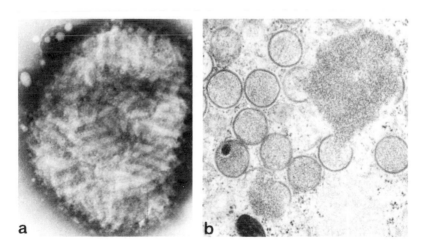

a   **b**

Fig. 10a. "Mulberry" form of vaccinia virus (poxvirus), by negative contrast. × 150,000. 10b. Immature forms of vaccinia virus in chick chorioallantoic cells. × 30,000. (Unpublished micrographs, courtesy of Prof. D. Peters.)

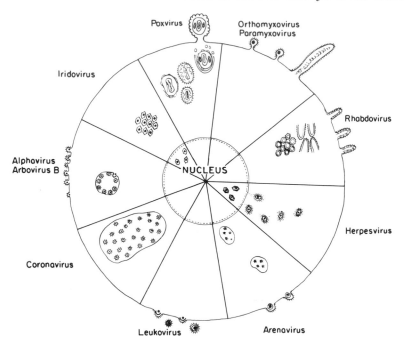

FIG. 11. Diagrammatic relationship between lipid-containing viruses and host cell membranes.

poxviruses; entomopoxviruses acquire an additional envelope by budding at the cell surface membrane (Devauchelle *et al.*, 1970, 1971).

The order of assembly of animal viruses and their relationship to preexisting cell membranes is shown in Fig. 11. It must be pointed out that, even though a virus may appear to derive the bulk of the lipids in its envelope from a preexisting membrane, evidence is accumulating that *de novo* synthesis of lipids or rearrangement of lipids occurs during virus infection, and these lipids may be incorporated into the virion. The relationship between viral infection and lipid metabolism is considered in greater detail in Section V.

III. Methods of Analysis of Viral Lipids

A. Purification of Virus

Until the development of tissue culture techniques, it was difficult to obtain any viruses in sufficiently large quantities to permit detailed study and lipid analysis. More recently, a wide variety of hosts has been used for enveloped viruses, including calf kidney (Kates *et al.*, 1961), bovine and canine kidney (Klenk and Choppin, 1970a), primary rabbit kidney (Kaplan, 1957), baby hamster kidney (Vaheri *et al.*, 1965), HeLa (David, 1971), chick embryo fibroblast (Weinstein and Blough, 1973), and chick scalp epithelium (White *et al.*, 1968), but many other systems may be used, some of which are listed by Hoyle (1968) and Kaplan (1969). An older established method is growth in the allantoic membrane of embryonated eggs (Hoyle, 1968), especially for the myxoviruses where suitable egg-adapted strains are available. It has been suggested that the results of lipid analysis of virus produced in tissue culture under single-step growth conditions may be more consistent than in virus grown under multiple-cycle conditions in eggs (Klenk and Choppin, 1970a).

Methods of harvesting the progeny virus vary according to whether the virus is released into the medium or retained intracellularly. Following propagation in eggs, the virus is released into the allantoic fluid, and this can be harvested free from cells, although contaminated by cellular debris and "normal cell particles" pinched off from the surface membrane of chorioallantoic cells (Hoyle, 1950). Intracellular virus is released by conventional disruptive techniques such as Dounce homogenizing following harvest of cells, and virus released from cultured cells is obtained by collection of the medium, involving centrifugation to remove cells if suspension cultures are used. Purification of virus from cellular debris can then follow comparable techniques irrespective of the manner of growth of the virus.

In studying the lipids of viruses, it is of critical importance to obtain specimens uncontaminated by cellular material, particularly in cases where the composition of viral lipids is to be compared with that of the host cell or parent membrane. Generally, a first step involves removal of the bulk of cellular contamination: this may involve (1) one or more cycles of differential centrifugation; (2) liquid chromatography, e.g., on columns of aluminum phosphate (Miller and Schlesinger, 1955) or DEAE cellulose (Fuscaldo *et al.*, 1971) and elution with a salt gradient or buffered saline; (3) by employing some specific but reversible adsorption property of the virus. Using the latter technique, for viruses which hemagglutinate, washed erythrocytes are added to the viral suspension, causing attachment of virus but not of cellular debris. After centrifugation to remove debris, the virus is dissociated from the cells by addition of fresh saline medium or by lowering the divalent cation concentration (Furukawa *et al.*, 1967), and further centrifugation separates virus and cells. In the case of influenza virus, the release is through the action of viral neuraminidase (Hoyle *et al.*, 1954). In some cases an inert adsorbent such as barium sulfate for influenza virus (Mizutani, 1963), may be used instead of erythrocytes. Additional techniques such as isoelectric focusing and density gradient electrophoresis have been used (e.g., Polson and Russell, 1967). Further purification usually involves banding of virus on a density gradient of sucrose, cesium or rubidium chloride or sulfate, or potassium tartrate (Blough *et al.*, 1967). Depending on the length of centrifugation and the concentrations necessary to achieve the desired densities, this procedure may prove disruptive of the virus (Norrby, 1969). For large quantities of virus, a considerable reduction of effort may be achieved by use of the zonal rotor; this has been found useful in separating influenza virus into spherical and filamentous populations (Reimer *et al.*, 1966). Isotope dilution techniques are frequently used to follow the extent of removal of contaminating host materials (Blough *et al.*, 1967; McSharry and Wagner, 1971); polyacrylamide gel electrophoresis may also be used with isotopically labeled host cell polypeptides as markers (Spear and Roizman, 1968; Holland and Kiehn, 1970). The above purification methods are necessarily brief and devoid of experimental detail; the reader is referred to standard virological texts for more detailed treatment (e.g., Brakke, 1967).

The adsorption methods of purification may be criticized on the grounds that no distinction is made between infectious and noninfectious particles, since only surface properties of the envelope are involved; similarly the use of erythrocytes may possibly lead to exchange of lipids with enveloped viruses, giving misleading results on lipid analysis.

B. Lipid Chemistry Techniques

In the past, compositional analyses of lipids in viruses were hindered not only by the unavailability of stocks of adequately purified virus, but also by inefficient biochemical techniques including methods of solvent extraction and separation and identification of individual species of lipid. The work of Folch *et al.* (1957) on extraction of lipids has led to a more systematic method of approach designed to free lipid classes from association with each other and with proteins. Workers differ in their preference for one solvent system or another, but most now use chloroform and methanol in various ratios. Most phospholipids and neutral lipids are removed by this means. An additional extraction with ethanol has been found to release an appreciable further amount of triglyceride, thought to be associated with envelope structural proteins of influenza virus (Tiffany and Blough, 1969a). Protocols of other workers differ largely in the proportions of solvents, temperatures and times of extraction, and the means of separating the lipid classes once extracted. The reader is referred to Kritchevsky and Shapiro (1967) for specific details on the isolation of viral lipids, and to Weinstein *et al.* (1969, 1970) for techniques of isolation and analysis of cell membrane lipids.

Once they are extracted, it is particularly important to guard against breakdown of sensitive lipids by storage at low temperatures under an inert atmosphere such as nitrogen or argon, and by the addition of anti-oxidants such as *t*-butyl hydroxyanisole (BHA) or di-*t*-butyl hydroxytoluene (BHT); thin-layer chromatographic separations of lipids may be carried out in the presence of anti-oxidant without interference (Blough and Lawson, 1968). Similarly, precautions should be taken to prevent breakdown of sialoglycolipids in aqueous solution by maintaining a neutral or alkaline pH.

Analysis of the lipids is carried out by well-established methods, largely detailed in the literature, e.g., Marinetti (1967), Renkonen (1967), or Dittmer and Wells (1969). Special techniques for certain classes of lipid may also be found elsewhere: e.g., Weinstein *et al.* (1970) for glycolipids; Baumann and Mangold (1966) and Baumann *et al.* (1970) for glyceryl ethers; White *et al.* (1968) for precursors of cholesterol biosynthesis; Renkonen (1967) for plasmalogens (phospholipids in which one acyl group is replaced by a long-chain-substituted vinyl ether group); Clamp *et al.* (1971) for carbohydrates. With the development of gas-liquid chromatography, many analyses formerly requiring considerable time and relatively large quantities of lipid may now be performed with microgram or even nanogram quantities.

Glycolipids remain among the most difficult classes of lipid to analyze, partly because they make up only a small proportion of the total lipid, but also because, in addition to acyl groups and a sphingosine base (together forming the ceramide portion of the molecule) they have a chain of sugars of variable length, which may be branched and which may also contain one, two, or three sialic acid units (Ledeen, 1966; Stoffel, 1971). Although glycolipids form only a small part of the total lipids of either viruses or membranes (Section IV, Table 2; Weinstein *et al.*, 1969), knowledge of their detailed composition is of importance since a possible role in cell fusion has been suggested for glycolipids (Blough and Lawson, 1968; Klenk and Choppin, 1970b).

Following initial separation of the glycolipid fraction from polar and neutral lipids, further fractionation into gangliosides, hematosides, and ceramide hexosides can be carried out by thin-layer chromatography (TLC) using known reference standards to give R_f values for each component (Klenk and Choppin, 1970b). Spots are scraped off the TLC plates and the glycolipids eluted from the gel with organic solvents, hydrolyzed, and converted to appropriate derivatives for analysis by gas-liquid chromatography (GLC): hexosamines and sialic acids as their trimethyl silyl ether derivatives; hexoses as alditol acetates following reduction and acetylation, using internal standards (Weinstein *et al.*, 1970). The N-acetyl- and N-glycolyl- moieties of neuraminyl ceramide hexosides may be separated by TLC and quantitated by the thiobarbituric acid assay of Warren (1959), or by the much more sensitive GLC methods of Clamp *et al.* (1971) or Craven and Gehrke (1968), or the spectrofluorometric method of Hess and Rolde (1964). Sequencing of the sugar units can be done by periodate oxidation or following hydrolysis by specific glycosidases, but this technique has not yet been applied to viral lipids.

Equally as important as the determination of the lipid content of enveloped viruses is information on the amounts and classes of lipid available in the cell for incorporation into the virus particle. In the case of viruses assembled at membranes ("template" viruses, see Section VI), the lipids may be selected from those available at the site of assembly, and may be substantially identical to those of the parent membrane. However, the pattern of synthesis and turnover of cellular lipids, and hence the membrane lipid composition, is not necessarily the same in infected as in uninfected cells.

Studies of lipid metabolism in virus-infected and in control uninfected cells have just begun in the authors' laboratory and elsewhere, using isotopic precursors of various components of lipid molecules. Thus, in studying synthesis and turnover of phosphatidylcholine, a double label might be used of glycerol-2-^{3}H to label the glycerol skeleton and acetate-^{14}C to label the fatty acid chains, or alternatively choline-^{3}H to label the base and glycerol-^{14}C for the glycerol backbone. The acetate label will also appear in glycerides, sterols, and free fatty acids, but these are readily separated from other neutral lipids by a unidimensional TLC system such as that of Freeman and West (1966). To determine specific activities, individual spots are scraped off the plate and divided into two portions; one is used for radioactive assay by scintillation counting, and the other for mass measurement by a method such as the charring technique of Marsh and Weinstein (1966). Alternative precursor molecules include inositol-^{3}H for phosphatidylinositol and glucosamine-^{3}H for glycolipids. It should be stressed that the use of specific activities rather than counting rates is mandatory if turnover methods are to have any meaning.

It is hoped that by appropriate pulse-chase techniques it will be possible to trace the biosynthesis and turnover of lipids in a variety of cell types, and, more importantly, to determine how the effects of infection by lipid-containing viruses on host cell metabolism are related to envelope biogenesis and cell-surface-mediated phenomena. The results of some of these experiments are given in Section V. It should be borne in mind that relatively little work of this type has as yet been done, and on relatively few different viruses. Conclusions on the overall effect of viral infection must therefore be considered tentative, until confirmation by other workers, and for a large number of viruses, is forthcoming.

The lipid compositions found experimentally for a number of viruses are considered in the next section.

IV. Composition of Viral Lipids

Viruses are obligate intracellular parasites and are not known to carry genetic coding for enzymes involved in lipid synthesis. Hence they generally contain the same classes of lipid as are found in the host cell or their membrane of assembly (Table II). Only one major lipid class has been found to be an exception: gangliosides are not detectable in the simian paramyxovirus SV5 but are present in the plasma membrane of the host cell (Klenk and Choppin, 1970b). The significance of this finding will be discussed later (Section VI).

Lipids are found to make up 20–35% by weight of most viruses; however, as mentioned earlier, there are exceptions such as vaccinia virus, which has only 5% lipid (Zwartouw, 1964) despite having a complex multimembrane envelope structure (Dales, 1963). Avian tumor viruses contain the most lipid, 31–35% (Rao *et al.*, 1966; Quigley *et al.*, 1971), and insect nuclear polyhedrosis virus the least, 1.6% (Bergold and Wellington, 1954). With animal viruses, the molar ratio of cholesterol to phospholipid is high (~ 1) if the virus is assembled at the cell surface membrane, but less in the case of cytoplasmic assembly (Blough, 1968). The lowest value for cholesterol is 4% for rabies virus grown in BHK-21 cells in chemically defined medium (Blough *et al.*, 1973), giving a cholesterol:phospholipid molar ratio of 0.5; this may reflect the site of assembly in BHK-21 cells, but some other mechanism may also be involved since some particles seen in thin sections appear to bud from the plasma membrane. Glycolipids make up 1–2% of the lipids of animal viruses, and these values (at least for viruses released by budding) are similar to those reported for plasma membranes (Weinstein *et al.*, 1970). Data on the lipids of other insect and plant viruses are largely lacking, but many of these are rhabdoviruses (e.g., potato yellow dwarf virus and wheat striate mosaic virus) and may resemble rabies or vesicular stomatitis virus in lipid content if not in detailed composition. Molecular models of some of the lipids found in viruses are depicted in Figs. 12a–c.

Compositional analyses of the lipids of viruses and of their parent membranes may be reported in two ways: (1) by comparing the lipids of

Table II
Compositional Analysis of Viral Lipids[a]

Virus	Host	Lipid (% of virion)	Phospholipid (% of virion)	Total cholesterol (% of virion)	Major phospholipids[b] (% of total phospholipid)	Neutral lipids (% of total neutral lipid)	Sphingoglycolipids (% of total lipid)	Reference
Sindbis	CEF	28	20.3	6.8	PC 34; Sph 8.5; PE 32; PS 21	ND	ND	Pfefferkorn and Hunter (1963b)
Sindbis	BHK-21	28	ND	ND	PC 26; Sph 18; PE 35; PS 20	ND	ND	David (1971)
Semliki Forest	BHK-21	30.7	19	8.7	PC 34; Sph 21; PE 26; PS 12	TG 3; DG 2; FA 2	2.6	Renkonen et al. (1971)
Influenza A_0/PR8/34	EE	20.2	10.3	7.7	PC 38; Sph 23; PE 12	TG 3; DG 3; MG 1; FA 9	0.4	Blough and Merlie (1970)
Influenza (incomplete) A_0/PR8/34	EE	24.2	14.1	4.6	PC 16; Sph 16; PE 31; PS 16	TG 3; DG 10; MG 6; FA 25	1.2	Blough and Merlie (1970)
Influenza A_0/PR8/34	EE	18.5	11.5	6.5	PC 28; Sph 35	ND	ND	Frommhagen et al. (1959)
Influenza Mel	CaK	16	11.5	6.5	PC 11; PA 64; PS + PE 13	ND	ND	Kates et al. (1961)
Newcastle disease B1	EE	24	13	6.5	PC 12; Sph 18; PE 35; PS 12	Total glycerides 9	ND	Blough and Lawson (1968)
Sendai	EE	28	16	7.2	Sph 12; PE 37; PS 15; PA 10	Total glycerides 11	ND	Blough and Lawson (1968)
SV5	HaK	19	12.4	4.2	PC 44; Sph 26; PE 17	TG 4.6e	ND	Klenk and Choppin (1969b)
SV5	MDBK	18.6	9.4	4.3	PC 24; Sph 27; PE 40	TG 6.3e	ND	Klenk and Choppin (1970a)

Virus	Cell type				Major phospholipids	Neutral lipids	FA	Reference
Rous sarcoma	CEF	31	21	9	PC 28; Sph 29 PE 30	ND	ND	Quigley et al. (1971)
Avian myeloblastosis	Myelo	35	21.3	11.7	PC 18; Sph 25 PE 34; PS 12	1.8	ND	Rao et al. (1966)
Vesicular stomatitis (Ind)	L	20	12	5.8	PC 16; Sph 21; PE 33; PS 17	TG 9; DG 11; MG 5; FA 4	ND	McSharry and Wagner (1971)
Rabies	BHK-21	24	15.8	4	PC 23; Sph 31; PE 34	TG 9; DG 12; MG 2; FA 14	1.5	Blough et al. (1973)
Potato yellow dwarf	Nicotiana rustica	19	ND	ND	ND	ND	ND	Ahmed et al. (1964)
Tomato spotted wilt	N. glutinosa	19	ND	ND	ND	ND	ND	Best (1968)
Lipovirus PM2	Pseudomonas BAL-31	15	14	—	PG 65–68; PE 28	ND	ND	Braunstein and Franklin (1971)
Herpesvirus	BHK-21	ND	22	ND	PC + PI 69; Sph 17; PE 14	ND	ND	Asher et al. (1969)
Fowlpox	CS	34	5.3	7.4[d]	ND	TG 28; DG 0.3; MG 0.2; FA 19	ND	White et al. (1968)
Vaccinia	Rabbit	5	2.2	1.5	ND	ND	ND	Zwartouw (1964)
Iridovirus FV 3	FHM	ND	ND	ND	PC 58; LPC 11; PS + PE 16	ND	ND	G. Houts and M. Gravell (personal communication, 1972)

[a] Abbreviations used: Cell type: CEF, chick embryo fibroblasts; EE, embryonated eggs; CaK, calf kidney; HaK, hamster kidney; MDBK, Madin Darby bovine kidney; Myelo, avian myeloblasts; L, mouse fibroblasts; BHK-21, baby hamster kidney; CS, chick scalp epithelium; FHM, fat head minnow. Lipids: PC, phosphatidylcholine; Sph, sphingomyelin; PE, phosphatidylethanolamine; PS, phosphatidylserine; PA, phosphatidic acid; PG, phosphatidylglycerol; PI, phosphatidyl inositol; LPC, lysophosphatidylinositol; TG, triglyceride; DG, diglyceride; MG, monoglyceride; FA, free fatty acid. ND = not determined.

[b] "Major phospholipids" indicates those present in amounts of 10% or more.

[c] Percentage of total lipid.

[d] Includes 5.9% cholesterol esters.

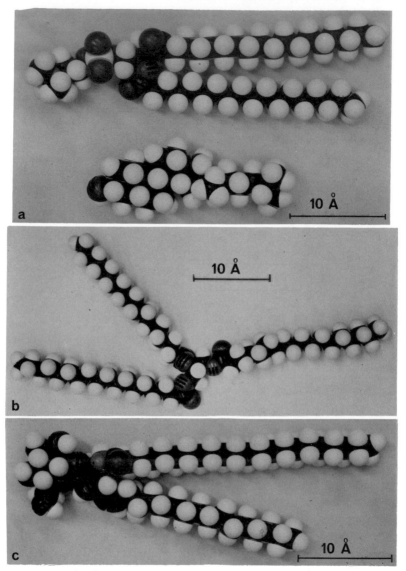

Fɪɢ. 12a. Molecular models of phosphatidylcholine and cholesterol. 12b,c. Molecular models of a triglyceride and a ceramide monohexoside.

different strains of the same virus propagated in homolog membranes, e.g., different strains of influenza virus in embryonated eggs (Tiffany and Blough, 1969a,b); (2) by comparing the lipids of purified virus with those of the isolated host membrane at which they are assembled. With several notable exceptions, phospholipid compositions (based on *polar group* analysis) are·essentially the same as those of the membrane from which the assembled virus originated (Klenk and Choppin, 1969b). Exceptions include Newcastle disease virus (strain Italy/Milano/1945), Sendai and influenza viruses in embryonated eggs (Blough and Lawson, 1968; Blough *et al.*, 1967); simian paramyxovirus SV5 in MDBK cells (Klenk and Choppin, 1970a); Sindbis virus in BHK-21 cells and chick fibroblasts (David, 1971); and avian myeloblastosis virus in myeloblasts (Rao *et al.*, 1966). The result with avian myeloblastosis virus is at variance with a recent report on the phospholipid composition of another leukovirus, Rous sarcoma virus (Quigley *et al.*, 1971). These authors employed orthophosphate-^{32}P labeling of chick embryo fibroblast host cells, and estimated the proportions of the different phospholipid classes from their radioactive content; essentially the same pattern of lipid classes as in the isolated host cell plasma membrane was reported for the Schmidt-Ruppin strain of Rous sarcoma virus, and also for Newcastle disease virus, Sendai virus, Sindbis virus, avian sarcoma virus B77, and another avian leukosis virus, RAV-2. However, under the conditions of labeling used by these workers, isotopic equilibrium might not be achieved, and further work is headed to resolve this point.

Paramyxoviruses (Blough and Lawson, 1968; Klenk and Choppin, 1969b), vesicular stomatitis virus (McSharry and Wagner, 1971), and rabies virus (Blough *et al.*, 1973) have all been found to contain more phosphatidylethanolamine than their parent membranes. Klenk and Choppin (1970a) observed that yields of paramyxovirus SV5 were higher in rhesus monkey kidney cells than in baby hamster kidney cells (BHK-21), and correlated this with a higher phosphatidylethanolamine:phosphatidylcholine ratio in plasma membranes of monkey kidney than in BHK-21 cells. The observed high values of phosphatidylethanolamine found in the other viruses mentioned above may be related in some way to this. Under conditions of high multiplicity of infection and repeated passage, alterations were noted in phospholipids, fatty acyl chains, and neutral lipids of incomplete influenza virus when compared to standard virus (Blough and Merlie, 1970).

The high level of phosphatidic acid found in influenza virus grown in calf kidney cells (Kates *et al.*, 1961) is most probably an artifact due to hydrolysis of other phospholipids during the extraction procedure, since no appreciable amount of phosphatidic acid has been reported by any other workers on ortho- or paramyxoviruses, using essentially similar techniques.

Fowlpox virus lipids include large amounts of plasmalogens (phospholipids having one acyl group replaced by a long-chain-substituted vinyl ether), which on hydrolysis yield both fatty acids and long-chain fatty aldehydes. The proportion of saturated to unsaturated aldehydes was found to be higher in fowlpox virus grown in chick scalp epithelium than in the host cells (White *et al.*, 1968). Plasmalogens were also detected in Venezuelan equine encephalitis (an alphavirus), but no separation into molecular species was performed (Heydrick *et al.*, 1970).

Neutral lipids consist mainly of cholesterol and cholesterol esters, glycerides, and free fatty acids. Bacterial virus PM2 and plant viruses are exceptions to this in containing no cholesterol or cholesterol esters (Table II). The ratio of free to esterified cholesterol is generally high, but the reverse is found to be true for fowlpox virus (White *et al.*, 1968). A higher proportion of cholesterol was found in Semliki Forest virus than in its parent membrane (Renkonen *et al.*, 1971), and a lower proportion in incomplete influenza virus (Blough and Merlie, 1970). Squalene, a hydrocarbon precursor of cholesterol biosynthesis, accounted for 16% of the lipids of the fowlpox virion, but only 0.6% of lipids of the uninfected cell (White *et al.*, 1968). These authors suggest that squalene may serve to solubilize the lipids of the virion.

Lipid analyses of viruses considered here are given in Table II, as well as an indication of the host cells in each case. These figures should not be used as a basis for comparison of viruses, since they depend in some cases on the choice of host (e.g., paramyxovirus SV5), and in others on the site of assembly or the number of membranes incorporated into the virion (e.g., herpesvirus; Kaplan, 1969). We have attempted to keep this table as simple as possible, and have therefore not expressed the results in terms of deviations from the parent membrane composition, although this is one of the most interesting ways of looking at the results.

Table III shows the fatty acid composition of the polar lipids (PL: largely phospholipids) and neutral lipids (NL: glycerides, free fatty acids, and cholesterol esters) for three strains of influenza virus, and also for the "normal cell particles" (NCP) or fragments of chorioallantoic cell surface membrane released into the allantoic cavity of embryonated hen's eggs (Tiffany and Blough, 1969b). For convenience, acyl chains have been grouped at the foot of the table into saturated, monoenoic, and polyenoic categories. This permits a rapid comparison of the different virus strains. It is clear that the saturated fatty acid content of NCP is much lower than in virus, especially in the NL fraction, where NCP have a greatly increased oleic:stearic (18:1/18:0) ratio. The overall composition of the viruses shows differences between all the strains; this is particularly marked in the individual long-chain polyenoic components such as 22:polyene, where A_0 has 8.4% in PL and none in NL, but A_2 has only 1% in PL and 5.6% in NL, and B has 3% in PL only. If lipid were passively incorporated from the host membrane during budding, we should expect

Table III

Fatty Acid Composition of Three Strains of Influenza Virus and Normal Uninfected Cell Particles[a,b]

Acyl chains[c]	A₀/PR8/34 PL	A₀/PR8/34 NL	A₂/Jap/305/57 PL	A₂/Jap/305/57 NL	B/Lee/40 PL	B/Lee/40 NL	Normal cell particles PL	Normal cell particles NL
12:0	Tr	ND	1.0	5.8	ND	14.2	1.5	ND
14:0	1.6	4.1	3.1	16.8	Tr	14.8	3.5	2.8
16:0	15.1	28.5	17.5	23.7	20.9	25.0	23.2	22.3
16:1	5.2	6.6	1.1	3.2	0.8	1.1	3.1	5.9
18:0	14.8	18.8	9.7	6.2	16.9	16.9	17.3	8.5
18:1	15.8	22.0	20.5	10.3	17.0	9.6	17.1	35.5
18:2	4.3	4.6	7.0	0.9	4.2	6.5	3.9	12.3
18:3	0.9	Tr	Tr	0.8	2.8	4.8	1.1	0.6
20:0	8.4	6.1	5.0	3.1	3.9	1.9	0.9	0.9
20:1	Tr	ND	ND	ND	ND	ND	ND	ND
20:4	4.2	4.9	14.4	14.1	13.4	1.6	12.9	4.0
22:0	13.7	4.4	9.6	4.7	7.3	2.0	1.2	Tr
22:1	Tr	ND	ND	ND	ND	ND	ND	ND
22:polyene	8.4	ND	1.1	5.6	3.0	ND	6.5	3.7
24:0	6.8	Tr	8.1	1.0	9.0	0.5	1.6	2.8
24:polyene	Tr	ND	1.8	ND	ND	ND	ND	ND
Uncharacterized	0.6	—	—	3.9	0.8	1.1	6.3	0.5
Saturated	60	62	54	61	58	75	49	37
Monoenoic	21	20	21	14	18	11	20	41
Polyenoic	18	9	24	21	20	13	24	21

[a] Reproduced from Tiffany and Blough (1969b) by kind permission of the American Association for the Advancement of Science.

[b] Abbreviations used: PL = polar lipids; NL = neutral lipids; ND = not detected; Tr = Trace ($\leq 0.5\%$).

[c] Acyl chains are indicated by number of carbon atoms: number of double bonds.

these compositions to be substantially the same; if the composition of the lipid were determined in some way by the nucleocapsid of the virion, A_0 and A_2 viruses might have a similar composition since these strains have a common internal antigen. The fact that none of these correspondences was found led to the hypothesis that lipid composition of the virion is determined by some envelope component, probably a structural protein (see Section VI).

Table IV shows the result of acyl chain analyses on individual phospholipid fractions from two strains of influenza virus belonging to different subtypes (A and B). Many considerable differences can be seen, not only between A and B viruses, but between the phospholipids of each strain.

Table IV

FATTY ACID COMPOSITION OF INDIVIDUAL PHOSPHOLIPIDS OF TWO STRAINS OF
INFLUENZA VIRUS DERIVED FROM HOMOLOG MEMBRANES[a,b]

Acyl chains[c]	PC		Sph		PE		PS	
	A	B	A	B	A	B	A	B
14:0	4.0	Tr	1.7	ND	Tr	2.3	2.9	ND
16:0	30.1	38.7	43.3	44.4	16.7	14.7	15.4	13.0
16:1	2.4	Tr	0.7	0.6	1.6	0.8	1.2	0.9
18:0	13.9	15.4	9.3	11.1	19.2	11.2	34.2	32.7
18:1	26.8	28.7	9.3	5.5	45.3	35.0	20.9	26.1
18:2	10.7	6.5	Tr	2.1	10.2	9.8	9.2	1.0
18:3	ND	0.7	Tr	Tr	Tr	1.8	1.8	ND
20:0	0.8	2.8	3.1	7.6	1.9	ND	2.3	Tr
20:4	5.3	7.0	2.7	3.1	4.1	24.4	3.6	10.3
22:0	0.9	ND	15.1	12.1	ND	ND	1.6	Tr
22:1	ND	ND	0.6	ND	ND	ND	ND	ND
22:polyene	4.9	ND	0.8	ND	1.1	ND	5.8	12.8
24:0	Tr	Tr	13.0	11.4	ND	ND	1.1	1.8
24:1	ND	ND	0.9	2.1	ND	ND	ND	ND

[a] Reproduced from Blough (1971a) by kind permission of Cambridge University Press.

[b] Abbreviations used: PC = phosphatidylcholine; Sph = sphingomyelin; PE = phosphatidylethanolamine; PS = phosphatidylserine; A = A_0/PR8/34 strain of influenza virus; B = B/Lee/40 strain of influenza virus; ND = not detected; Tr = Trace ($\leq 0.5\%$).

[c] Acyl chains are indicated by number of carbon atoms: number of double bonds.

For example, 16:0 content is roughly the same for A and B within any phospholipid class, but varies widely from class to class; the same is true for 18:1, varying between 5.5% in sphingomyelin and 35% in phosphatidylethanolamine of B virus. Almost all long-chain saturated acids (22:0 and 24:0) are in sphingomyelin. There is, however, no consistent pattern of acyl chain incorporation such as might be ascribed to selection of host lipids during budding only on the basis of their polar groups.

The neutral glycolipid content of paramyxovirus SV5, and of both the whole host cell and its plasma membrane, is given in Table V. It is not possible to compare the amounts of each of these lipids in membranes and virions in terms of micrograms of lipid per milligram of protein, since different proteins are inserted into the plasma membrane during budding; it can be seen, however, that the proportion of the ceramide tetrahexoside is much greater in the virion than in the parent membrane, and this may reflect a stimulation of glycosyltransferases during infection. Such differences have also been observed in the glycolipids of Semliki Forest virus

Table V

Neutral Glycolipid Content of MDBK Cells, Plasma Membranes, and SV5 Virus Grown in These Cells[a]

Glycolipid[b]	Whole cells	Plasma membranes	SV5 virions
	(μg per 100 mg protein)		
Glc-Cer	160	1300	1550
GalNAc-Gal-Gal-Glc-Cer	510	2200	3000

[a] Reproduced from Klenk and Choppin (1970b) by kind permission of the authors and the Editors of *Proceedings of the National Academy of Sciences*, Washington.

[b] Cer = ceramide; Glc = glucose; Gal = galactose; GalNAc = N-acetyl galactosamine.

and BHK-21 cells (Renkonen *et al.*, 1971), and in incomplete versus normal influenza virus (Weinstein and Blough, quoted in Blough and Merlie, 1970).

A summary of differences between viral and host cell lipids is given in Table VI.

V. The Effects of Viral Infection on Host Cell Lipid Metabolism

The earliest studies on the effect of infection by fowl plague virus on host cell lipids were based on the incorporation of orthophosphate-^{32}P into chick cells and comparison of the specific activity of phospholipids of the virus with those of the host cell (Wecker, 1957). This was followed by the first definitive study on the origin of influenza virus lipids by Kates *et al.* (1961). Primary calf kidney cells were prelabeled with orthophosphate-^{32}P for 72 hours prior to infection, and the specific activities of the phospholipids of subcellular fractions of the host cells were compared to those of purified influenza virus grown in the same cell system. It was concluded that, with the exception of phosphatidic acid, newly synthesized lipids were not incorporated into the virion. Similar studies were made on Sindbis virus lipids by Pfefferkorn and Hunter (1963a,b), who demonstrated that the specific activities of viral sphingomyelin, phosphatidylcholine, and phosphatidylethanolamine were the same in the virus as in the host chick embryo fibroblast cell. They concluded that the lipids of arboviruses were preformed and that *de novo* synthesis of lipids did not play a role in the assembly of these viruses. The use of orthophosphate-^{32}P to study phospholipid turnover is open to

Table VI

SUMMARY OF DIFFERENCES IN LIPIDS BETWEEN HOST CELL AND ITS
MEMBRANES AND VIRUS

Differences noted	Viruses	References
1. Acyl chain composition	Influenza, Newcastle disease	Tiffany and Blough (1969a,b)
	Incomplete influenza virus	Blough et al. (1969)
	Sendai	Blough and Lawson (1968)
	Paramyxovirus SV5	Klenk and Choppin (1970a)
	Vesicular stomatitis	McSharry and Wagner (1971)
	Sindbis	David (1971)
2. Absence of sialoglycolipids (gangliosides) in virus	Paramyxovirus SV5	Klenk and Choppin (1970b)
3. High cholesterol ester:free cholesterol ratio	Fowlpox	White et al. (1968)
4. Quantitative differences in polar groups of phospholipids	Newcastle disease, Sendai	Blough and Lawson (1968)
	Semliki Forest	Renkonen et al. (1971)
	Avian myeloblastosis	Rao et al. (1966)
	Iridovirus FV 3	E. Houts and M. Gravell (personal communication, 1972)
	Lipovirus PM2	Braunstein and Franklin (1971)
	Incomplete influenza virus	Blough and Merlie (1970)
	Vesicular stomatitis	McSharry and Wagner (1971)
	Paramyxovirus SV5	Klenk and Choppin (1970a)
5. Ratio of saturated to unsaturated plasmalogens	Fowlpox	White et al. (1968)
6. High concentration of unusual lipid in virion	Fowlpox	White et al. (1968)
7. Quantitative differences in neutral glycolipids	Paramyxovirus SV5	Klenk and Choppin (1970b)
	Sindbis	Renkonen et al. (1971)
8. Quantitative differences in cholesterol	Semliki Forest	Renkonen et al. (1971)
	Incomplete influenza virus	Blough and Merlie (1970)
9. Quantitative differences in glycerides	Incomplete influenza virus	Blough and Merlie (1970)
	Vesicular stomatitis	McSharry and Wagner (1971)
	Fowlpox	White et al. (1968)

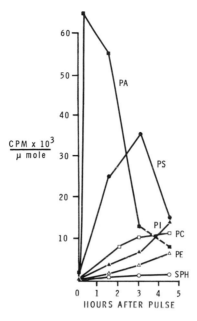

FIG. 13. Pulse chase studies on uninfected chick embryo fibroblasts. Cells grown in a chemically defined medium, pulsed for 7½ minutes with orthophosphate-^{32}P and chased in carrier-free medium containing 10 mM α-glycerol phosphate (Weinstein and Blough, 1973).

question because it appears compartmentalized in an organic pool turning over slowly (Fig. 13).

Before embarking on any extensive description of measurements of lipid metabolism, we should define some of the terms used and give an indication of the ways in which they can be measured. *Synthesis* is the amount of a lipid produced in the cell, and may include newly formed material *de novo* as well as that formed by reutilization, or only that newly formed from small precursor subunits. It is measured by the rise in specific activity of a lipid class following uptake of a small isotopically labeled precursor molecule such as glycerol, choline, or acetate. *Turnover* is the balance between complete *de novo* synthesis of a class of lipid from its fundamental parts (choline, glycerol, phosphate, etc.) and its catabolism into simpler subunits. *Interconversion* or *exchange* is the transfer of individual moieties from one class of lipids to another without *de novo* synthesis or catabolism. Some authors will refer to this as *incomplete turnover*. Equilibrium labeling involves growth of the cell in medium containing an isotopically labeled precursor until the precursor pools within the cell have reached isotopic equilibrium and specific activity of a particular lipid class is maximal. To measure turnover, the cell is *pulsed* by supplying a labeled precursor for a short period, and then *chased* in medium containing unlabeled precursor. Using short pulses, as much as 85% of acetate label appears in acyl chains of glycerides and phosphoglycerides as well as sterols and free fatty acids: however, the source of label in a lipid class may be complex if multiple pools are operative. Choline gives preferential labeling of zwitterionic phospholipids (phosphatidylcholine and sphingomyelin) and inositol is a useful label for phosphatidylinositol as it is not synthesized *de novo* in most mammalian cells. Glycerol is incorporated largely into glycerides and phosphoglycerides; in short pulses 95% of the label may enter these classes. In general, ^{32}P is the most widely used isotope, but is not specific for phospholipids since other molecules are also labeled (e.g., nucleotides). Compartmentalization and recycling into phospholipid synthetic pathways from these pools is possible, suggesting that ^{32}P is not a good precursor for the study of phospholipid synthesis and turnover. Similarly, if glycerol-1-^{3}H is used, tritium is lost during oxidation and decarboxylation of the molecule and may feed back into lipid via multiple pathways: the tritium label in glycerol-2-^{3}H is more stable and there is little or no randomization of label into other lipid precursor moieties. Studies in the authors' laboratory confirm the work of Bailey *et al.* (1964) that as little as 0.5% serum in the medium inhibits the synthesis of both phospholipids and neutral lipids by as much as 50%. Such large shifts in lipids may entirely mask changes in the level of a minor component if serum is present. Therefore all studies in the author's laboratory were done in chemically defined medium using fatty acid-poor bovine serum albumin in place of serum.

Recent studies by Pasternak and Bergeron (1970) have shown that in cultured mammalian cells in the presence of serum there are at least two classes of phospholipid, an "unstable" one consisting largely of phosphatidylcholine, and a "stable" one containing most of the sphingomyelin. Turnover rates for phospholipid using long pulses suggest a half-life of 18–24 hours for phosphatidylcholine in Novikoff rat hepatoma cells (Plagemann, 1971) and for mastocytoma cells in culture (Pasternak and Bergeron, 1970). Recently, however, Gallaher *et al.* (1972) found by using short pulses of 30 minutes and a double label of glycerol-2-^{3}H and acetate-^{14}C that the half-life of some phospholipids in BHK-21 cells and in chick embryo fibroblasts in confluent or nonconfluent monolayers is as low as 2–2½ hours. The half-lives of phospholipids are not all the same; using very short pulses of 7½ minutes on chick embryo fibroblasts, Weinstein and Blough (1973) have found that the turnover rate for phospholipids is multiple not only in separate classes (e.g., phosphatidylserine vs. phosphatidylethanolamine) but even within individual species.

A. RNA VIRUSES

RNA synthesis has been shown to be necessary to maintain phospholipid synthesis. In Sindbis virus-infected cells, synthesis of total proteins and host cell RNA appeared to decline more rapidly than phospholipid synthesis. Waite and Pfefferkorn (1970) used temperature-sensitive (*ts*) mutants of Sindbis virus which do not make RNA at 42.5°. Chick fibroblasts infected with the *ts* at the nonpermissive temperature failed to shut off phospholipid synthesis whereas wild-type virus did so. Using temperature-shift experiments and an RNA⁻ mutant, it was possible to show that the depression in phospholipid synthesis occurred at 2–3 hours after infection, and paralleled the inhibition of host cell macromolecular synthesis (Fig. 14). At 28°, the small amount of viral RNA synthesized was enough to account for this inhibition. In addition, variability of response in different cell types was evident: in BHK-21 cells, phospholipid synthesis was not inhibited until 8–10 hours after wild-type infection.

Studies on phospholipid synthesis and renewal in influenza virus-infected cells were undertaken in the authors' laboratory using glycerol-2-³H to label the glycerol skeleton and acetate-¹⁴C to label the fatty acid chains, sterols, and free fatty acids (Weinstein and Blough, 1973). It was found that the level of *de novo* synthesis of phospholipids continued unchanged up to 7 hours after infection of chick fibroblasts with A₀/WSN influenza virus (Fig. 15) at low input multiplicities (3–5 pfu/cell), and up to 4 hours with higher multiplicities (10–30 pfu/cell) (Blough and Weinstein, 1972).

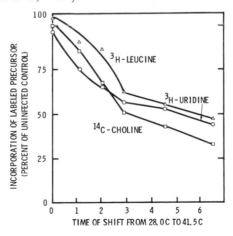

FIG. 14. Shutoff of phospholipid synthesis in chick embryo fibroblasts infected with a temperature-sensitive mutant of Sindbis virus, showing its dependence on RNA synthesis. From Waite and Pfefferkorn (1970).

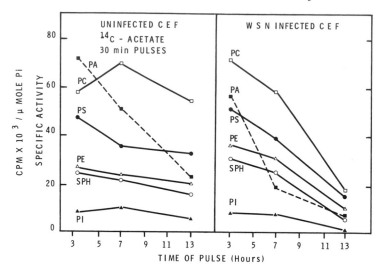

FIG. 15. Effect of influenza virus (A₀/WSN) on phospholipid synthesis in chick fibroblasts using a double label of glycerol-2-³H and acetate-¹⁴C. Cells were pulsed for 30 minutes at various time intervals after infection and sampled immediately. Depression of synthesis of various phospholipid species is seen to occur 7 hours after infection.

With influenza virus, all lipid synthesis was depressed between 8 and 12 hours following infection (Weinstein and Blough, 1972). This disproved the conclusion that *de novo* synthesis of lipid did not occur in virus-infected cells and stresses the importance of using multiple techniques of isotopic labeling.

Turnover studies were less conclusive. Short pulses with glycerol-³H and acetate-¹⁴C were done at various time intervals after infection. In the chick embryo fibroblast system, there appears to be an overall depression of all lipid synthesis 8 hours after infection, but turnover of the glycerol backbone (during a 4-hour chase) appears enhanced in infected cells in the case of phosphatidylcholine and phosphatidylserine. The fact that turnover rates appear remarkably similar in controls and infected cells despite an 80–90% decrease in phospholipid synthesis at these times is a paradox. A possible explanation is that preformed phospholipid molecules are transported for assembly in viral envelopes (see Section VI,A). Alternatively, the portion of lipid which is labeled may be a labile fraction whose turnover is necessary for viral envelope biogenesis.

It has been shown by Lands (1965) that enzymes of the monoacyl-diacyl phosphoglyceride cycle are responsible for the renewal of fatty acyl chains in a variety of tissues. These enzymes are located primarily in the microsomal and mitochondrial fractions of cells (Stoffel and

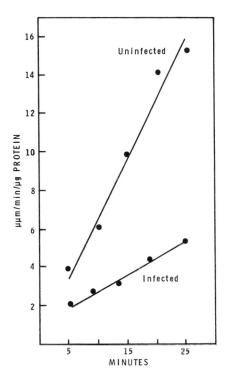

Fɪɢ. 16. Inhibition of host cell acyl-CoA : phosphoglyceride acyl transferase activity following infection with influenza virus. The reaction mixture contained 20 mμmoles of lysophosphatidylcholine as the acceptor, 200 μg of microsomal protein from chick chorioallantoic cells, and 5,5'-dithio-*bis*-nitrobenzoic acid (DTNB); the molar adsorptivity was used to calculate the release of free mercaptan. Microsomes were isolated 30 minutes after infection. From Blough and Smith (1973).

Schiefer, 1968; Turkki and Glenn, 1968; Eibl *et al.*, 1970). Due to the varying acyl chain composition observed in different strains of myxoviruses grown in embryonated eggs (Tiffany and Blough, 1969a,b) the myxovirus/chick cell system was investigated to see if influenza or Newcastle disease viruses could alter host cell enzymes responsible for phospholipid renewal. Microsomal fractions of chorioallantoic cells were isolated at various times after infection, and compared with uninfected controls; it was seen that the acyl-CoA:phosphoglyceride acyl transferase level was reduced to approximately 70% of that of uninfected controls (Fig. 16); this effect was noted within 30 minutes following infection. Acyl-CoA hydrolase was enhanced threefold with incomplete influenza virus of the von Magnus type at 40 hours postinfection (Fig. 17). These enzymes were *not* detected within the virion. The conclusion of these studies was that, *in ovo,* the enzymes of the monoacyl-diacyl phospho-

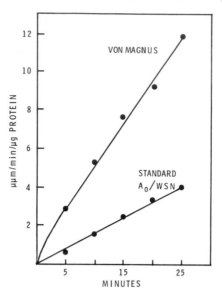

FIG. 17. Acyl-CoA hydrolase activity of the microsomal fraction of chick chorioallantoic cells infected with von Magnus influenza virus, compared to cells infected with standard virus. The reaction mixture is the same as for the experiment of Fig. 16, except that the acceptor molecule (lysophosphatidylcholine) has been omitted. Microsomal fractions were obtained 40 hours after infection or from 13-day-old uninfected chorioallantoic membranes. From Blough and Smith (1973).

glyceride cycle did not play a major role in determining the molecular species of phospholipid incorporated into the viral envelope (Blough and Smith, 1973).

Experiments were also designed to try to test the hypothesis that altered lipid metabolism in certain viruses (e.g., in cells infected with incomplete influenza virus) or certain nonpermissive cell types (e.g., HeLa cells) are responsible, in part, for failure of viral assembly. Influenza virus which has been passed at high multiplicity pleomorphic and loses a portion of its genome (Pons and Hirst, 1969), behaving in fact like a deletion mutation—the so-called incomplete or von Magnus virus. When compared to standard virus this virus has an altered lipid composition and shows obvious defects in the viral envelope (Blough and Merlie, 1970). When incorporation studies with glycerol-^{3}H and acetate-^{14}C were done, there was an immediate 50% decrease in diglyceride synthesis and a 75% increase in free fatty acids when compared to cells mock-infected with sterile allantoic fluid (Table VII). This correlated well with the studies on compositional analysis of von Magnus virus

Table VII

Effect of Incomplete Influenza Virus on Incorporation of Glycerol-³H
and Acetate-¹⁴C into Neutral Lipids of Chick Fibroblasts[a,b]

	Glycerol-³H			Acetate-¹⁴C		
Lipid class	Control	Infected	Change (%)	Control	Infected	Change (%)
Monoglyceride	40,029	51,821	+29	44,000	46,607	+6
Diglyceride	613,760	521,503	−15	272,552	135,134	−50
Triglyceride	167,193	186,184	+11	14,570	15,225	+5
Fatty acids	—	—	—	10,175	17,809	+75
Cholesterol	—	—	—	79,351	64,210	−19
Cholesterol esters	—	—	—	766	762	No change

[a] Specific activities in cpm/μmole of neutral lipid.
[b] Samples taken immediately after a 30-minute pulse.

(Blough and Merlie, 1970), in which free fatty acids were increased in comparison to standard virus. Furthermore, preliminary studies (Blough and Weinstein, 1973) suggest that phosphatidylcholine and phosphatidylethanolamine synthesis is enhanced in chick embryo cells infected with von Magnus virus.

In HeLa cells infected with A_0/WSN influenza virus, viral structural polypeptides are synthesized, as are all the species of RNA, yet viral assembly does not occur (Lerner and Hodge, 1969). In HeLa cells, influenza virus (3–5 pfu/cell) affects both the synthesis and turnover of lipids immediately; diglyceride synthesis is inhibited by 15% and all phospholipids are inhibited by 27–80% (using glycerol-³H label). Phosphatidylethanolamine and sphingomyelin turnover are decreased, whereas phosphatidylserine turnover was increased by 50% over controls. These studies suggest that host cell lipid metabolism plays an important role in determining whether or not some cell systems are permissive or not for certain viruses. In addition an uncoupling of synthesis and turnover of neutral lipids and phospholipids was evident (Blough, 1971b; Weinstein and Blough, 1973). Such systems provide a unique opportunity to study the interrelationship of host cell regulatory mechanisms and viral envelope biogenesis at the molecular level and are worthy of further exploration.

Fusion, a process whereby the viral envelope joins with the cellular membrane to form a coherent membrane is the means of entry of viral nucleocapsid into the cell under certain circumstances (Morgan and Rose, 1968). The molecular events responsible for fusion are unknown (Poste, 1970). Using BHK-21 cells infected with Newcastle disease virus (NDV), and the appropriate conditions for fusion to occur, a twofold to fourfold depression of the synthesis of all lipid classes was noted immediately, which is quite different from results with orthomyxoviruses. This inhibition could be duplicated during a cytolytic infection with NDV in calcium-free medium or late in a productive infection (Gallaher and Blough, 1972); again, the phospholipid composition of the cells remained remarkably constant.

As mentioned earlier, SV5, a paramyxovirus, contains neutral glycolipids rather than the hematosides or gangliosides present in the host cell membrane; BHK-21 cells contain N-acetylneuraminyl lactose ceramide, and virtually none was detected in the virion produced in these cells (Klenk and Choppin, 1970b). Recent studies in sphingolipid synthesis have been done using choline-^{3}H and glucosamine-^{3}H as precursors (A. A. Scheid and P. W. Choppin, personal communication, 1972); in MDBK (Madin Darby bovine kidney) cells following SV5 infection, sphingomyelin synthesis decreases whereas globoside doubles. It had previously been shown by Hakomori (1970) that confluent cells had higher levels of sphingoglycolipids than had sparsely plated cells. Thus SV5 infection seems to produce the same effect as the attainment of confluence by a cell monolayer (A. A. Scheid and P. W. Choppin, personal communication, 1972). Hakomori et al. (1971) have studied the relationship of glycolipid synthesis to transformation of chick embryo fibroblasts by Rous sarcoma virus. Viral transformation led to a decrease in glycolipids with nonreducing terminals (e.g., disialosyl and monosialosyl hematosides), and increased amounts of precursor molecules (ceramides and glucosyl ceramides) within cells. At 20 hours after infection, when 30% of the cells were transformed, disialosylhematoside began to drop and reached barely detectable levels at 48 hours, when 70% of the cells were transformed. The decrease of hematoside was followed by an increase in neutral sphingoglycolipids. On the other hand, incorporation studies with glucosamine-^{14}C revealed a 50% increase in glycolipid synthesis in cells transformed by Rous virus (Hakomori et al., 1971), suggesting a rapid turnover of the sugar moieties in virally transformed cells. In contrast Warren et al. (1972), using palmitate-1-^{14}C as a precursor, failed to show any major differences in the incorporation of this precursor into glycolipids of normal chick fibroblasts, those transformed by Rous virus (Schmidt-Ruppin strain), or cells transposed with a ts mutant (TF) which reverted to normal following growth at 41.5°. These differences may result from variability in "pool equilibria" with different isotopes (Hakomori et al., 1971), or from palmitate exchange. Obviously, more studies along these lines are needed to map out the molecular events responsible for cell fusion, transformation, lysis, and death.

B. DNA Viruses

Studies of lipid metabolism in cells infected with DNA-containing viruses have been limited to three viral classes: herpesviruses, poxviruses, and lipovirus. It is the paucity of work on DNA viruses which accounts for the shortness of this section, rather than the authors' interests in the RNA-containing viruses.

1. *Herpesviruses*

Lipid synthesis in primary rabbit kidney cells infected with pseudo-rabies virus was studied using different radioactive precursors (Ben-Porat and Kaplan, 1971). These studies were based on the experimental design of Kates *et al.* (1961) for influenza virus except that 16- and 90-hour pulses of orthophosphate-^{32}P and choline-^{3}H were used instead of a single pulse of 72 hours. Several important findings were noted. First, the level of radioactivity of the inner nuclear membrane and that of purified virus closely resembled each other, confirming the morphological studies of Siegert and Falke (1966), which indicated that the virus acquired its envelope from this membrane. Second, the specific activities of the nuclear membrane and virion were quite different, suggesting to Ben-Porat and Kaplan (1972) that the viral envelope was derived from more metabolically active sites of the inner nuclear membrane than the remainder of the nuclear envelope. Ben-Porat and Kaplan (1972) prelabeled rabbit

Table VIII

TRANSFER OF PHOSPHOLIPIDS FROM CYTOPLASMIC TO NUCLEAR MEMBRANES AFTER INFECTION WITH PSEUDORABIES VIRUS[a]

Experiment	Time after infection[b] (hours)		Cytoplasmic	Nuclear	
				Outer	Inner
1	4.5	Infected	25,600[c]	3560[c]	5820[c]
		Uninfected	26,100	3120	3430
2	7	Infected	29,900	6780	5980
		Uninfected	33,500	3890	3020

[a] Reprinted from Table 2 of Ben-Porat and Kaplan (1972) by courtesy of Macmillan Press.

[b] Primary rabbit kidney cell monolayers were incubated in medium containing 3% bovine serum and 0.2 μCi/ml choline-^{3}H for 72 hours prior to mock infection or infection with 20 pfu/cell of pseudorabies virus, and chased with unlabeled medium.

[c] Values are in cpm/culture.

kidney cells with choline-^{3}H for 72 hours, and then isolated cellular organelles at various times following infection with pseudorabies virus. During the chase period, there was a 40% drop in radioactivity (cpm/culture dish) in the cytoplasm, and a doubling of radioactivity in the nuclear membrane at 7 hours postinfection (Table VIII), suggesting a flow of lipid from the cytoplasm to the nucleus for viral assembly. Since sphingomyelin and phosphatidylcholine turn over at different rates in P815Y cells (Pasternak and Bergeron, 1970) as well as in other cell types (Weinstein and Blough, 1973), it is surprising that they were found in the same ratio in infected and uninfected cells during the chase.

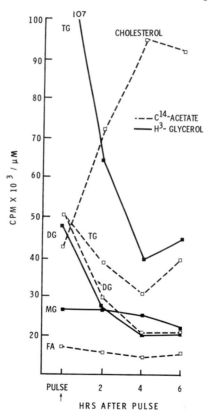

Fig. 18. a and b. Metabolism of glycerol-^{3}H (2 μCi/ml) and acetate-^{14}C (0.5 μCi/ml) by BHK-21 cells infected with herpes simplex virus. Cells were pulsed for 30 minutes at 2 hours after infection or mock-infection and samples taken after the pulse and during a 6-hour chase period. Fig. 18a. Control BHK cells. (MG = monoglycerides; DG = diglycerides; TG = triglycerides; FA = free fatty acids.) From Weinstein and Blough (1973).

Studies were done in the authors' laboratory on herpes simplex virus infection of BHK-21 cells using relatively short pulses of 30 minutes with glycerol-2-³H and acetate-¹⁴C, and various chase periods; both neutral lipids and phospholipids were analyzed. Very early in the infectious cycle (2 hours after infection), there was a preferential stimulation of phosphatidylserine and sphingomyelin synthesis over other phospholipids, whereas triglycerides were inhibited. At 3 to 5 hours, phosphatidylserine was inhibited, and all neutral lipids stimulated. At 8 hours, there was a stimulation of both isotopic precursors flowing into all lipids (Weinstein and Blough, 1973); this is the time of cell fusion and cytopathology. The different rates of uptake of acetate and glycerol into the same lipids suggest multiple pools are operative. Despite the cyclic changes in phospho-

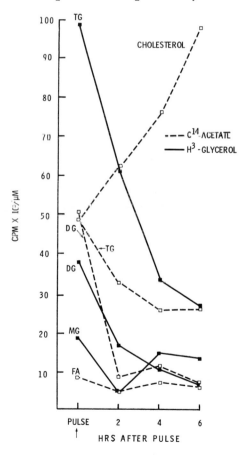

Fɪɢ. 18b.   Herpesvirus-infected cells. See Fig. 18a legend.

lipids in herpesvirus-infected cells, the composition of host-cell lipid during the infectious cycle is stable (Gallaher and Blough, 1972), and increased levels of lysophosphatides are not detected. This suggests that monoacylated phospholipids do not play a part in cell fusion. Turnover of diglycerides and triglycerides is the same in infected and uninfected cells, that is, 2- to 2½-hour half-lives for both molecules. Fatty acids, sterols, and monoglycerides do not turn over under these experimental conditions (Figs. 18a,b). With phospholipids, the glycerol skeleton shows different patterns of turnover in phosphatidylserine and phosphatidylcholine, in comparing infected to uninfected cells. Turnover did not appear to follow first-order kinetics and the possibility of ^{3}H exchange in the case of glycerol-^{3}H could not be ruled out. It may well be that definitive measurements of turnover must await the isolation and quantitation of isotopic precursor and cellular product pool sizes. Obviously there may be a great deal of variation of lipid synthesis and turnover in cultured cells, which no doubt reflects cell types (multiple in the case of primary chick embryo fibroblasts), cell cycle conditions, contact inhibition, and other physiological and metabolic events responsible for cell growth and division.

2. Poxviruses

Vaccinia virus lipid biosynthesis was investigated in L cells using choline-^{3}H as a precursor (Dales and Mosbach, 1968); 92–98% of the radioactivity was found in phosphatidylcholine; the ratio of stearic acid ($C_{18:0}$) to oleic acid ($C_{18:1}$) was 1.0 in purified virions and 0.5 in microsomal fractions of the host cell, suggesting de novo synthesis of lipids. Inhibitor studies with streptovitacin A revealed that translation of messenger RNA was required before viral envelope biogenesis occurred at 3 hours postinfection.

3. Lipovirus PM2

Studies on the lipid composition of the bacteriophage PM2 and its host cell Pseudomonas BAL-31 suggest de novo synthesis or rearrangement of lipid for virus assembly. Within 60 minutes after infection there is a shift in the distribution of lysophosphatidylethanolamine and phosphatidic acid in the host cell (Braunstein and Franklin, 1971). Phosphatidic acid is a trace component only in uninfected cells, but makes up 2–4% of viral lipid. Phosphatidylethanolamine drops from 75% to 43% of cellular phospholipid and phosphatidylglycerol rises from 23% to 36%, following infection.

VI. Viral Assembly and Structure

A. PATTERNS OF ASSEMBLY

Apart from electron microscopic observations on the site of synthesis or accumulation of viral material, and the relationship of this site to that of subsequent assembly of the virion, little is known about the assembly or transport of lipid molecules to cell membranes. The work of Kates *et al.* (1961) indicated no disturbance of lipid patterns of the host cell following viral infection; in contrast to this, *de novo* synthesis of lipid has been found to occur in chick embryo fibroblasts infected with influenza virus (see Section V). It is postulated that some of the differences in acyl chain composition seen in a variety of viruses may be due to the transport of newly synthesized (or preformed) lipid from the endoplasmic reticulum to the plasma membrane; in the case of viruses maturing at other membranes, such as herpesvirus, this transport would be toward the nuclear membrane. The most likely candidate to undertake this transport is an envelope structural polypeptide (Tiffany and Blough, 1970a). There is a precedent for this in the binding of lipid to enzymes of eukaryotic cells in the fatty acid synthetase system of yeast, where the apolar lipid binds to hydrophobic sites of the enzyme and allows transport of this multienzyme complex through the cell sap (Lynen *et al.*, 1968). Another transport system has been shown to operate in rat liver (Wirtz and Zilversmit, 1969), whereby phospholipids are transported from their site of synthesis in the endoplasmic reticulum to mitochondria.

The "inverted toadstool" model of Tiffany and Blough (1970a) for the structure of the envelope of influenza virus (considered in more detail below) suggests that the first step in the assembly process may be a phase transition of lipid within the cell membrane to a micellar state similar to that suggested by Lucy (1964). This would present an array of polar head groups of lipids with porelike spaces between them which would allow the hydrophilic parts of the external envelope polypeptides of the virus to be inserted through the cell membrane (Fig. 19). This is not unlike the "closed" to "open" pillar change in the membrane model of Kavanau (1963). There is either a lateral displacement of host cell membrane macromolecules or a dissolution of the preexisting membrane components to make room for the incoming polypeptides. The former mechanism has been shown to apply in the case of herpesvirus (Heine *et al.*, 1972).

The complexity of the problem of assembly is increased when one considers the need to glycosylate the glycolipids and the envelope polypep-

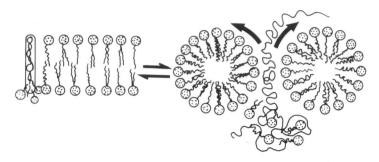

Fig. 19.   Method of inserting viral polypeptide into a membrane. Polar groups
of lipid in the micellar form feed the polypeptide through the membrane. The possible transition to a lamellar phase with an interdigitated polypeptide is shown on
the left.

tides (which make up the surface projections of a large number of enveloped viruses). It seems that the majority of proteins exposed on the
outer faces of cell surface membranes are also glycoproteins, and it has
been proposed that the carbohydrate moiety promotes passage of glycoproteins across cell membranes (Eylar, 1966). This requires the presence
in the cell of a battery of glycosylating enzymes. These are specific for
each monosaccharide, and together build a host-specific carbohydrate
structure, leading to observations such as that on Sindbis virus, where
the carbohydrate moiety of envelope glycoproteins depends on the host
cell (Grimes and Burge, 1971). Ortho- and paramyxoviruses grown in
cells exhibiting blood group and Forssman antigen activities have been
shown to possess the same surface activities, but not when grown in hosts
without these groups (Isacson and Koch, 1965; Rott et al., 1966). Burge
(quoted by Scheele and Pfefferkorn, 1969) is reported to have been unable to find a pool of free glycosylated glycopeptide in the cytoplasm of
cells infected with Sindbis virus. The enzymes responsible for glycosylation have been found in the microsomal fraction of cells (Grimes and
Burge, 1971) and Golgi membranes (J. J. M. Bergeron, personal communication, 1972); thus far, no studies on the glycosylation of glycolipids in virus-infected cells have been reported. It is postulated that
the glycosyltransferases responsible for addition and chain elongation
of sugars are at the site of viral maturation. Klenk and Choppin
(1970b) noted the absence of sialic acid in sphingoglycolipids synthesized in cells infected with the paramyxovirus SV5, and also showed
the absence of detectable surface sialic acid in the budding virus envelope
by electron microscopic staining (Klenk et al., 1970b). It has yet to be
determined whether this is a defect in glycolipid synthesis at the CMP-
sialotransferase level, or the result of viral neuraminidase action. It seems
unlikely that viral neuraminidase alone is responsible for total removal of

sialic acid, since nonterminal sialic acid is not readily removed from gangliosides by sialidases (Burton, 1963). However, sialic acid has been found in both glycoproteins and glycolipids of viruses which do not contain neuraminidase (Burge and Strauss, 1970; Burge and Huang, 1970; Klenk and Choppin, 1971). Budding is thought to occur when the envelope polypeptides reach a critical concentration or form a patch of critical area (Fig. 20). The ionic strength of the medium appears to play a part in the assembly process of enveloped viruses (Waite and Pfefferkorn, 1970). The separation of virus from the cell surface, endoplasmic reticulum, or nuclear membrane is probably mediated through electrostatic repulsive forces which shear the particle from its placental membrane.

Viruses such as PM2 (Harrison *et al.*, 1971a) and the envelope of more complex viruses such as poxviruses, baculoviruses, and possibly iridoviruses (Dales and Mosbach, 1968; Harrap, 1969; E. Houts and M. Gravell, personal communication, 1972), appear to be formed independently of any preexisting membrane, their proteins and lipids interacting directly to form a lipoprotein shell; the ordering of protein and lipid by hydroprobic interaction, or nonpolar protein-protein interactions, provide a net entropy decrease which is responsible for the self-assembly phenomenon. It is suggested that lipids bearing appropriate acyl chains are

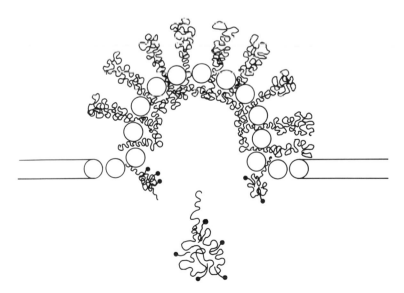

Fɪɢ. 20. Diagrammatic expression of the budding process of enveloped viruses at a cell membrane. Note molecules of lipid bound to structural polypeptide with polar groups on the exterior (●), facilitating transport through the cell cytoplasm. Spheres represent micelles of lipid.

necessary in order to provide or preserve configurations of some polypeptides which are needed for assembly. The incorporation of lipid permits a unique plasticity of structure not possible in the isometric viruses. It should be noted that lipid-protein structures are not necessarily devoid of an ordered structure; Pollard *et al.* (1969) found that low-density lipoproteins consisted of a core containing most of the neutral lipid, surrounded by a shell composed of the phospholipid and twenty protein subunits arranged in a dodecahedral pattern with icosahedral symmetry. It appears certain that union of protein and lipid occurs rapidly and probably leads to an almost instant encapsidation of viruses such as PM2. The functional need for lipids in this encapsidation process might be thought to resemble the lipid requirement in the model suggested by Green and Perdue (1966) for the assembly of lipid-depleted mitochondrial membrane building blocks. The hydrophobic protein regions of the virion may be considered as "lipid-depleted subunits"; the binding of lipid represents "information" at the molecular level, in which the stretches of hydrophobic amino acids specify the amount and type of lipid bound.

Some viruses such as entomopoxviruses (Devauchelle *et al.*, 1970, 1971), and some herpesviruses (Heine *et al.*, 1971), appear to be formed by a combination of "scaffolding template" and *de novo* synthesis. Why different viruses assemble at a specific site, such as poxviruses in cytoplasmic "factories" (Dales, 1963) or herpesvirus at the nuclear membrane (Morgan *et al.*, 1959), is at present unknown, although the availability of lipids bearing specific acyl chains is probably of paramount importance. Reference to Section II shows that many RNA viruses assembled in the cytoplasm will fall into the "scaffolding template" category, and some DNA viruses will fall into the *de novo* or mixed categories, but there are too many exceptions for this to be used as a basis for general classification of enveloped viruses.

Obviously these are extremely tentative hypotheses and a great deal more work is required to give them more formal substance. The isolation and characterization of unique hydrophobic polypeptides has not yet been achieved, and it is at present unknown whether the large DNA-containing viruses such as vaccinia, FV 3, etc., can induce or have the genetic capacity to code for enzymes which are necessary for lipid biosynthesis.

Figure 21 shows a general scheme for *de novo* synthesis of viruses.

B. MODELS OF STRUCTURE

With the awakening of interest in the structure, composition, and function of membranes, and the realization that viral envelopes could be con-

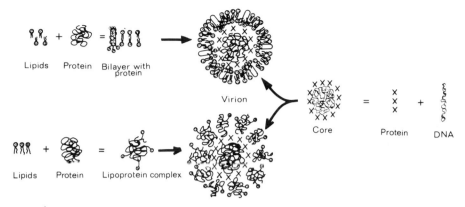

FIG. 21.   Simplified diagram of self-assembly of lipid-containing viruses.

sidered as a special case in which a relatively small number of proteins was associated with lipid, much attention has been focused on the structure of viral envelopes, and it is probably safe to say that more papers have appeared on this subject in the last 3 years than in the 10 preceding years. The results up to the present cannot be considered complete for any single virus. It is the express purpose of this section to show the diversity of opinion that exists on envelope structure and to point out that not all lipid-containing viruses are constructed in the same fashion.

Prior to 1969 it was thought that the envelope of viruses was produced at cellular membranes by a simple budding process; the envelope lipids were therefore assumed in all cases to have the same composition as the host membrane, and to retain the presumed bimolecular leaflet structure of the cell membrane. The virus was pictured as a nucleocapsid core surrounded by a liposome-like structure in which were embedded repeating surface subunits. This posed a number of problems, chief among which was how the polypeptides forming the external projections of the virion were transferred from the cytoplasm to the outer side of the lipid bilayer prior to and during budding. This transport of charged materials through the hydrophobic interior of the lipid bilayer membrane would require considerable amounts of energy, and any involvement of a transmembrane pore system, such as might be used for macromolecular uptake or exclusion from the cell, would seem unlikely as host membrane proteins forming the pore might then be found in the viral envelope. This was shown not to be the case for influenza virus (Holland and Kiehn, 1970). With the application of high-resolution gas-chromatographic techniques, it became evident that the lipid composition of the virion did not necessarily mimic that of the uninfected host cell membrane from which it was derived (Tiffany and Blough, 1969a,b). The greatest differences were noted in the acyl groups of neutral lipids and phospholipids.

It has been suggested that viruses which contain lipid in an envelope do so in part because of the unique hydrophobicity of one or more of the envelope structural polypeptides. According to this hypothesis, viruses may have a predilection for maturing at certain membranes because of the phospholipid and glyceride (and hence acyl chain) composition at these points, or because of a favorable lipid transport process to this site; the virus may assemble incorrectly if the composition of the lipid available is altered, e.g., by growing virus in the presence of vitamin A (Blough, 1963) or an exogenous fatty acid (Blough and Tiffany, 1969), in incomplete influenza virus or influenza virus in a nonpermissive cell system (Blough, 1971b). As indicated in Section V, changes of lipid metabolism in the host cell following infection may be responsible for shifts in lipid composition at the site of assembly, or at the site of "charging" of transport proteins, thus accounting for at least some of the observed differences between virus and host lipids.

Of the viruses which possess classical cubic symmetry only those of the herpesvirus group appear to be enveloped, but the envelope itself has no such regularity and is capable of considerable variation in shape, such as during preparation for electron microscopy when ballooning may occur as negative stain penetrates within the envelope (Fig. 6a). Other regular viruses are known to contain lipid (e.g., lipovirus and frog virus FV 3), but in these the lipid appears to play a more integral part in the structure of the internal portion of the virion than in the true envelope. Some of the other enveloped viruses appear to possess an underlying network structure or scaffolding within the envelope which may be composed of hexamers and pentamers, in particular influenza C (Apostolov and Flewett, 1969), and the regular spacing of surface projections revealed by negative staining of some strains of influenza A has suggested a greater degree of regularity of envelope structure than had been previously considered (Almeida and Waterson, 1967, 1970; Tiffany and Blough, 1970b).

The external projections of the envelope of animal viruses have been found to be glycoproteins in all cases so far studied (Stollar, 1969; Compans et al., 1970; Schulze, 1970; Burge and Strauss, 1970; Compans, 1971; Chen et al., 1971), and recent studies confirm that an envelope structural protein of the type postulated by Blough (1969) and Tiffany and Blough (1970a) may be found within the lipid region of the envelope or just beneath it (Schulze, 1970, 1972; Compans et al., 1970; Neurath et al., 1972). In all cases the envelope must be regarded as an essential part of the virion since treatment with organic solvents or phospholipases, or the presence of "nonenveloped" particles occurring naturally, e.g., in herpesvirus-infected cells, are all associated with a lower infectivity (Watson et al., 1964). Approaches to a plausible envelope structure can

be made by the construction of molecular models based on the compositional analysis of the virion, the possible type of molecular interaction
between components' of the virion, electron-microscopic appearance
(using negative contrast, positively-stained thin sections, and freeze-
etching), and the effect on virus structure of various enzymes such as
proteases and phospholipases. We should stress, however, that the
geometrical considerations (the packing of lipid, cross-sectional areas of
molecules, etc.) are particularly important, since no matter what model
of structure is chosen, it must be possible to pack all the components into
the available space without incompatibility of hydrophobic and hydrophilic regions. Data from ultracentrifugal or polyacrylamide gel electrophoresis studies of individual polypeptides must be used with caution,
since molecular weights so derived may be considerably in error, especially in the case of glycoproteins (Segrest *et al.*, 1971). An alternative
approach is to use powerful tools such as X-ray diffraction and magnetic
resonance spectroscopy in an attempt to discern the arrangement of lipid
and protein within the virion (Harrison *et al.*, 1971a,b; Landsberger *et al.*,
1971). However, such methods are insufficient to solve the problem by
themselves. At the present time there is enough information to construct
tentative models for at least four groups of viruses: myxoviruses, rhabdoviruses, alphaviruses, and lipovirus. Models proposed for other viruses
are also noted below.

1. *Myxoviruses*

We shall consider here principally influenza A virus as representative
of the orthomyxoviruses, since almost all the work on structure has employed this type, although not always the same strain. There is also
evidence that influenza C differs quite considerably in structure from
influenza A and B (Apostolov and Flewett, 1969). These viruses are assembled at the cell surface membrane ("scaffolding template" viruses)
and possess an envelope with regularly spaced projections 90–130 Å long.
From measurements of spike spacing Tiffany and Blough (1970b) determined that a particle of overall diameter 1000 Å was covered by 500–
600 spikes, in contrast to the frequently quoted figure of 2000; uncritical
acceptance of this latter figure probably delayed attempts to establish
a structure for the influenza virus envelope by leading to confusing esti-
mates of numbers of functional molecules per virion (Kendal *et al.*,
1968). Protease digestion studies (Kendal *et al.*, 1969), negative-contrast electron microscopy (Berkaloff and Thiéry, 1963; Nermut and
Frank, 1971), and freeze-etching studies (Bächi *et al.*, 1969) have all
indicated the presence of "nanogranules" about 40 Å in size in the
envelope; these appear to be embedded in the envelope toward the inner

side, and to correspond roughly to the positions of the spikes. Such a particle of protein would have a molecular weight of about 25,000.

The model proposed by Tiffany and Blough (1970a) was the first to attempt to rationalize the state of knowledge of the composition and structure of this virus by applying simple geometrical principles to the then available data on the nature and amounts of the constituent molecules of the envelope. At that time no detailed information was published on the proportions and molecular weights of the individual polypeptides, such as shortly afterwards became available from polyacrylamide gel electrophoresis studies (Compans et al., 1970; Haslam et al., 1969, 1970a,b; Schulze, 1970; Skehel and Schild, 1971). Nevertheless, this study led to some interesting conclusions and permitted some predictions to be made, particularly that there is an envelope structural protein underlying the lipid-containing region of the envelope; other parts of the model have been more seriously questioned, and in the light of more recent evidence require modification. The salient features of this model are given here, together with some indication of the data from other laboratories which reinforce or conflict with the model.

Typically a particule of influenza A (e.g., strain A_0/PR8/34) is spherical and 1000 Å in diameter with surface projections 100 Å long and 65 Å apart and an envelope 90–100 Å thick. The particle contains about 20% lipid (approximately 12% phospholipid and 8% cholesterol) and roughly 70% protein; protein has been estimated to weigh 4.2×10^{-16} gm per particle (Reimer et al., 1966), and nucleocapsid to account for about 40% of this (Laver, 1964). We calculate that there are 550 spikes on this particle (Tiffany and Blough, 1970b), and by taking a typical value of 0.7 ml/gm for the partial specific volume of the proteins, and typical dimensions for the spikes (Laver and Valentine, 1969), we find that the total protein volume per particle is 2.94×10^8 Å^3, of which about 9.5×10^7 Å^3 is in the nonspike part of the envelope. A lipid bilayer structure similar to that proposed by Schulze (1972) was first considered, but comparison of the area occupied by the viral lipid in the form of a bilayer, and the area available in the envelope for such a bilayer, led to abandonment of this method of lipid arrangement. Taking De Bernard's (1958) figure of 50.3 Å^2 per molecule for the mean cross-sectional area of a lipid molecule at the observed cholesterol:phospholipid molar ratio of 1.5, the lipid is calculated to occupy 3.3×10^6 Å^2 as a bilayer. Other strains of influenza virus have been observed to have cholesterol:phospholipid molar ratios closer to unity, in which case the area per molecule is about 55 Å^2 but the bilayer area is still 3.4×10^6 Å^2. The largest area of bilayer which could be accommodated in the envelope (forming a shell of mean radius about 370 Å on the outer side of the envelope) is only $1.54 \times 10^6 \text{ Å}^2$. There hence appeared to be twice as much lipid present as would be required in the bilayer model, and the problem reduced to one of distributing this lipid in some uniform manner. Previous studies (Tiffany and Blough, 1969a) had suggested some hydrophobic interaction between lipids and an envelope protein; it was therefore postulated that the envelope protein might be arranged in the form of a shell of units with "stalks" directed outward and acting as supports for the external spikes. The spaces between the "stalks" would be filled by roughly spherical micelles of lipid, equal in number to the external spikes, and part of the lipid would also be bound to the units in the protein shell (Figs. 22 and 23). Because of the shape of the base and "stalk" this was referred to as the "inverted toadstool" model. The stalk is not necessarily to be thought of as an integral part of the toadstool; it is included with the base since their total volume was calculated as that of the nonspike envelope proteins, and it was in fact suggested that the stalk might form part of the spike. Assuming that the lipid-binding capacity of the toadstool base was similar to that of the lipid-binding chloroplast protein studied by Ji and Benson (1968), i.e., about 18 phos-

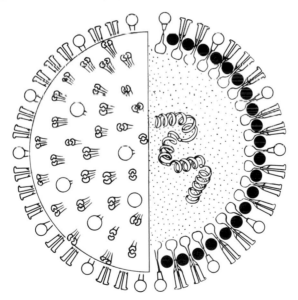

Fig. 22. Model of the influenza virus particle (Tiffany and Blough, 1970a). Right half shows internal fragmented nucleocapsid (coil) with "linker" molecules; the toadstool-shaped structural polypeptide goes through the membrane and interdigitates with envelope lipid in micellar form (black spheres). Surface projections are hemagglutinin and neuraminidase (sphere-topped spike). Left half shows an external view of the viral envelope with glycoprotein projections.

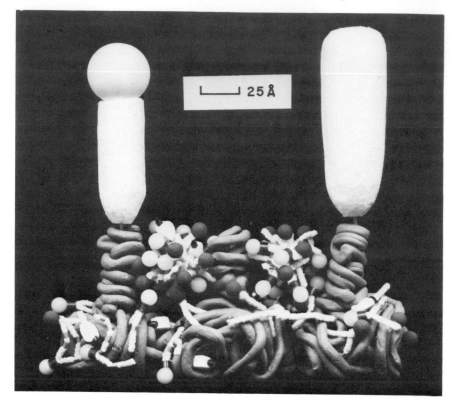

Fig. 23. Molecular model of micelles of lipid plus toadstool (viral envelope structural proteins). Acyl chains of lipid molecules are represented by pipe cleaners and their polar groups by small balls. Hemagglutinin (flat-topped projection) and neuraminidase (spherical-tipped projection) surmount the toadstools. The projection on the middle toadstool has been omitted. (From Blough, 1969, reprinted by courtesy of the Bulletin of the World Health Association.)

pholipid molecules bound per 23,000 molecular weight of protein, about 25% of the viral lipid would be hydrophobically bound, and the rest would form 550 spherical micelles 54 Å in diameter. This lipid, but not that hydrophobically bound, would be susceptible to lipase attack; Schulze (1970) found that 70% of the viral lipid was removed by this means. It seemed likely also that the bound lipid might confer greater resistance to proteolytic enzyme action on the base protein, and the toadstool bases would appear as "nanogranules" in partially digested particles (Kendal et al., 1969). The appearance of the envelope in positively stained ultrathin sections would probably sufficiently resemble that of a conventional lipid bilayer structure to be interpreted as such. The molecular weight of the base would be about 120,000, and the stalk about

40,000; it was considered that the base might be composed of subunits of 20,000–25,000 molecular weight. This model also simplifies the assembly process at the cell membrane by permitting insertion of spike proteins through the membrane following a local phase change to the micellar form, induced by the presence of envelope proteins (Fig. 19).

Recently results have been published from several laboratories, indicating that there is in fact a shell of envelope structural protein underlying the lipid region (Compans *et al.*, 1970; Haslam *et al.*, 1969, 1970a,b; Schulze, 1970; Skehel and Schild, 1971), but as yet no studies showing lipid-binding properties have been reported for this protein. Schulze (1970, 1972) and Klenk *et al.* (1972) concluded, from the smooth appearance and resistance to proteolytic enzymes of influenza particles whose external spikes had been removed by bromelain treatment, that the lipid was probably in the form of a bilayer surrounding the outer part of the envelope, and that protein "stalks" supporting the spikes did not penetrate this lipid region. This view was reinforced by the spin-label studies of Landsberger *et al.* (1971). An unpaired-electron spin label was introduced into the virion by incorporating nitroxy-labeled analogs of stearic acid and androstane. A comparison was made of purified influenza virus (strain A_0/WSN) and human erythrocyte ghosts following labeling at 4° for 4–15 hours. Striking similarities between the spectra for human erythrocyte membranes and virus were noted (Fig. 24): the rotation of the nitroxy-label was more hindered when the label was close to the carboxyl end of the stearic acid molecule than when it was close to the terminal methyl group, and this was taken to be indicative of a bilayer type lipid structure. Taking values for the cross-sectional areas of the lipids which correspond more nearly to the packings achieved in crystals, 46.7 Å^2 for phospholipid and 35 Å^2 for cholesterol (Levine and Wilkins, 1971), Landsberger *et al.* (1971) calculated that the lipid of the virus could in fact all be contained in a bilayer shell.

Obviously the model of Tiffany and Blough (1970a) must be modified if it is to be brought into agreement with later results; it would, for instance, require little change to replace the lipid micelles by a bilayer through which the spikes protrude. De Bernard's (1958) values for cross-sectional areas of lipids have been criticized as being derived from monolayer studies at too low a value of surface pressure. However the figures chosen by Landsberger *et al.* (1971) may also be criticized since there is no evidence that the degree of lipid packing in the viral envelope approaches that in the solid phase. Engelman's (1969) calculations on the hydrophobic volume of lipids in a bilayer suggest a larger molecular area should be taken, especially as the virus is normally assembled at about 37°, whereas most area measurements on monolayers and packed

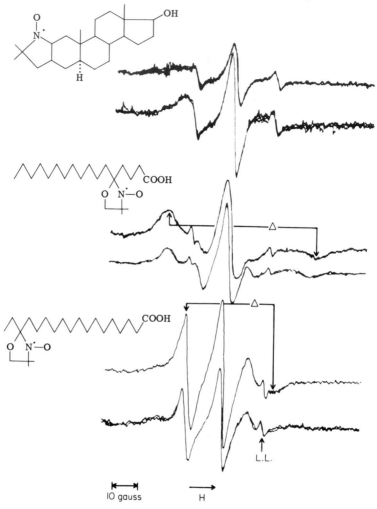

Fig. 24. Electron spin resonance traces for influenza virus particles (upper trace) and erythrocyte ghosts (lower trace). Nitroxy-derivatives of androstane and stearic acid were used. Δ = splitting between low- and high-magnetic-field peaks ("broad-line spectrum"). LL = high-field peak or "liquid lines." H = magnetic field. (Reprinted from Landsberger *et al.*, 1971, by courtesy of Dr. R. W. Compans and the Editors of the *Proceedings of the National Academy of Sciences.*)

lipids have been made at room temperature and the lipids can be expected to occupy significantly larger areas at the higher temperature. A control experiment which has not been performed is the determination of the spectrum of a micellar solution of lipids in which the micelles are *the same size* as those postulated in the model of Tiffany and Blough; it is possible that this would not differ significantly from the erythrocyte membrane trace. Recent work by Lesslauer *et al.* (1972) indicates that the introduction of a bulky label into a lipid may cause a considerable change in the interactions of the membrane lipids. The above comments, rather than attempting to detract from the results of Landsberger *et al.*, indicate that the problem of the structure and function of the lipids of influenza virus is still not yet fully determined. The model of Tiffany and Blough (1970a) has served a useful purpose in postulating the presence of a structural protein whose existence was subsequently confirmed in several laboratories, and in promoting the use of a simple geometrical approach to the determination of envelope structure which is proving of use with other viruses (see below).

There appear to be two main reasons for the discrepancy in the amounts of lipid in the two models (bilayer and micellar). The first is the use by Tiffany and Blough of the value obtained by Reimer *et al.* (1966) of 4.2×10^{-16} gm of protein per virus particle, based on a Lowry protein determination and particle counting. This figure was also used by Skehel and Schild (1971) in calculating the numbers of molecules of each of the polypeptides per virion and may contribute to the differences found between the results of these authors and those of Compans *et al.* (1970). Alternatively, one may estimate the total molecular weight of viral lipid from the observed percentages of lipid and RNA and the molecular weight of the RNA, assuming one genome-equivalent per particle. Taking the RNA content to be 1% (Frisch-Niggemeyer and Hoyle, 1956), the lipid content as 20% (Blough *et al.*, 1967), and the molecular weight of one genome of RNA as 3.9×10^6 (Skehel, 1971), then the total molecular weight of lipid is 7.8×10^7; for a cholesterol:phospholipid molar ratio of unity this gives 6.75×10^4 molecules each of cholesterol and phospholipids, and using the cross-sectional area figures of Levine and Wilkins (1971) we find a lipid bilayer area of 2.8×10^6 Å^2. The available area from Landsberger *et al.* (1971) is only 1.47×10^6 Å^2, again indicating an excess of lipid. The lower limit found for the molecular weight of influenza virus RNA by Pons and Hirst (1969) is 2.4×10^6; use of this figure reduces the bilayer area to 1.7×10^6 Å^2, which is still greater than the figure of Landsberger *et al.*, and does not allow for the space occupied by the proximal ends of the spikes inserted into the outer leaflet of the bilayer. If we are to be able to bring the lipid areas calculated by different methods into agreement, it would seem necessary at least to reassess the figure for the proportion of RNA in the virion, and preferably the amount of protein per particle also. The second reason for the discrepancy between the two models is the value of 250×10^6 for the total molecular weight of the virion used by Compans *et al.* (1970) in calculating the numbers of constituent polypeptides. This is much lower than the value calculated from the protein analysis of Reimer *et al.* (1966) of about 360×10^6.

The major difference still remaining between the two basic models is the question of whether the spikes are supported by "stalks" penetrating the lipid layer, or whether they float in the outer half of the lipid bilayer, stabilized partly by hydrophobic interactions between their bases and the acyl chains of the lipids surrounding them, and partly by electrostatic repulsive forces between the exposed parts of the spikes. Proteins traversing a membrane have been found in other systems (Bretscher, 1971), and such an interdigitated polypeptide would simplify the assembly problem.

Despite the considerable volume of knowledge which has been amassed on the paramyxoviruses, in particular on SV5 by Choppin and his co-workers (Compans *et al.*, 1966; Caliguiri *et al.*, 1969; Chen *et al.*, 1971; Klenk and Choppin, 1969a,b, 1970a,b, 1971; Klenk *et al.*, 1970a), no model comparable to that described above for orthomyxoviruses has yet been produced. It seems likely, however, that the role of lipids in the structure of the paramyxovirus envelope will closely parallel that in the orthomyxovirus envelope. Variation in the fatty acyl composition of lipids from different strains of Newcastle disease virus (Tiffany and Blough, 1969b) may indicate a lipid selection by envelope polypeptides such as was suggested for influenza virus (Tiffany and Blough, 1969a); differences of lipid composition between Newcastle disease virus and Sendai virus grown in the same host (Blough and Lawson, 1968) indicate that some process other than passive incorporation of normal cellular lipids takes place. If we perform the same kind of calculation on the extent of SV5 viral lipid in the form of a bilayer as given above for influenza virus, taking 0.9% RNA of molecular weight $5.7–6.8 \times 10^6$ and 20% lipid (Klenk and Choppin, 1969a) and a cholesterol:phospholipid molar ratio of 0.9 (Klenk and Choppin, 1969b), we find a bilayer area of $4.4–5.2 \times 10^6 \text{ Å}^2$, corresponding to a spherical shell of mean diameter 1180–1290 Å. These figures are roughly the same as those given by Klenk and Choppin (1969a) for the diameter of the whole virion, including spikes. The diameter of a bilayer lipid shell in these particles would probably be 920–1000 Å, allowing 100 Å for the spike length and 40 Å for the bilayer thickness, so it appears that there is at least 60% too much lipid for a bilayer. It would seem reasonable here to reassess the diameter of the particle as seen in the electron microscope, making due allowance for shrinkage during specimen preparation. The particle size range of other paramyxoviruses is generally taken to be 1500–3000 Å.

2. Rhabdoviruses

Rabies virus is a rhabdovirus consisting of five or six polypeptides (Sokol *et al.*, 1971; Neurath *et al.*, 1972), 24% lipid (Blough *et al.*, 1973), and a single continuous nucleocapsid. The major part of the nucleocapsid is helically coiled into a hollow cylinder, with the remainder coiled in reducing turns to form a hemispherical end-cap (Matsumoto, 1970). Electron micrographs occasionally show released particles with the lipid-containing envelope ballooning at one end (Hummeler *et al.*, 1967); it is not known whether this is an error of assembly, or an artifact of preparation for electron microscopy. It is also not known whether the envelope is rigid or sufficiently elastic to distribute itself smoothly over the core when the particle is free from the parent membrane, in cases where ballooning is seen during budding. It seems possible that some of these ballooned regions of envelope are merely eversions of the invaginated portion lining the cylinder of nucleocapsid. Hummeler *et al.* (1967) refer to the flat or slightly reentrant base as "nocked" like the butt end of an arrow, and their results suggest that this is the normal form of the base. The surface area of the envelope has been calculated to be about 5.5×10^6 Å^2, taking the cap to be a hemisphere and the base flat. A hexagonal arrangement of surface projections can be seen in electron micrographs, with a row separation of about 75 Å; from this it can be calculated that there are about 790 surface projections per virion, covering the sides and cap. It is not known at present whether the base carries projections or not. Kuwert *et al.* (1972) confirm that the surface area of the envelope is about 5×10^6 Å^2. Calculations have been made which suggest that there may be rather less lipid than required to form a bilayer over the entire surface of the virion (Blough *et al.*, 1973); it has also been found that treatment of rabies virus with diethyl ether in the presence of Tween 80 detergent reduced infectivity but left the majority of the particles morphologically intact (Crick and Brown, 1970). These observations suggest that there may be some penetration of proteins through the lipid region of the envelope, rather in the manner proposed for the lipovirus PM2 (Harrison *et al.*, 1971a), and such an arrangement seems also to be suggested by Neurath *et al.* (1972) in drawing attention to the close correspondence between the numbers of the various polypeptide components of the envelope. These aspects of the structure of rabies virus obviously require further investigation. Kuwert *et al.* (1972) suggest the presence of hexagonal subunits over the surface of the particle and calculate that there are 580 of these on a particle 2000 Å long, but at present there seems to be no obvious connection between this and the other observations mentioned above.

Despite work on the structure of the nucleocapsid (Nakai and Howatson, 1968), and identification of the polypeptides of the virion (Wagner et al., 1969), little seems to have been done to elucidate the structure of the envelope of another rhabdovirus, vesicular stomatitis virus. McSharry and Wagner (1971) have concluded from differences between viral and host lipids that a selection of lipids by polypeptides of vesicular stomatitis virus probably occurs, as in the case of myxoviruses (Tiffany and Blough, 1969a,b) and Sindbis virus (David, 1971), but as yet no specific interactions have been shown.

3. Lipoviruses

The marine bacteriophage PM2 contains 15% lipid, of which 90% is phospholipid consisting mainly of phosphatidylglycerol (67%) and phosphatidylethanolamine (27%) and a circular molecule of DNA of molecular weight 6×10^6 (Braunstein and Franklin, 1971). Harrison et al. (1971a) studied this virus intensively by combined electron microscopic, biochemical, and X-ray diffraction techniques. From the staining patterns using both positive and negative stains, it was possible to define "solvent excluding areas" occupied by nucleoprotein and lipid, and the electron density distribution in the solvent excluded areas was determined by X-ray diffraction. A deep minimum in electron density was found at a distance of 220 Å from the center of the particle and was considered to correspond to the hydrocarbon chain region of a lipid bilayer. Between 240 and 250 Å from the center was an area corresponding to the region of positive staining in thin section, which probably represented the polar head groups of the lipid interacted with protein. In the wide-angle X-ray scattering photograph shown in Fig. 25 the broad 4.6 Å band (middle) represents the lipid bilayer, while scatter in the 10 Å region is protein, and the inner 3.4 Å band is DNA. The lipid present in the virion (1.3×10^4 molecules, largely phospholipid) appears sufficient only to cover about 65% of the 220 Å shell as a bilayer. This suggests the presence of fenestrations or patches where protein might protrude through the lipid layer. The outer shell may be protein with a triangulation number of at least 12 or 13 (Caspar and Klug, 1962). Harrison et al. (1971a) suggest the virus is assembled de novo by condensation of protein and lipid around a core of DNA. A diagrammatic representation of the structure of PM2 is shown in Fig. 26.

4. Alphaviruses

Sindbis virus consists of only three proteins, two of which are envelope glycoproteins (of similar size or mobility in polyacrylamide gel electrophoresis), and the third a core protein associated with the single-

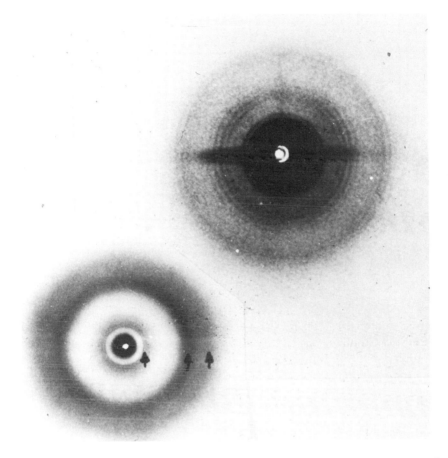

FIG. 25. X-ray diffraction pattern of marine bacteriophage PM2. Upper: small-angle pattern; the sharpness of the rings suggests the particles are isometric and identical. Lower: wide-angle pattern; arrows indicate sharp reflections at 12 Å, 4.6 Å, and 3.4 Å. (Reprinted from Harrison *et al.*, 1971a, by courtesy of Dr. R. M. Franklin and Macmillan Press.)

stranded RNA (Burge and Strauss, 1970; Schlesinger *et al.*, 1972); X-ray diffraction suggests that the envelope lipid is present in the form of a bilayer (Harrison *et al.*, 1971b).

Another member of this group, Semliki Forest virus, has been studied by Renkonen *et al.* (1971) and is found to have a cholesterol:phospholipid molar ratio near unity. These authors calculate, from data on the total molecular weight of the envelope, that there are about 10,000 cholesterol-phospholipid pairs in the viral envelope. Taking the electron-microscopic measurements of Acheson and Tamm (1967) and a cross-

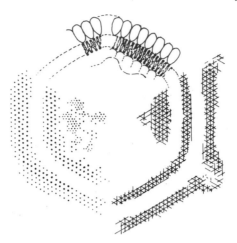

FIG. 26. Model of the structure of the lipid-containing bacteriophage PM2. (Reprinted from Harrison *et al.*, 1971a, by courtesy of Dr. R. M. Franklin and Macmillan Press.)

sectional area of about 100 Å^2 for each cholesterol-phospholipid pair, they calculate that 7000–8000 such pairs could be accommodated on the surface of the envelope; hence roughly twice this number could be incorporated in the form of a bilayer. These authors hence seem justified in concluding that a bilayer structure may be present. It may, however, be noted that according to the above calculation there is less lipid than required to form a complete bilayer, and there may therefore be penetration of a protein component through the lipid region, as was suggested above for rabies virus and influenza virus.

5. *Poxviruses*

Mitchiner (1969) suggested that the outer envelope of orf and vaccinia viruses is proteolipid in nature since these viruses are degraded by chloroform-methanol or 2-chloroethanol treatment, but not by carbon tetrachloride, acetone, ether, or lipolytic enzymes; however, treatment with ether produced a marked decrease in infectivity (Zwartouw, 1964). Mitchiner also proposed a model for the vaccinia envelope. This consists of (1) an internal envelope composed of a shell of laterally adherent blocks of envelope subunit protein, partially separated by deep clefts, and associated on both inner and outer faces and in the clefts with the polar groups of phospholipids and acyl chains of triglycerides; (2) an external membrane of closely associated protein and lipid. Spaces between the two membranes, and in the clefts, contain the cholesterol. However, although this model seems to agree with electron microscopic observations and resistance to disruptive agents, a number of objections can be made. The amount of lipid present (2.1% phospholipid, 1.7% neutral lipid, and 1.2% cholesterol) seems inadequate to form the two membrane structures as envisaged in this model. There also seems no reason to suppose that the phospholipid associates with the envelope subunit protein only through its polar groups, since specific protein-acyl chain interactions have been shown to exist in some systems (DePury and Collins, 1966; Ji and Benson, 1968). There is also no evidence that triglycerides and phospholipids associate on a one-to-one basis as implied in the model. The indicated width of clefts between protein units (15–20 Å) seems insufficient to contain a double layer of phospholipid and triglyceride, as well as the cholesterol.

A model of this type seems even less acceptable in the case of fowlpox virus, where only 16% of the total lipid is phospholipid; the overall lipid composition is predominantly neutral, with 23% triglyceride, 16.8% squalene, and 17.6% cholesteryl esters (White *et al.*, 1968). The biological significance of this unusual pattern of lipid has not been elucidated.

6. Leukoviruses

Rao *et al.* (1966) analyzed the lipids of avain myeloblastosis virus, finding that total lipid made up 35% of the viral mass, comprising 21.3% phospholipid, 11.7% cholesterol, and only 1.8% "neutral fat." These authors also described the manner of assembly of the virion as seen in the electron microscope: barely discernible electron-dense material, probably either viral RNA or ribonucleoprotein, accumulates close to the plasma membrane and forms a segment of a sphere, enclosing material of even lower electron density; a second shell (referred to in the mature particle as the "inner membrane"), continuous with the cytoplasm, forms around the first, and during budding both these structures are enclosed in an external envelope continuous with the plasma membrane. Previous studies (Bonar and Beard, 1959) had established the dry weight of the virion as 7.5×10^{-16} gm, giving a lipid mass of 2.6×10^{-16} gm per virion; the mean overall diameter of the particle is 1000 Å. Using these figures, taking the average molecular weight of lipid to be 750 and the cross-sectional area per lipid molecule to be 88 Å^2, and assuming that the lipid is contained in a bimolecular lipid leaflet at the periphery of the virus particle, Rao *et al.* (1966) calculate that only 30% of the viral lipid can be accommodated in a shell of this size. It therefore appears that a large part of the lipid must be in the interior of the particle, possibly in the "inner membrane." This calculation is open to question since it takes much too high a value for the area per molecule, and seems to have confused the average molecular weight of all lipids with that of phospholipid; however a recalculation using the lipid area figures of Levine and Wilkins (1971) shows there are 1.45×10^5 molecules of cholesterol and 1.34×10^5 molecules of phospholipid per virion and these occupy an area of 5.67×10^6 Å^2 in the form of a bilayer. The area of bilayer forming a spherical shell 1000 Å in external diameter is 2.8×10^6 Å^2, indicating that there is twice as much lipid in the virion as can be accommodated in this single spherical shell. The lipid shell of the outer membrane may in fact be even smaller, since this calculation does not take into account the size of the external projections of the envelope.

7. Nuclear Polyhedrosis Virus of Lymantria dispar

Chemical analysis of this insect virus indicated a lipid content of only 1.3%; however this low value may depend on the virus isolation technique or the lipid extraction procedure used. Alternatively, the apparent viral content may be low because of multigenomic particles or it may be low if not all capsids are enveloped.

Harrap (1969) suggests that the envelope of nuclear polyhedrosis virus is composed of an outer layer, presumably of protein, showing no regularity of structure, covering a layer of hexagonally packed subunits 200 Å in diameter beneath which is a bilayer of lipid 40 Å thick. The nucleic acid is complexed with protein to form a rodlike structure; this is encased by an inner protein shell composed of structural subunits 20–25 Å across packed in a rhomboidal lattice. A tentative model of this complex virus is presented in Fig. 27. Further confirmation of the envelope structure will have to await more detailed studies of purified virus from insect tissue culture.

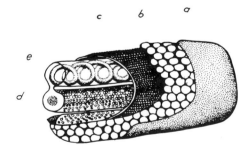

FIG. 27. Schematic representation of an enveloped bundle of *Lymantria dispar* nuclear polyhedrosis virus. a. surface layer; b. peplomers; c. virus membrane; d. virus capsid; e. coiled internal component. a, b, and c constitute the viral envelope; d and e represent the nucleocapsid. (Courtesy of Dr. K. A. Harrap.)

C. Factors Influencing the Composition of Viral Lipids

In concluding this section, we may list some of the factors most likely to influence the composition of viral lipids; some of these have already been covered in greater detail above.

1. Envelope Structural Polypeptides

Irrespective of the type of model favored for the structure of the envelope of a lipid-containing virus (i.e., basically a lipid-bilayer shell or a lipoprotein-complex structure), some lateral interaction of lipid and protein takes place. The closeness of packing of lipid acyl chains with nonpolar side chain regions of protein will be determined largely by the sequence and conformation of the amino acids in these regions, and this interaction will in turn influence the nature and degree of cohesion between other neighboring lipid molecules. The great importance of unsaturated chains in promoting or preventing close packing of lipid molecules in membranes has been stressed by Vandenheuvel (1963).

2. Alterations in Host Cell Catabolic and Biosynthetic Pathways

Host cell biosynthesis and catabolism of lipid during viral infection have not yet been extensively explored; however, compositional analyses of a variety of viruses and their host cell membranes show differences in lipid polar groups and precursors of cholesterol. Recent studies on virus-infected cells and uninfected controls reveal an uncoupling of phospholipid and neutral lipid biosynthesis which might account for some of the differences seen in viral lipids (see Section V,A).

3. Environmental Factors

Free fatty acids inoculated into embryonated eggs before infection with influenza virus (Blough and Tiffany, 1969) or added to tissue culture fluids (Klenk and Choppin, 1970a) were incorporated into the virion; differences in viral morphology and hemagglutinating ability were noted with branched-chain phytanic acid (Blough and Tiffany, 1969). Similarly, vitamin A alters the morphology of influenza virus from spherical to filamentous particles and this is accompanied by changes in polar lipids and acyl chains (Blough, 1963; Blough et al., 1967). This points to the necessity, when comparing viruses and membranes, of using the same batches of serum and medium throughout a series of experiments.

4. Virally-Coded Catabolic Enzymes

The absence of detectable sialic acid in either glycolipids or glyco-proteins of myxoviruses following release from the host cell, despite the demonstration of its presence in areas of the host surface membrane not involved in budding, has been discussed above. Klenk and Choppin (1970b) have suggested that viral neuraminidase is responsible for the removal of sialic acid, rather than a host enzyme, since vesicular stomatitis virus, grown in the same host but possessing no viral neuraminidase, has the same hematoside (neuraminosyl-galactosyl-glucosyl-ceramide) as its host cell plasma membrane.

5. Physiological State of the Host Cell

In cells where sterol metabolism has been altered by long passage in tissue culture, some functions such as the ability to desaturate desmo-sterol have been lost; this results in the replacement of cholesterol by desmosterol in vesicular stomatitis virus as well as in the mouse L cell in which it was grown (Bates and Rothblat, 1972). The biological ac-tivity and morphology of the virion were in this case unaffected. A virion may also mimic the acyl chain composition of the host cell in those cul-tured cells which have lost the ability to chain elongate or desaturate fatty acids. The flexibility of higher microorganisms, such as *Mycoplasma* strain Y, is striking in this respect; 97% of all its fatty acyl chains may be replaced with elaidic (*trans*-oleic) acid with little effect on growth (Rodwell, 1968).

6. Multiplicity of Infection

Infection of chick embryo fibroblasts with 10–30 plaque-forming units (pfu) per cell of influenza virus causes an inhibition of cell lipid metab-olism at 4 hours after infection, whereas infection with 3–5 pfu per cell delays the onset of this inhibition until 7 hours after infection (Blough and Weinstein, 1972). In addition, infection at multiplicities sufficient to produce incomplete virus (von Magnus, 1951) causes an immediate alteration in host cell phospholipid and neutral lipid metabolism.

VII. Functional Role of Lipids

Despite the considerable accumulation of knowledge on the nature, amount, and composition of lipids of viruses and their hosts, it must be admitted that the role played by these components is still largely un-known. Several possible functions for lipids are suggested below; the list is not considered to be exhaustive, and much more work obviously remains to be done before these suggestions can be conclusively proved or disproved.

A. Molecular Architecture of the Envelope

As mentioned earlier, viruses which possess lipid may do so in order to preserve or provide configurational changes in those polypeptides which are required for assembly of the envelope. Loss of viral activity on treatment with various agents, e.g., organic solvents (Andrewes and Horstmann, 1949), bile salts (Smith, 1939), or phospholipase C (Mizutani and Mizutani, 1964; Simpson and Hauser, 1966; Friedman and Pastan, 1969; Schulze, 1970), is brought about by removal of lipid and subsequent breakup of the envelope. The presence of a coherent envelope is in many cases necessary for normal levels of infectivity of the virus, presumably because the envelope carries the specific groups responsible for attachment to the host cell surface or for triggering the engulfment of the particle.

B. Transport

From experiments on the release of polypeptides by detergent, and the reaggregation of the envelope subunits on the removal of detergent, some at least of the viral envelope proteins have been shown to have extensive hydrophobic regions on their surfaces (Laver and Valentine, 1969). It seems unlikely that these regions will only be exposed by a configurational change after the proteins have reached the assembly site of the virus. Lipids could therefore fulfill a critical role in assisting the transport of these molecules from the site of synthesis to the site of assembly by shielding the hydrophobic portion. This would entail the formation of a partial micelle about these regions of the polypeptides; the lipids involved might not in all cases be those subsequently incorporated into the viral envelope, since the lipids conferring structural integrity on the envelope may requre properties other than solely that of solubilizing the polypeptide. This transport role could apply to both "template" type assembly and to *de novo* synthesis of the envelope.

C. Assembly

In Section VI a model of envelope assembly was discussed in which external envelope proteins were fed through the lipid region of the template membrane, probably mediated by a local phase transition of membrane lipids to a micellar form. Once assembled, the viral lipids confer the unique plasticity seen in enveloped viruses, and the surface projections would be supported in a matrix which permitted sufficient lateral mobility for electrostatic repulsive forces between adjacent projections to maintain a uniform spacing (Hoyle, 1968; Schulze, 1972). This would be especially true if the lipid-bilayer model proves to be correct. In either a micellar or a lamellar configuration, polar groups of lipid would be on the exterior and interior of the lipid region of the envelope and could help to maintain the spacing of the projections as well as binding the nucleocapsid to the budding envelope (Schulze, 1972). Recent studies have shown that monovalent hemagglutinin solubilized from Newcastle disease virus, which had lost its ability to agglutinate erythrocytes, regained this biological activity when mixed with phosphatidylethanolamine, indicating reforming of a structure with functional groups directed outward (Iinuma et al., 1971). Studies on the reconstitution of envelope subunits and surface projections have important biological implications, and this field merits further investigation. A report that lipid restores the infectivity of RNA from Newcastle disease virus (Dhar et al., 1963) has never been verified.

D. RELEASE

Naked herpesvirus capsids closely resemble non-lipid-containing viruses such as adenovirus or polyoma virus, which are also assembled in the nucleus but which show full infectivity without any envelope. Both naked and enveloped herpesvirus particles are found in infected cells, but only enveloped particles are found in extracellular fluids (Roizman et al., 1968). It is not altogether clear whether only enveloped particles are infectious (Siegert and Falke, 1966; Watson et al., 1964). The question may therefore be raised of why herpesvirus needs an envelope. During budding of the herpesvirus core through the inner nuclear membrane, virally coded polypeptides are incorporated into the membrane, which then forms the envelope. Morgan et al. (1959) have indicated that the enveloped virus is enclosed in vacuoles which are released from the cell by a process of "reverse phagocytosis." This is questioned by Schwartz and Roizman (1969), who found evidence for a network of branching tubules established in the cytoplasm of productively infected HEp-2 cells following infection with herpes simplex virus. The membranes lining these ducts were continuous at one end with the outer nuclear envelope, and at the other end with the cell surface membrane, thus offering a means of egress from the cell for the virus without being exposed to the degradative or uncoating enzymes of the cytoplasm. The observations of Darlington and Moss (1968) are consistent with this hypothesis, but as yet no other confirmation of this mode of release has been reported. Schwartz and Roizman (1969) also suggest that the vacuoles containing virus seen by other workers are in fact cross sections of the tubules.

Two possible reasons for the acquisition of the envelope can be formulated. (1) The virus can only penetrate the inner nuclear membrane by this means, but having done so can escape from the cell by direct opening of the cytoplasmic tubules to the medium at the plasma membrane. (2) The envelope acts as a carrier for virally coded polypeptides which play some active part in the release process, such as by inducing vacuole formation in the cytoplasm, and expulsion of virus from the cell within vacuoles.

E. Fusion

Herpesvirus and some paramyxoviruses (e.g., Sendai and Newcastle disease virus) are capable of causing cell fusion, one form of which— "fusion from without" (Bratt and Gallaher, 1969)—arises from direct contact between the virus particles and the surface membranes of the cells. Monoacylated phospholipids such as lysophosphatidylcholine have been shown to be capable of producing membrane fusion (Howell and Lucy, 1969, Poole et al., 1970), and it has been suggested that similar monoacylated phospholipids are responsible for cell fusion and hemolysis during viral infection (Rubin, 1967), and that the virus may carry a lipoid "fusion factor"; however, such lipids do not accumulate in cells infected with herpesvirus or Newcastle disease virus (Gallaher et al., 1973) and do not make up significant amounts of the lipids of Newcastle disease or Sendai viruses (Blough and Lawson, 1968). Lysophosphatidylcholine has been shown not to be important in fusion of cells by Sendai (Falke et al., 1967) or SV5 viruses (Elsbach et al., 1969). In addition, exogenous monoacylated phospholipid inactivates the "fusion factor," suggesting that an intact viral envelope is necessary for fusion to occur (Kohn and Klibansky, 1967; Hosaka, 1970). While glycolipids have also been implicated as having a function in cell fusion (Blough and Lawson, 1968; Klenk and Choppin, 1970b), there is no supporting evidence for this at present. The possibility that the virus contains degradative enzymes, e.g., a sphingomyelinase (Moberly et al., 1958; Hosaka, 1958), has not been verified by isolating such an enzyme from the virus and doing *in vitro* studies.

F. Penetration

In those viruses which fuse to cell membranes, lipids probably facilitate entry of the nucleocapsid (Morgan and Rose, 1968) by producing phase transitions at the site of entry (Bächi and Howe, 1972). This might involve the same type of mechanism as in virus-mediated cell fusion, but may involve a different "fusion factor" in the case of viruses which do not cause true fusion.

VIII. Conclusion

In the preceding pages we have attempted to indicate the large number of classes of lipid-containing viruses, their manner of assembly, and their lipid compositions, where this has been determined. It can be seen from Table II that the lipid analyses thus far available are few and incomplete, and do not in most cases cover all the common hosts for a given virus. It seems that we shall not be able to form a true picture of the function of lipids in the formation and structure of viruses until we have more consistent information on a number of fronts:

(1) More thorough compositional analyses are needed for many viruses; where extensive analysis has been carried out, confirmation is required from other workers in the field, including virus grown in different hosts.

(2) A thorough investigation is required on the vexing question of whether or not the lipid composition of template viruses is the same as that of their parent membranes; this involves more detailed knowledge of the changes in host cell lipid metabolism induced by viral infection, and hence of the varieties and relative amounts of different classes of lipids available during assembly. The major difficulty appears to be obtaining samples of the lipids of the parent membrane from the infected cell, without also including those regions of membrane at which the virus is budding. If there is appreciable lateral mobility of lipids in the membrane at this time, this may not prove possible.

(3) Further examination of virus particles by physical techniques such as X-ray diffraction and spin resonance spectroscopy is needed to establish the structure of the particle, and hence the degree of interaction of structural proteins and lipid. Isolation of structural proteins and investigation of their lipid-binding properties may also give valuable information.

In view of the wide variation in the proportion of lipid in different viruses, it seems unlikely that any unified structural pattern will emerge which is capable of dealing with the virion as a whole. It is however possible that a common minimal structure will be discerned, upon which variations can be constructed. This may well be the lipid bilayer in association with an underlying layer of structural protein; where insufficient lipid is present in the virion to provide a complete bilayer shell, penetrating regions of protein can be expected, as suggested in structural models mentioned in Section VI. When too much lipid is present, the excess either may be accommodated in ill-defined association with the internal component of the virion or may form a concentric structure within the basic envelope.

ACKNOWLEDGMENTS

The senior author would like to thank Dr. Charles Pasternak, University of Oxford, and Dr. Ossi Renkonen, University of Helsinki, for the generous hospitality of their laboratories during the writing of this review. This review would also not have been possible without the enthusiastic and stimulating work of our colleagues Drs. W. R. Gallaher and D. B. Weinstein. This work was supported in part by the Commission on Influenza, Armed Forces Epidemiological Board, through the U. S. Army Medical Research and Development Command, Department of the Army (Research Contract No. DADA-17-67-C-7128), and by a Senior Post-Doctoral Fellowship of the National Multiple Sclerosis Society to H. A. Blough.

We should also like to thank Drs. P. W. Choppin, A. Granoff, K. A. Harrap, C. Howe and B. Ruizman for permission to use unpublished data for inclusion in this review, Drs. M. S. Bretscher, W. R. Gallaher, K. A. Harrap, J. B. Marsh, C. A. Pasternak and H. Pollard for their stimulating discussions and criticism, and Dr. W. R. Gallaher in particular for his critical reading of the manuscript and many helpful suggestions. In addition, we are grateful to Ms. C. Court for the excellent technical illustrations.

References

Acheson, N. H., and Tamm, I. (1967). *Virology* **32**, 128.
Ahmed, M. E., Black, L. M., Perkins, E. G., Walker, B. L., and Kummerow, F. A. (1964). *Biochem. Biophys. Res. Commun.* **17**, 103.
Almeida, J. D., and Waterson, A. P. (1967). *J. Gen. Microbiol.* **46**, 107.
Almeida, J. D., and Waterson, A. P. (1970). *In* "The Biology of Large RNA Viruses" (R. D. Barry and B. W. J. Mahy, eds.), p. 27. Academic Press, New York.
Andrewes, C. H., and Horstmann, D. M. (1949). *J. Gen. Microbiol.* **3**, 290.
Apostolov, K., and Flewett, T. H. (1969). *J. Gen. Virol.* **4**, 365.
Archetti, I., Jemolo, A., and Steve-Bocciarelli, D. (1967). *Arch. Gesamte Virusforsch.* **20**, 133.
Armbruster, O., and Beiss, U. (1958). *Z. Naturforsch. B* **13**, 75.
Asher, Y., Heller, M., and Becker, Y. (1969). *J. Gen. Virol.* **4**, 65.
Bächi, T., and Howe, C. (1972). Submitted for publication.
Bächi, T., Gerhard, W., Lindenmann, J., and Mühlethaler, K. (1969). *J. Virol.* **4**, 769.

Bailey, J. M., Gey, G. O., and Gey, M. K. (1964). *Proc. Soc. Exp. Biol. Med.* **113**, 747.

Bates, S. R., and Rothblat, G. H. (1972). *J. Virol.* **9**, 883.

Baumann, W. J., and Mangold, H. K. (1966). *Biochim. Biophys. Acta* **116**, 570.

Baumann, W. J., Takahashi, T., Mangold, H. K., and Schmid, H. H. O. (1970). *Biochim. Biophys. Acta* **202**, 468.

Becker, W. B., McIntosh, K., Dees, J. H., and Chanock, R. M. (1967). *J. Virol.* **1**, 1019.

Ben-Porat, T., and Kaplan, A. S. (1971). *Virology* **45**, 252.

Ben-Porat, T., and Kaplan, A. S. (1972). *Nature (London)* **235**, 165.

Bergold, G. H., and Wellington, E. F. (1954). *J. Bacteriol.* **67**, 210.

Berkaloff, A., and Thiéry, J. P. (1963). *J. Microsc. (Paris)* **2**, 583.

Best, R. J. (1968). *Advan. Virus Res.* **13**, 65.

Blough, H. A. (1963). *Virology* **19**, 349.

Blough, H. A. (1964). *Cell. Biol. Myxovirus Infect., Ciba Found. Symp., 1964* p. 120.

Blough, H. A. (1968). *Wistar Inst. Symp. Monogr.* **8**, 55.

Blough, H. A. (1969). *Bull. WHO* **41**, 487.

Blough, H. A. (1971a). *J. Gen. Virol.* **12**, 317.

Blough, H. A. (1971b). *Proc. Int. Congr. Virol., 2nd, 1971* p. 133.

Blough, H. A., and Lawson, D. E. M. (1968). *Virology* **36**, 286.

Blough, H. A., and Merlie, J. P. (1970). *Virology* **40**, 685.

Blough, H. A., and Smith, W. R. (1973). *J. Gen. Virol.* (in press).

Blough, H. A., and Tiffany, J. M. (1969). *Proc. Nat. Acad. Sci. U. S.* **62**, 242.

Blough, H. A., and Weinstein, D. B. (1973). *In* "Biology of the Fibroblast" Sigrid Jusélius Fd. Symp. (E. Kulonen and J. Pikkarainen, eds.). Academic Press, London. (in press).

Blough, H. A., Weinstein, D. B., Lawson, D. E. M., and Kodicek, E. (1967). *Virology* **33**, 459.

Blough, H. A., Merlie, J. P., and Tiffany, J. M. (1969). *Biochem. Biophys. Res. Commun.* **34**, 831.

Blough, H. A., Aaslestad, H. G., and Tiffany, J. M. (1973). In press.

Bonar, R. A., and Beard, J. W. (1959). *J. Nat. Cancer Inst.* **23**, 183.

Bonissol, C., and Sisman, J. (1968). *C. R. Acad. Sci., Ser. D* **267**, 1337.

Brakke, M. K. (1967). *In* "Methods in Virology" (K. Maramorosch and H. Koprowski, eds.), Vol. 2, p. 119. Academic Press, New York.

Bratt, M. A., and Gallaher, W. R. (1969). *Proc. Nat. Acad. Sci. U. S.* **64**, 536.

Braunstein, S. N., and Franklin, R. M. (1971). *Virology* **43**, 685.

Bretscher, M. S. (1971). *J. Mol. Biol.* **58**, 775.

Burge, B. W., and Huang, A. S. (1970). *J. Virol.* **6**, 176.

Burge, B. W., and Strauss, J. H. (1970). *J. Mol. Biol.* **42**, 452.

Burton, R. M. (1963). *J. Neurochem.* **10**, 503.

Caliguiri, L. A., Klenk, H.-D., and Choppin, P. W. (1969). *Virology* **39**, 460.

Carver, D. H., and Marcus, P. I. (1968). *Abstr. 68th Annu. Meet. Amer. Soc. Microbiol.* V216.

Caspar, D. L. D., and Klug, A. (1962). *Cold Spring Harbor Symp. Quant. Biol.* **27**, 1.

Caspar, D. L. D., Dulbecco, R., Klug, A., Lwoff, A., Stoker, M. G. P., Tournier, P., and Wildy, P. (1962). *Cold Spring Harbor Symp. Quant. Biol.* **27**, 49.

Chen, C., Compans, R. W., and Choppin, P. W. (1971). *J. Gen. Virol.* **11**, 53.

Clamp, J. R., Bhatti, T., and Chambers, R. E. (1971). *Methods Biochem. Anal.* **19**, 229.

Compans, R. W. (1971). *Nature (London), New Biol.* **229**, 114.

Compans, R. W., and Dimmock, N. J. (1969). *Virology* **39**, 499.

Compans, R. W., Holmes, K. V., Dales, S., and Choppin, P. W. (1966). *Virology* **30**, 411.

Compans, R. W., Klenk, H.-D., Caliguiri, L. A., and Choppin, P. W. (1970). *Virology* **42**, 880.

Cota-Robles, E., Espejo, R. T., and Haywood, P. W. (1968). *J. Virol.* **2**, 56.

Craven, D. A., and Gehrke, C. W. (1968). *J. Chromatogr.* **37**, 414.

Crick, J., and Brown, F. (1970). *In* "The Biology of Large RNA Viruses" (R. D. Barry and B. W. J. Mahy, eds.), p. 133. Academic Press, New York.

Dahlberg, J. E., and Franklin, R. M. (1970). *Virology* **42**, 1073.

Dales, S. (1963). *J. Cell Biol.* **18**, 51.

Dales, S., and Mosbach, E. H. (1968). *Virology* **35**, 564.

Dales, S., and Siminovitch, L. (1961). *J. Biophys. Biochem. Cytol.* **10**, 475.

Darlington, R. W., and Moss, L. H. (1968). *J. Virol.* **2**, 48.

Darlington, R. W., Granoff, A., and Breeze, D. C. (1966). *Virology* **29**, 149.

David, A. E. (1971). *Virology* **46**, 711.

De Bernard, L. (1958). *Bull. Soc. Chim. Biol.* **40**, 161.

DePury, G. G., and Collins, F. D. (1966). *Chem. Phys. Lipids* **1**, 1.

de Thé, G., and O'Connor, T. E. (1966). *Virology* **28**, 713.

Devauchelle, G., Bergoin, M., and Vago, C. (1970). *C. R. Acad. Sci., Ser. D* **271**, 1138.

Devauchelle, G., Bergoin, M., and Vago, C. (1971). *J. Ultrastruct. Res.* **37**, 301.

Dhar, M. M., Babbar, O. P., and Choud'hury, B. L. (1963). *Experientia* **12**, 100.

Dittmer, J. C., and Wells, M. A. (1969). *In* "Methods in Enzymology" (J. M. Lowenstein, ed.), Vol. 14, p. 483. Academic Press, New York.

Dourmashkin, R. R., and Simons, P. J. (1961). *J. Ultrastruct. Res.* **5**, 505.

Eibl, H., Hill, E. E., and Lands, W. E. M. (1970). *Eur. J. Biochem.* **9**, 250.

Elsbach, P., Holmes, K. V., and Choppin, P. W. (1969). *Proc. Soc. Exp. Biol. Med.* **130**, 903.

Engelman, D. M. (1969). *Nature (London)* **223**, 1279.

Espejo, R. T., and Canelo, E. S. (1968a). *Virology* **34**, 738.

Espejo, R. T., and Canelo, E. S. (1968b). *J. Virol.* **2**, 1235.

Eylar, E. H. (1966) *J Theor. Biol.* **10**, 80.

Falke, D., Schiefer, H.-G., and Stoffel, W. (1967). *Z. Naturforsch. B* **22**, 1360.

Fenner, F. (1968). "Biology of Animal Viruses," Vol. 1, Chapters 1–3. Academic Press, New York.

Folch, J., Lees, M., and Sloane Stanley, G. H. (1957). *J. Biol. Chem.* **226**, 497.

Franklin, R. M. (1962). *Progr. Med. Virol.* **4**, 1.

Freeman, C. P., and West, D. (1966). *J. Lipid Res.* **7**, 324.

Friedman, R. M., and Pastan, I. (1969). *J. Mol. Biol.* **40**, 107.

Frisch-Niggemeyer, W., and Hoyle, L. (1956). *J. Hyg.* **54**, 201.

Frommhagen, L. H., Knight, C. A., and Freeman, N. K. (1959). *Virology* **8**, 176.

Furukawa, T., Plotkin, S. A., Sedwick, W. D., and Profeta, M. L. (1967). *Proc. Soc. Exp. Biol. Med.* **126**, 745.

Fuscaldo, A. A., Aaslestad, H. G., and Hoffman, E. J. (1971). *J. Virol.* **7**, 233.

Gallaher, W. R., and Blough, H. A. (1972). *Abstr. 72nd Annu. Meet. Amer. Soc. Microbiol.* V179.

Gallaher, W. R., Weinstein, D. B., and Blough, H. A. (1973). Submitted for publication.

Gelderblom, H., Bauer, H., and Graf, T. (1972). *Virology* **47**, 416.

Gourley, R. N. (1971). *J. Gen. Virol.* **12**, 65.

Granoff, A. (1969). *Curr. Top. Microbiol. Immunol.* **50**, 107.

Green, D. E., and Perdue, J. F. (1966). *Proc. Nat. Acad. Sci. U. S.* **55**, 1295.

Grimes, W. J., and Burge, B. W. (1971). *J. Virol.* **7**, 309.

Grimley, P. M., and Friedman, R. M. (1970). *Exp. Mol. Pathol.* **12**, 1.

Hakomori, S.-I. (1970). *Proc. Nat. Acad. Sci. U. S.* **67**, 1741.

Hakomori, S.-I., Saito, T., and Vogt, P. K. (1971). *Virology* **44**, 609.

Harrap, K. A. (1969). Ph.D. Dissertation, Oxford University.

Harrison, S. C., Caspar, D. L. D., Camerini-Otero, R. D., and Franklin, R. M. (1971a). *Nature (London), New Biol.* **229**, 197.

Harrison, S. C., David, A. E., Jumblatt, J., and Darnell, J. E. (1971b). *J. Mol. Biol.* **60**, 523.

Haslam, E. A., Cheyne, I. A., and White, D. O. (1969). *Virology* **39**, 118.

Haslam, E. A., Hampson, A. W., Egan, J. A., and White, D. O. (1970a). *Virology* **42**, 555.

Haslam, E. A., Hampson, A. W., Radiskevics, I., and White, D. O. (1970b). *Virology* **42**, 566.

Heine, U., Ablashi, D. V., and Armstrong, G. R. (1971). *Cancer Res.* **31**, 1019.

Heine, J. W., Spear, P. J., and Roizman, B. (1972). *J. Virol.* **9**, 431.

Hess, H. H., and Rolde, E. (1964). *J. Biol. Chem.* **239**, 3215.

Heydrick, F. P., Comer, J. F., and Wachter, R. F. (1970). *J. Virol.* **7**, 642.

Holland, J. J., and Kiehn, E. D. (1970). *Science* **167**, 202.

Holmes, I. H., and Warburton, M. F. (1967). *Lancet* **2**, 1233.

Horne, R. W., Waterson, A. P., Wildy, P., and Farnham, A. E. (1960). *Virology* **11**, 79.

Hosaka, Y. (1958). *Biken J.* **1**, 90.

Hosaka, Y. (1970). *In* "Biology of Large RNA Viruses" (R. D. Barry and B. W. J. Mahy, eds.), p. 684. Academic Press, New York.

Hotz, G., and Schäfer, W. (1955). *Z. Naturforsch. B* **10**, 1.

Howatson, A. F. (1970). *Advan. Virus Res.* **16**, 196.

Howell, J. I., and Lucy, J. A. (1969). *FEBS Lett.* **4**, 147.

Hoyle, L. (1950). *J. Hyg.* **48**, 277.

Hoyle, L. (1952). *J. Hyg.* **50**, 229.

Hoyle, L. (1968). *Virol. Monogr.* **4**, 1.

Hoyle, L., Jolles, B., and Mitchell, R. G. (1954). *J. Hyg.* **52**, 119.

Hummeler, K., Koprowski, H., and Wiktor, T. J. (1967). *J. Virol.* **1**, 152.

Ie, T. S. (1964). *Neth. J. Plant Pathol.* **70**, 114.

Iinuma, M., Yoshida, T., Nagai, Y., Maeno, K., Matsumoto, T., and Hoshino, M. (1971). *Virology* **46**, 663.

Isacson, P., and Koch, A. E. (1965). *Virology* **27**, 129.

Ji, T. H., and Benson, A. A. (1968). *Biochim. Biophys. Acta* **150**, 686.

Johnson, M., and Mora, P. T. (1967). *Virology* **31**, 230.

Kaplan, A. S. (1957). *Virology* **4**, 435.

Kaplan, A. S. (1969). *Virol. Monogr.* **5**, 1.

Kates, M., Allison, A. C., Tyrrell, D. A. J., and James, A. T. (1961). *Biochim. Biophys. Acta* **52**, 455.

Kavanau, J. L. (1963). *Nature (London)* **198**, 525.

Kendal, A. P., Biddle, F., and Belyavin, G. (1968). *Biochim. Biophys. Acta* **165**, 419.

Kendal, A. P., Apostolov, K., and Belyavin, G. (1969). *J. Gen. Virol.* **5**, 141.

Kilbourne, E. D. (1963). *Progr. Med. Virol.* **5**, 79.

Kitajima, E. W. (1965). *Virology* **26**, 89.

Kitajima, E. W., and Costa, A. S. (1966). *Virology* **29**, 523.

Klenk, H.-D., and Choppin, P. W. (1969a). *Virology* **37**, 155.

Klenk, H.-D., and Choppin, P. W. (1969b). *Virology* **38**, 255.

Klenk, H.-D., and Choppin, P. W. (1970a). *Virology* **40**, 939.

Klenk, H.-D., and Choppin, P. W. (1970b). *Proc. Nat. Acad. Sci. U. S.* **66**, 57.
Klenk, H.-D., and Choppin, P. W. (1971). *J. Virol.* **7**, 416.
Klenk, H.-D., Caliguiri, L. A., and Choppin, P. W. (1970a). *Virology* **42**, 473.
Klenk, H.-D., Compans, R. W., and Choppin, P. W. (1970b). *Virology* **42**, 1158.
Klenk, H.-D., Rott, R., and Becht, H. (1972). *Virology* **47**, 579.
Kohn, A., and Klibansky, C. (1967). *Virology* **31**, 385.
Kritchevsky, D., and Shapiro, I. L. (1967). In "Methods in Virology" (K. Maramorosch and H. Koprowski, eds.), Vol. 3, p. 77. Academic Press, New York.
Kuwert, E., Böhme, U., Lichfeld, K. G., and Böhme, W. (1972). *Zentralbl. Bakteriol., Parasitenk., Infektionskr., Hyg., Abt. 1: Orig. A* **219**, 39.
Lands, W. E. M. (1965). *Annu. Rev. Biochem.* **34**, 313.
Landsberger, F. R., Lenard, J., Paxton, J., and Compans, R. W. (1971). *Proc. Nat. Acad. Sci. U. S.* **68**, 2579.
Laver, W. G. (1964). *J. Mol. Biol.* **9**, 109.
Laver, W. G., and Valentine, R. C. (1969). *Virology* **38**, 105.
Ledeen, R. (1966). *J. Amer. Oil Chem. Soc.* **43**, 57.
Lerner, R. A., and Hodge, L. D. (1969). *Proc. Nat. Acad. Sci. U. S.* **64**, 544.
Lesslauer, W., Cain, J. E., and Blasie, J. K. (1972). *Proc. Nat. Acad. Sci. U. S.* **69**, 1499.
Levine, Y. K., and Wilkins, M. H. F. (1971). *Nature (London) New Biol.* **230**, 69.
Lucy, J. A. (1964). *J. Theor. Biol.* **7**, 360.
Lwoff, A., Horne, R. W., and Tournier, P. (1962). *Cold Spring Harbor Symp. Quant. Biol.* **27**, 51.
Lynen, F., Oesterholt, D., Schweitzer, E., and Willeke, K. (1968). "Cellular Compartmentalization and Control of Fatty Acid Metabolism," Fed. Eur. Biochem. Soc. Symp., p. 1, Universitetsforlaget, Oslo.
McCombs, R. M., Brunschwig, J. P., and Rawls, W. E. (1968). *Exp. Mol. Pathol.* **9**, 27.
McSharry, J. J., and Wagner, R. R. (1971). *J. Virol.* **7**, 59.
Marinetti, G. V., ed. (1967). "Lipid Chromatographic Analysis," Vol. 1. Dekker, New York.
Marsh, J. B., and Weinstein, D. B. (1966). *J. Lipid Res.* **7**, 574.
Matsumoto, S. (1970). *Advan. Virus Res.* **16**, 257.
Miller, H. K., and Schlesinger, R. W. (1955). *J. Immunol.* **75**, 155.
Milne, R. G. (1970). *J. Gen. Virol.* **6**, 267.
Mitchiner, M. B. (1969). *J. Gen. Virol.* **5**, 211.
Mizutani, H. (1963). *Nature (London)* **198**, 109.
Mizutani, H., and Mizutani, H. (1964). *Nature (London)* **204**, 781.
Moberly, M. L., Marinetti, G. V., Witter, R. F., and Morgan, H. R. (1958). *J. Exp. Med.* **107**, 87.
Morgan, C., and Rose, H. M. (1968). *J. Virol.* **2**, 925.
Morgan, C., Rose, H. M., and Moore, D. H. (1956). *J. Exp. Med.* **104**, 171.
Morgan, C., Rose, H. M., Holden, M., and Jones, E. P. (1959). *J. Exp. Med.* **110**, 643.
Morgan, C., Howe, C., and Rose, H. M. (1961). *J. Exp. Med.* **113**, 219.
Murphy, F. A., Halonen, P. E., and Harrison, A. K. (1968). *J. Virol.* **2**, 1223.
Murphy, F. A., Webb, P. A., Johnson, K. M., Whitfield, S. G., and Chappell, W. A. (1970). *J. Virol.* **6**, 507.
Nakai, T., and Howatson, A. F. (1968). *Virology* **35**, 268.
Nermut, M. V., (1970). *Acta Virol. (Prague), Engl. Ed.* **14**, 185.
Nermut, M. V., and Frank, H. (1971). *J. Gen. Virol.* **10**, 37.

Neurath, A. R., Vernon, S. K., Dobkin, M. B., and Rubin, B. A. (1972). *J. Gen. Virol.* **14,** 33.

Norrby, E. (1969). *Virol. Monogr.* **7,** 115.

Pasternak, C. A., and Bergeron, J. J. M. (1970). *Biochem. J.* **119,** 473.

Peters, D., and Müller, G. (1963). *Virology* **21,** 266.

Peters, D., Müller, G., and Geister, R. (1963). *Arch. Gesamte Virusforsch.* **13,** 435.

Pfefferkorn, E. R., and Hunter, H. S. (1963a). *Virology* **20,** 433.

Pfefferkorn, E. R., and Hunter, H. S. (1963b). *Virology* **20,** 446.

Plagemann, P. G. W. (1971). *J. Lipid Res.* **12,** 715.

Pollard, H., Scanu, A. M., and Taylor, E. W. (1969). *Proc. Nat. Acad. Sci. U. S.* **64,** 304.

Polson, A., and Russell, B. (1967). *In* "Methods in Virology" (K. Maramorosch and H. Koprowski, eds.), Vol. 2, p. 391. Academic Press, New York.

Pons, M., and Hirst, G. K. (1969). *Virology* **38,** 68.

Poole, A. R., Howell, J. I., and Lucy, J. A. (1970). *Nature (London)* **227,** 810.

Poste, G. (1970). *Advan. Virus Res.* **16,** 303.

Quigley, J. P., Rifkin, D. B., and Reich, E. (1971). *Virology* **46,** 106.

Rao, P. A., Bonar, R. A., and Beard, J. W. (1966). *Exp. Mol. Pathol.* **5,** 374.

Reimer, C. B., Baker, R. S., Newlin, T. E., and Havens, M. L. (1966). *Science* **152,** 1379.

Renkonen, O. (1967). *Advan. Lipid Res.* **5,** 329.

Renkonen, O., Kääriäinen, L., Simons, K., and Gahmberg, C. G. (1971). *Virology* **46,** 318.

Řimen, J., Korb, J., and Michlová, A. (1972). "Virus-Cell Interactions and Viral Antimetabolites," *Fed. Eur. Biochem. Soc. Symp.* (D. Shugar, ed.). **22,** 99.

Robinson, W. S., and Duesberg, P. M. (1968). *In* "Molecular Basis of Virology" (H. Fraenkel-Conrat, ed.), p. 255. Van Nostrand-Reinhold, Princeton, New Jersey.

Rodwell, A. (1968). *Science* **160,** 1350.

Roizman, B., Spring, S. B., and Schwartz, J. (1968). *Fed. Proc., Fed. Amer. Soc. Exp. Biol.* **28,** 1890.

Rott, R., Drzeniek, R., Saber, M. S., and Reichert, E. (1966). *Arch. Gesamte Virusforsch.* **19,** 273.

Rubin, H. (1967). *In* "The Specificity of Cell Surfaces" (B. D. Davis and L. Warren, eds.), p. 181. Prentice-Hall, Englewood Cliffs, New Jersey.

Scheele, C. M., and Pfefferkorn, E. R. (1969). *J. Virol.* **3,** 369.

Schlesinger, M. J., Schlesinger, S., and Burge, B. W. (1972). *Virology* **47,** 539.

Schulze, I. T. (1970). *Virology* **42,** 890.

Schulze, I. T. (1972). *Virology* **47,** 181.

Schwartz, J., and Roizman, B. (1969). *Virology* **38,** 42.

Segrest, J. P., Jackson, R. L., Andrews, E. P., and Marchesi, V. T. (1971). *Biochem. Biophys. Res. Commun.* **44,** 390.

Siegert, R. S., and Falke, D. (1966). *Arch. Gesamte Virusforsch.* **19,** 230.

Simpson, R. W., and Hauser, R. E. (1966). *Virology* **30,** 684.

Skehel, J. J. (1971). *J. Gen. Virol.* **11,** 103.

Skehel, J. J., and Schild, G. C. (1971). *Virology* **44,** 396.

Smith, K. M. (1967). "Insect Virology," Chapter 2. Academic Press, New York.

Smith, W. (1939). *J. Pathol. Bacteriol.* **48,** 557.

Sokol, F., Stanček, D., and Koprowski, H. (1971). *J. Virol.* **7,** 241.

Spear, P. G., and Roizman, B. (1967). *Nature (London)* **214,** 713.

Spear, P. G., and Roizman, B. (1968). *Virology* 36, 545.
Spear, P. G., and Roizman, B. (1972). *J. Virol.* 9, 143.
Spring, S. B., and Roizman, B. (1967). *J. Virol.* 1, 294.
Spring, S. B., and Roizman, B. (1968). *J. Virol.* 2, 979.
Stoffel, W. (1971). *Annu. Rev. Biochem.* 40, 57.
Stoffel, W., and Schiefer, H.-G. (1968). *Z. Phys. Chem.* 349, 1017.
Stollar, V. (1969). *Virology* 39, 426.
Tiffany, J. M., and Blough, H. A. (1969a). *Science* 163, 573.
Tiffany, J. M., and Blough, H. A. (1969b). *Virology* 37, 492.
Tiffany, J. M., and Blough, H. A. (1970a). *Proc. Nat. Acad. Sci. U. S.* 65, 1105.
Tiffany, J. M., and Blough, H. A. (1970b). *Virology* 41, 392.
Turkki, P. R., and Clenn, J. L. (1968). *Biochim. Biophys. Acta* 152, 104.
Vaheri, A., Sedwick, W. D., and Plotkin, S. A. (1965). *Proc. Soc. Exp. Biol. Med.* 125, 1086.
Vandenheuvel, F. A. (1963). *J. Amer. Oil Chem. Soc.* 40, 455.
van Kammen, A., Henstra, S., and Ie, T. S. (1966). *Virology* 30, 574.
von Magnus, P. (1951). *Acta Pathol. Microbiol. Scand.* 28, 278.
Wagner, R. R., Schaitman, T. C., and Snyder, R. M. (1969). *J. Virol.* 3, 395.
Waite, M. R. F., and Pfefferkorn, E. R. (1970). *J. Virol.* 6, 637.
Warren, L. (1959). *J. Biol. Chem.* 234, 1971.
Warren, L., Critchley, D., and MacPherson, I. (1972). *Nature (London)* 235, 275.
Watson, D. H., Wildy, P., and Russell, W. C. (1964). *Virology* 24, 523.
Wecker, E. (1957). *Z. Naturforsch. B* 12, 208.
Weinstein, D. B., and Blough, H. A. (1973). Submitted for publication.
Weinstein, D. B., Marsh, J. B., Glick, M. C., and Warren, L. (1969). *J. Biol. Chem.* 244, 4103.
Weinstein, D. B., Marsh, J. B., Glick, M. C., and Warren, L. (1970). *J. Biol. Chem.* 245, 3928.
White, H. B., Powell, S. S., Gafford, L. G., and Randall, C. C. (1968). *J. Biol. Chem.* 243, 4517.
Wilcox, W. C., and Ginsberg, H. S. (1963). *J. Exp. Med.* 118, 295.
Wildy, P. (1971). *In* "Monographs in Virology" (J. L. Melnick, ed.), Vol. 5, p. 28. Karger, Basel.
Wirtz, K. W. A., and Zilversmit, D. B. (1969). *Biochim. Biophys. Acta* 193, 105.
Woodson, B., and Joklik, W. K. (1965). *Proc. Nat. Acad. Sci. U S.* 54, 946.
Zwartouw, H. T. (1964). *J. Gen. Microbiol.* 34, 115.

Author Index

Numbers in italics refer to the pages on which the complete references are listed.

Subject Index

A

Acilius sulcatus, 227, 228, 230, 256
Aedes aegypti, 259
Alphaviruses, 271, 273
  structure of, 322–324
Androstenedione, 225, 226
Antheridiol, 197
Anthonomus grandis, 233
Apis mellifera, 233
Arbovirus group A, 271, 273
Arbovirus group B, 271, 273
Arenaviruses, 271, 275
Arthrobacter simplex, 163, 164, 182
Aulocara elliotti, 222

B

Baculoviruses, 271, 277
Bile acids, 55
  in animals, degradation of, 186, 187
  conjugated, hydrolysis of, 146–149
  dehydroxylation of, 149–154
  excretory products of, 160–162
  microbial degradation of, 162–187
    intermediates in, 185, 186
    pathways for, 171–185
    of side chain, 173, 174
  microbiological transformation of, 143–188
    in intestinal tract, 144–162
    miscellaneous reactions, 157–160
    oxidation of alcohols to ketones, 154–157
Bile duct obstruction, *see* Cholestasis
Blattella germanica, 223–226, 229, 234
Blood-brain barrier
  deficiency of essential fatty acids, 136, 137
    of thiamine, 137
  fatty acids and, 112–126, *see also* Fatty acids in brain
  lipids and, 110–112
    effect of age, 111

radioactive markers, 110, 111
routes of entry, 111, 112
malnutrition and, 136, 137
Bombyx mori, 229, 230, 233
Brain, *see also* Blood-brain barrier
  polar lipids in, 131–133

C

Calcium ion, precipitation of serum lipoproteins, 71–73
Calliphora stygia, 227, 230, 249, 252
Calliphora vicina, 225, 227, 232, 252
Campesterol, 229, 232, 236
(4R)-4-[4α-(2-Carboxyethyl)-3aα-perhydro-7α,β-methyl-5-oxoindan-1β-yl]valeric acid, 165, 166, 174–182
Ceramide monohexoside in viruses, 288
Cholestanol, 223–225
Cholestanone, 223, 224
Cholestasis, 39–46
  lipoproteins in, 41–46
Cholestatrienol, 223, 224, 237
Cholesterol
  in erythrocytes, 57
  guinea pigs fed, 34–39
  high density lipoproteins and, 39
  in insects
    conjugation, 231, 232
    as dealkylation product, 229
    esterification and hydrolysis of, 221–223
    hydroxylation of, 226–228
    as oxidation product, 225
    as reduction product, 223, 224
    side-chain cleavage, 230
  low density lipoproteins and, 9, 10, 37, 38
  as membrane component, 195
  in plants, 198, 233–235
  of plasma lipoprotein
    concentration of, 35
    plasma membranes and, 2

359